S0-ATI-551

Semigroups

Contributors

L. W. ANDERSON
MAHLON M. DAY
EDWIN HEWITT
KARL HEINRICH HOFMANN
R. P. HUNTER
R. J. KOCH
PAUL S. MOSTERT
W. D. MUNN
JOHN RHODES
M. ROSENBLATT
TAKAYUKI TAMURA
BRET R. TILSON
ALEXANDER DONIPHAN WALLACE
HERBERT S. ZUCKERMAN

SEMIGROUPS

Proceedings of a Symposium on Semigroups Held at Wayne State University, Detroit, Michigan, June 27–29, 1968

Edited by KARL W. FOLLEY

DEPARTMENT OF MATHEMATICS
WAYNE STATE UNIVERSITY
DETROIT, MICHIGAN

1969

ACADEMIC PRESS New York and London

ACADEMIC PRESS INC.
111 Fifth Avenue, New York, New York 10003

United Kingdom Edition published by
ACADEMIC PRESS INC. (LONDON) LTD.
Berkeley Square House, London W.1

LIBRARY OF CONGRESS CATALOG CARD NUMBER: 77-84228

AMS 1968 SUBJECT CLASSIFICATION 2092

PRINTED IN THE UNITED STATES OF AMERICA

List of Contributors

Numbers in parentheses indicate the pages on which the authors' contributions begin.

L. W. ANDERSON (1), Department of Mathematics, Pennsylvania State University, University Park, Pennsylvania

MAHLON M. DAY (5), Department of Mathematics, University of Illinois, Urbana, Illinois

EDWIN HEWITT (55), University of Washington, Seattle, Washington

KARL HEINRICH HOFMANN* (85), Tulane University, New Orleans, Louisiana and The Institute for Advanced Study, Princeton, New Jersey

R. P. HUNTER (1), Department of Mathematics, Pennsylvania State University, University Park, Pennsylvania

R. J. KOCH (101), Louisiana State University, Baton Rouge, Louisiana

PAUL S. MOSTERT* (85), Tulane University, New Orleans, Louisiana and The Institute for Advanced Study, Princeton, New Jersey

W. D. MUNN (107), University of Stirling, Stirling, Scotland

JOHN RHODES (125), Department of Mathematics, University of California, Berkeley, California

M. ROSENBLATT (209), Department of Mathematics, University of California San Diego, La Jolla, California

TAKAYUKI TAMURA (221), Department of Mathematics, University of California, Davis, California

BRET R. TILSON (163), Department of Mathematics, University of California, Berkeley, California

ALEXANDER DONIPHAN WALLACE (261), Department of Mathematics, University of Florida, Gainsville, Florida

HERBERT S. ZUCKERMAN (55), University of Washington, Seattle, Washington

* Present address of both authors: Tulane University, New Orleans, Louisiana.

Preface

The papers published in this volume are based on lectures presented in connection with the Symposium on Semigroups held at Wayne State University, Detroit, Michigan, June 27–29, 1968. This Symposium, which was sponsored by the National Science Foundation under Grant No. GY-3981, was a part of the Centennial Celebration of Wayne State University.

The purpose of the Symposium was to bring together distinguished mathematicians engaged in research in the theory of semigroups and its applications, and have them report on recent results in their areas of specialization. In particular, the Symposium was to emphasize the algebraic structure of semigroups, the structure of topological semigroups, and harmonic analysis on semigroups. Other important areas such as probability theory on semigroups and the theory of automata and machines were to be considered also. Professor Constantine Kassimatis initiated the plans for our symposium, and was instrumental in its organization. His death in September 1967 was a great shock to his colleagues; and for a short period there was some discussion concerning future plans for the Symposium. A departmental committee was formed to complete the arrangements; and we all feel that the Symposium was a great success.

I would like to take this opportunity to thank Professors A. T. Bharucha-Reid and T. Nishiura for their assistance in arranging the publication of this volume and program arrangements, respectively, and Miss Yara Zubalskyj who served as Symposium Secretary.

At the present time the general theory of semigroups is an active area of mathematical research; and applications of the general theory are of importance in several branches of mathematics, as well as in the theory of machines and languages (M. Arbib, *Algebraic Theory of Machines, Languages, and Semigroups*, Academic Press, 1968) and the analysis of metabolic processes in biological systems. We sincerely hope these Proceedings of the Wayne State University Symposium on Semigroups will stimulate further research activity and serve as a valuable guide to the various rapidly developing branches of the subject.

May 1969 KARL W. FOLLEY

Contents

Problems about Compact Semigroups

Karl Heinrich Hofmann and Paul S. Mostert

A Survey of Results on Threads

R. J. Koch

Some Recent Results on the Structure of Inverse Semigroups

W. D. Munn

Algebraic Theory of Finite Semigroups: Structure Numbers and Structure Theorems for Finite Semigroups

John Rhodes

Appendix to "Algebraic Theory of Finite Semigroups": On the p Length of p-Solvable Semigroups: Preliminary Results

Bret R. Tilson

Stationary Measures for Random Walks on Semigroups

M. Rosenblatt

The Study of Closets and Free Contents Related to Semilattice Decomposition of Semigroups

Takayuki Tamura

Recent Results on Binary Topological Algebra

Alexander Doniphan Wallace

Semigroups

Remarks on the Algebraic Subsemigroups of Certain Compact Semigroups

L. W. ANDERSON AND R. P. HUNTER

Department of Mathematics
Pennsylvania State University
University Park, Pennsylvania

We should like to determine the algebraic subsemigroups of a compact semigroup. Of course, our present discussion falls somewhat short of achieving this goal and will, in fact, be restricted to some rather general remarks regarding compactifications of semigroups.

Before continuing, let us consider the first question one might ask: can every semigroup be embedded (algebraically) in a compact semigroup? The answer is, of course, no as demonstrated by the following examples.

EXAMPLE 1. The bicyclic semigroup is the semigroup generated by two elements $\{p, q\}$ subject to the relation $pq = 1$. As is wellknown, this semigroup is unstable and cannot be embedded in a stable semigroup. Thus, the bicyclic semigroup cannot be a subsemigroup of a compact semigroup.

EXAMPLE 2. This example is due to Šain. Consider the full transformation semigroup on the positive integers. Let A be all constant mappings, i.e., $a_i(x) = i$ for all x and let B be the set of all mappings b such that $b(1) = 1$, $b(2) = 2$ and $b(n) \in \{1, 2\}$ for $n = 3, 4, \ldots$. Now $C = A \cup B$ is the desired semigroup. Suppose C were contained in a compact semigroup and that a_{n_i} converges to α and b_{n_i} converges to β. One easily sees that

$$a_{n_i}\{b_{n_i}, b_{n_{i+1}}, \ldots\} \supset \{a_1, a_2\},$$

an obvious contradiction.

EXAMPLE 3. As noted by von Neumann and Wigner, the group $SL(2, Q)$, where Q denotes the rationals, cannot be embedded in a compact group (hence, of course, not in a compact semigroup). The reason for this is that $SL(2, Q)$ contains elements a such that for each $n \geqslant 1$, there is a b_n such that $a^n = b_n a b_n^{-1}$. Except for the identity, no element in a compact group may enjoy this property.

Following P. Hall, we shall say that a semigroup enjoys a certain property P residually (subresidually) if any pair of points can be separated by a homomorphism onto (into) a semigroup having property P.

Following P. Holm we define the Bohr compactification of a semigroup S as a pair $(\hat{S}, \delta)$, where $\hat{S}$ is a compact semigroup, δ is a dense homomorphism of S into $\hat{S}$ with the property that the diagram

$$\begin{array}{ccc} \hat{S} & & \\ \delta \uparrow & & \\ S & \xrightarrow[\gamma]{} & T \end{array}$$

where γ is a dense homomorphism into the compact semigroup T, completes to the diagram

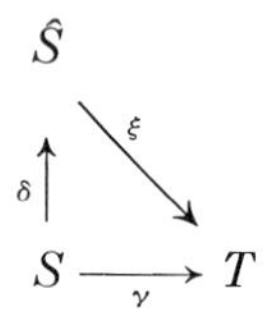

where ξ is a continuous homomorphism of $\hat{S}$ onto T.

Observe that a semigroup is subresidually compact if, and only if, δ is one-to-one.

It is quite clear that the Bohr compactification of a semigroup need not be particularly nice. To illustrate, let G be an Abelian group; then one sees that $\hat{G} = ch(ch(G)$ discrete). If, for example, Z is the integers, $\hat{Z}$ is the character group of the discrete circle group. Further, if B is the bicyclic semigroup (Example 1), then $\hat{B} = \hat{Z}$.

PROBLEM. If S is a semilattice, $\hat{S}$ totally disconnected?

If S is a linearly ordered semilattice, one can show that $\hat{S}$ is totally disconnected and linearly ordered. In this regard, consider:

Theorem 1. A semigroup S is residually finite if, and only if, $x, y \in S$ with $\delta(x)$ and $\delta(y)$ in the same component of $\hat{S}$ implies $x = y$.

We now consider which *simple* semigroups can be embedded in a compact semigroup. First, note that if S is a simple subsemigroup of a stable semigroup, then either S has an idempotent and is completely simple or S has no idempotent and has trivial $\mathscr{D}$ classes. Thus, a subresidually compact simple semigroup is either completely simple or is

$\mathscr{D}$ trivial without idempotents. We consider the completely simple case first.

Let $S = (X, Y, G, p)$ be a completely simple semigroup and suppose $\delta : S \to \hat{S}$ is one-to-one. We may as well assume that S is a dense subsemigroup of $\hat{S}$ so that $\hat{S}$ is also completely simple, say $\hat{S} = (X', Y', G', p')$. One verifies that $X' = \beta X$, $Y' = \beta Y$, G' is a compact group (perhaps not $\hat{G}$) containing G densely and $p' : X' \times Y' \to G'$ is a continuous extension of $p : X \times Y \to G$. Thus we see that for S completely simple if S is subresidually compact then $p : X \times Y \to G'$ has a continuous extension to $p' : \beta X \times \beta Y \to G'$. The validity of the converse is rather transparent. We may now apply the condition of Frölich which states: $p : X \times Y \to G'$ has a continuous extension to $\beta X \times \beta Y$ if and only if for each entourage V on G' there are sets $U_1, \ldots, U_n$ in X and $V_1, \ldots, V_n$ in Y such that $\{U_i \times V_i\}$ covers $X \times Y$ and if x and y are in $U_i \times V_i (i = 1, \ldots, n)$ then $(f(x), f(y)) \in V$. To summarize we have:

Theorem 2. A completely simple semigroup is subresidually compact if, and only if, it satisfies the condition of Frölich.

We now turn our attention to simple semigroups without idempotents. As noted previously, if it is subresidually compact, it must be $\mathscr{D}$ trivial. Unfortunately, this observation just about exhausts our knowledge of this subject. We remark that every compact, connected non-Abelian group contains a subsemigroup which is countable, simple, and without idempotents (hence $\mathscr{D}$ trivial). Thus we are assured of the existence of subresidually compact, simple semigroups without idempotents. On the other hand, consider the following:

EXAMPLE 4. Let S be the semigroup of matrices $\left(\begin{smallmatrix} x & y \\ 0 & 1 \end{smallmatrix}\right)$, where x and y are positive and rational. Then S is simple, $\mathscr{D}$ trivial, and without idempotents. Now if S were embedded densely in a compact semigroup, say T, then T would be a compact group. However, we have

$$\begin{pmatrix} n & 1 \\ 0 & 1 \end{pmatrix}\begin{pmatrix} 1 & 1 \\ 0 & 1 \end{pmatrix} = \begin{pmatrix} 1 & 1 \\ 0 & 1 \end{pmatrix}^n \begin{pmatrix} n & 1 \\ 0 & 1 \end{pmatrix}$$

which, as we have previously noted, is not admissible in a compact group.

PROBLEM. Find a necessary and sufficient condition for a simple, $\mathscr{D}$-trivial semigroup without idempotents to be subresidually compact.

Proofs of the statements in this note may be found in a forthcoming paper by the authors entitled, "On the infinite subsemigroups of certain compact semigroups."

Semigroups and Amenability

MAHLON M. DAY

Department of Mathematics
University of Illinois
Urbana, Illinois

1. Introduction

This chapter is a survey of the properties of and relations among semigroups which have invariant means on their bounded functions, with applications to numerous related properties of operator semigroups and of locally compact groups.

The subject began with a theorem of Banach (1923) who showed, as a consequence of the Hahn-Banach theorem, that there exists a mean on the bounded functions on the integers (or the reals) which is invariant under all translations. Hausdorff (1914, p. 469) showed that there is no such mean on the bounded functions on the surface of a sphere in 3 space which is invariant under all rotations of the sphere. Von Neumann (1929) showed that the reason for this failure is the excessive noncommutativity of the rotation group of the sphere; once dimension 2 has been passed, free non-Abelian subgroups of the rotation group of the n sphere are plentiful.

A semigroup Σ is called *left* [*right*] *amenable* if there is on the Banach space $m(\Sigma)$ of all bounded real (or complex) functions on Σ a mean μ (that is, an element of $m(\Sigma)^*$ for which $\| \mu \| = 1$ and $\mu(x) \geqslant 0$ if $x \geqslant 0$ on Σ) which is invariant under left [right] translations of elements of $m(\Sigma)$ by elements of Σ.

This paper surveys the available information about amenable, or only left-amenable, semigroups, and discusses many properties which are implied by, or are equivalent to, amenability.

For example, which semigroups are amenable, which surely not? What combinations of amenable pieces are amenable? Which semigroups have unique invariant means or few such means? What other interesting properties of semigroups are related to invariant means?

Section 2 contains definitions and two basic results. Section 3 lists (with hints of proof) many known properties of, and relations among amenable semigroups. Section 4 reviews the properties of the l_1 algebra of a semigroup and of its second conjugate algebra.

The later sections of this paper are devoted to: strong amenability and Følner's arithmetic-mean criterion; fixed points for left-amenable semigroups of affine continuous maps of compact convex sets; Mitchell's "stationary" semigroups; ergodic theorems; almost convergence; Granirer's work on few invariant means; spectra and norms for convolution operators by nonnegative elements of $l_1(\Sigma)$, extending Kesten's results for countable discrete groups; then passing to locally compact groups and work of Hulanicki, Reiter, Dieudonné, Namioka, and Greenleaf; extremely left-amenable semigroups of Mitchell and Granirer; invariant extensions of linear operators of Silverman.

Until recent years the principal results on amenability were known only for discrete semigroups, where the Abelian semigroups and the finite groups are the basic good systems.

Some general results on topological semigroups will be indicated as we go along. The theory for locally compact groups now closely parallels that for discrete groups, following breakthroughs by Rickert (1965) and Hulanicki (1966), consolidated and organized by Greenleaf (1966). Appropriate results will be indicated as we go along except that the locally compact-group version of the pattern in Section 3 is held back to the end of Section 13.

We shall refer to "Normed Linear Spaces" (Day, (1962) for general facts about such spaces, and to "Abstract Harmonic Analysis" (Hewitt and Ross, 1963) for facts about locally compact groups and Haar measure and convolution. The first large discussion of amenable semigroups, mostly for the discrete case, is given by Day (1957). A later expository account is by Hewitt and Ross (1963, Section 17). A very full discussion of amenability and many related topics for locally compact groups is found in the lecture notes of Greenleaf (1966).

2. General Definitions and First Criteria for Invariant Means

If Σ is a set, then $l_p(\Sigma)$ and $m(\Sigma)$ are, as usual, the spaces of real or complex functions on Σ which are pth power summable, or bounded; e is the constantly one function on Σ. There are standard theorems [see, for example, Day (1962, Chapter II, Section 2)] asserting the isometry of $l_1(\Sigma)^*$ with $m(\Sigma)$ and of $m(\Sigma)^*$ with the space $\mathbf{BV}(\Sigma)$ of all finitely additive set functions of bounded variation defined on the family of all subsets of Σ.

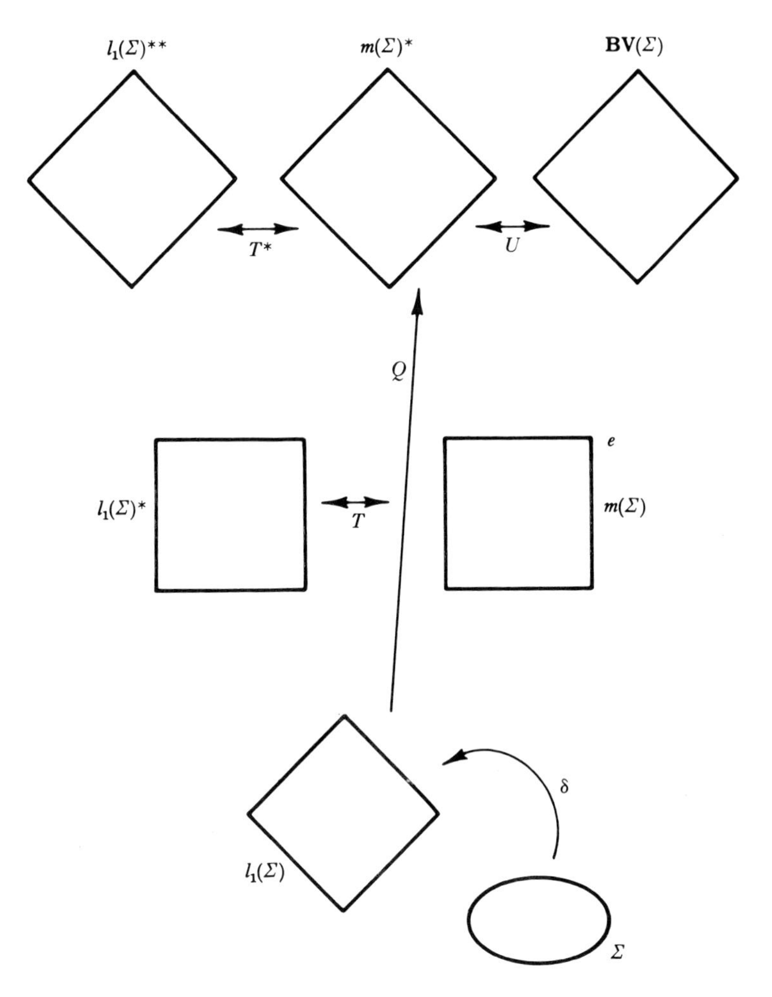

FIGURE 1.

If $x \in m(\Sigma)$, then $x^\vee = Tx$ in $l_1(\Sigma)^*$ is defined by $x^\vee(\alpha) = \sum_{s\in\Sigma} x(s)\,\alpha(s)$ for all α in $l_1(\Sigma)$.

If $\mu \in m(\Sigma)^*$, then $\mu^\vee = U\mu$ in $\mathbf{BV}(\Sigma)$ is defined by $\mu^\vee(E) = \mu(\chi_E)$ for all $E \subseteq \Sigma$.

If $s \in \Sigma$, then $\delta_s(t) = 1$ if $s = t$; $\delta_s(t) = 0$ if $s \neq t$.

If $\alpha \in l_1(\Sigma)$, then $Q\alpha$ is that element of $m(\Sigma)^*$ for which $Q\alpha(x) = x^\vee(\alpha)$ for all x in $m(\Sigma)$.

M, the set of means on $m(\Sigma)$, is the set of those elements μ in $m(\Sigma)^*$ such that for each x in $m(\Sigma)$, $\mu(x)$ is in the closed convex hull of the range of x. Clearly, $\| \mu \| = 1 = \mu(e)$, and $\mu(x) \geqslant 0$ if $x \geqslant 0$; any two of these properties characterize the elements of M (Day, 1957).

P, the set of probability densities, or *countable means, on Σ* is the set of nonnegative elements of norm one in $l_1(\Sigma)$; P_0, *the set of finite means on Σ*, is the subset of P containing those elements with only finitely many nonzero entries.

In a locally compact group G with left Haar measure H, $L_\infty(G)$ replaces $m(G)$. P becomes the set of nonnegative elements of norm one in $L_1(G)$ and P_0 becomes the set of those elements of P with compact support in G. P_{00} is the set of continuous elements of P_0. (It is well known that P_{00} is dense in P.)

If Σ is a semigroup, then for each s in Σ define l_s and r_s from $m(\Sigma)$ into $m(\Sigma)$ by: for each x in $m(\Sigma)$ and all t in Σ

$$l_s x(t) = x(st) \qquad \text{and} \qquad r_s x(t) = x(ts).$$

Then, to say that μ in $m(\Sigma)^*$ is *left invariant* [*right invariant*] {*invariant*} means that for each x in $m(\Sigma)$ and s in Σ

$$\mu(l_s x) = \mu(x) \qquad [\mu(r_s x) = \mu(x)] \qquad \{\text{both}\}.$$

Rephrasing this in terms of fixed points of adjoint operators [see Day (1962, p. 27) for some general properties] yields:

(2A) μ is left [right] invariant if and only if for each s in Σ

$$l_s^* \mu = \mu \qquad [r_s^* \mu = \mu].$$

A semigroup Σ is called *left amenable* [*right amenable*] {*amenable*} if there exists at least one mean μ on $m(\Sigma)$ which is left invariant [right invariant] {both}.

For any operator semigroup $\mathscr{S}$ in a Banach space B, define $\mathscr{D}(\mathscr{S})$ to be the closed linear manifold spanned by the differences $Sx - x$, where S runs over $\mathscr{S}$ and x over B. Also let $\mathscr{F}(\mathscr{S})$ be $\{x \in B \mid Sx = x \text{ for all } S \text{ in } \mathscr{S}\}$; that is, $\mathscr{F}(\mathscr{S})$ is the (closed linear) set of all common fixed points of the S in $\mathscr{S}$.

Lemma 2.1. (Dixmier, 1950; Følner, 1955). Σ is left [right amenable if and only if e is at distance 1 from $\mathscr{D}(l(\Sigma))$ [$\mathscr{D}(r(\Sigma))$]; that is, if and only if for each choice of x_i in $m(\Sigma)$ and s_i in Σ, setting

$h = \sum_{i \leqslant n} (x_i - l_{s_i} x_i)$ $[h = \sum_{i \leqslant n} (x_i - r_{s_i} x_i)]$, we have $\sup_{s \in \Sigma} \operatorname{Re} h(s) \geqslant 0$. Σ is amenable if and only if both conditions hold.

PROOF. First, a continuous linear functional on $m(\Sigma)$ is left [right] invariant if and only if it vanishes on all $x - l_s x$ $[x - r_s x]$; hence, on $\mathscr{D}(l(\Sigma))$ [on $\mathscr{D}(r(\Sigma))$].

But if $\mu(e) = 1$ and μ is, say, left invariant, then $1 = \mu(e - h) \leqslant \| e - h \|$ for all h in $\mathscr{D}(l(\Sigma))$. Hence $\| e + th \| \geqslant 1$ for all h and all t, from which a simple geometric argument shows that $\sup_s \operatorname{Re}(h(s)) = -\epsilon < 0$ is impossible.

For the converse, $\sup_s \operatorname{Re} h(s) \geqslant 0$ for all h in a dense subset of $\mathscr{D}(l(\Sigma))$ implies that distance from e to $\mathscr{D}(l(\Sigma)) = 1$; the Hahn-Banach theorem gives a μ vanishing on $\mathscr{D}(l(\Sigma))$ and 1 at e and of norm 1; such a μ is a left-invariant mean.

If Σ is amenable, it is both left and right amenable, so both $\mathscr{D}(l(\Sigma))$ and $\mathscr{D}(r(\Sigma))$ are at distance 1 from e. If, conversely, both are at distance 1 from e, then there exist a left-invariant mean μ and a right-invariant mean ν. (3B) shows that $\mu * \nu$ is a two-sided invariant mean. [(3B) is proved in the algebra $m(\Sigma)^*$ with no use of $\mathscr{D}(l(\Sigma))$.]

Følner (1957) showed for groups that if G is not left amenable, then $\mathscr{D}(l(\Sigma))$ is dense in $m(\Sigma)$. Earlier I showed (Day, 1950) that if $m(\Sigma) = \bigcup_{s \in \Sigma} l_s(m(\Sigma))$ (a condition trivially true in groups), then for a ν in $m(\Sigma)^*$, ν^+ is left invariant if ν is left invariant. Namioka (1967) removed the restriction on Σ.

Lemma 2.2. If ν is a left- [right-] invariant element of $m(\Sigma)^*$, then ν^+, the positive part of ν, is also left [right] invariant. Hence Σ is left [right] amenable if and only if $\mathscr{D}(l(\Sigma))$ $[\mathscr{D}(r(\Sigma))]$ is not $m(\Sigma)$.

PROOF. $\nu^+ \geqslant \nu$ and $\nu^+ \geqslant 0$; hence $l_s^*(\nu^+) \geqslant l_s^*(\nu) = \nu$, and, of course, $l_s^*(\nu^+) \geqslant 0$. Hence $l_s^*(\nu^+) > \nu^+$, or $l_s^*(\nu^+) - \nu^+ \geqslant 0$, so

$$\| l_s^*(\nu^+) - \nu^+ \| = (l_s^*(\nu^+) - \nu^+)(e) = \nu^+(l_s e) - \nu^+(e) = 0,$$

so $l_s(\nu^+) = \nu^+$.

For the last statement, there is a left-invariant nonzero ν in $m(\Sigma)^*$ if and only if $\mathscr{D}(l(\Sigma)) \neq m(\Sigma)$.

Von Neumann's work (1929) was phrased in terms of finitely additive set functions. As we have mentioned earlier, the relation $\mu \leftrightarrow \mu^\vee$ is a linear isometry between $m(\Sigma)^*$ and $\mathbf{BV}(\Sigma)$. μ is a mean if and only if

(1) $\mu^\vee(\Sigma) = 1$, and

(2) $\mu^\vee(E) \geqslant 0$ for all $E \subseteq \Sigma$.

If Σ is a semigroup, define $s^{-1}E$ $[Es^{-1}]$ to be $\{t \mid st \in E\}$ $[\{t \mid ts \in E\}]$.

Then μ is left [right] invariant if and only if the following condition is met.

(3) For each s in Σ and $E \subseteq \Sigma$, $\mu^\vee(s^{-1}E) = \mu^\vee(E)$ [$\mu^\vee(Es^{-1}) = \mu^\vee(E)$].

Von Neumann worked with finitely additive measures in groups; he called G "messbar" if there existed $\mu^\vee$ in $\mathbf{BV}(\Sigma)$ satisfying conditions (1)–(3). Since this is equivalent to left amenability of G, we naturally give von Neumann credit for the many fundamental results on means which he stated in terms of set functions.

My own paper (Day, 1942) on ergodic theorems for Abelian semigroups is also formulated in terms of set functions; there I prove that every Abelian semigroup has an invariant $\mu^\vee$.

3. Properties of the Family of Amenable Semigroups

Much of the following section can be found in Day (1957): it is also organized in a similar way in Hewitt and Ross (1963, Section 17).

(3A) If Σ is both left and right amenable, then it is amenable.

[If μ is left invariant and ν right invariant, then $\mu * \nu$ is both, as seen from Section 4 of Day (1957, p. 515).]

(3B) A left- [right-] amenable group is right [left] amenable, hence amenable [Day (1957, p. 515).] (The mapping $g \to g^{-1}$ interchanges left and right.)]

(3C) If Σ is left [right] amenable and f is a homomorphism of Σ onto a semigroup Σ', then Σ' is left [right] amenable. [See von Neumann (1929) for groups; Day (1957, p. 515. Define $[Fx](s) = x(f(s))$; then $F^*\mu$ has whatever invariance μ has.]

(3D) If Σ_n is a family of subsemigroups of a semigroup Σ, if $\Sigma = \bigcup_n \Sigma_n$, if for each m, n there is p such that $\Sigma_p \supseteq \Sigma_m \cup \Sigma_n$, and if each Σ_n is left [right] amenable, then Σ is left [right] amenable. [See von Neumann (1929) for increasing sequences of subgroups; see Day (1957, p. 516) in general.]

(3D′) Every direct limit of (left-) amenable groups is (left) amenable [(Day (1957, p. 517)]. Hence the following:

(3D″) The weak direct product (i.e., the direct sum) of amenable groups is amenable.

This proof begins with (3G) to get the product of two amenable factors amenable; then induction to finite products, and (3D′) to complete the proof [Day (1957, p. 517)].

It is shown in Day (1957, p. 517), as a consequence of (3J), that *full direct products, or inverse limits, of families of amenable groups need not be amenable.*

(3D‴) A group G is amenable if and only if every finitely generated subgroup of G is amenable [Day (1957, p. 517)].

(3D^{iv}) A semigroup Σ is left amenable if and only if each countable subsemigroup of Σ is contained in a countable left-amenable subsemigroup of Σ. (Sufficiency follows from (3D); necessity requires strong amenability, see Section 4) (Granirer, 1963a).

(3E) Every Abelian semigroup is amenable. [See von Neumann (1929) for groups; see Day (1942) for semigroups. A simple proof is given in Section 6.]

(3F) If G is an amenable group, every subgroup of G is amenable.

This has no semigroup theorem of comparable strength. Day (1957, p. 516), gave an example of a nonamenable semigroup in an amenable semigroup. Hochster, (1968) has just shown that the free semigroup on two generators can be found in an amenable group. See the remark after Section 7.5 (Day, 1957, p. 516; Følner, 1955).

(3G) If H is a normal subgroup of the group G, and if H and G/H are amenable, then so is G (von Neumann, 1929).

(3H) If the chain of commutator subgroups of G reaches the identity in finitely many steps, then G is amenable; hence every solvable group is amenable (von Neumann, 1929).

(3I) Every finite group is amenable, and the invariant mean is unique.

Some finite semigroups have no invariant means. For example, let Σ be a set with at least two elements and define products by $st = s$ for each pair of elements s, t of Σ. Then, by (3L″), every left-invariant μ would have to be supported on each singleton set; that is, there are no left-invariant means. On the other hand, every r_s is the identity operator in $m(\Sigma)$, so all means are right invariant.

(3I′) A finite semigroup Σ is left amenable if and only if it has a unique minimal right ideal R. Then this right ideal is the union of the disjoint minimal left ideals $L_1, \ldots, L_k$ of Σ; each left ideal is a group, and all these groups are isomorphic. If u_i is the identity element of the group L_i, then $u_i u_j = u_j$ for all $i, j \leqslant k$, and if U is the set of these u_i, $R = L_i \times U$, and the left-invariant means on Σ are supported on R and are exactly averaging over L_i crossed with arbitrary means on U (Rosen, 1956).

(3I″) A finite semigroup is amenable if and only if it has a unique minimal left ideal L and a unique minimal right ideal R and $R = L$.

Then there is precisely one left- or right-invariant mean on Σ, the unique invariant mean of the finite group R. (Rosen does these and the analog for compact semigroups. See Section 10.)

(3J) The free group (semigroup) on two generators is not amenable (von Neumann, 1929).

With (3C) and (3F) this yields the following.

(3J′) No amenable group has a subgroup or factor group which is free on more than one generator (von Neumann, 1929).

(3K) Each group G contains a normal amenable subgroup N which (1) contains every normal amenable subgroup of G, and (2) is contained in every maximal amenable subgroup of G. [Day (1957, p. 518) shows (1); (2) follows from the second isomorphism theorem for groups.]

(3L) If Σ is a left-amenable semigroup and if Γ is a subsemigroup of Σ for which there is a left-invariant mean μ on $m(\Sigma)$ such that $\mu^{\vee}(\Gamma) > 0$, then Γ has a left-invariant mean (Day, 1957, p. 518).

(3L′) If Σ is a left-amenable semigroup and Γ is a right ideal in Σ, then Γ is left amenable; in fact, each left-invariant μ on $m(\Sigma)$ is already concentrated on Γ; that is $\mu^{\vee}(\Gamma) = 1$ (Frey, 1960).

(3L″) If Σ is left [right] amenable, then the right [left] ideals of Σ have the finite intersection property.

(3L‴) Σ is left amenable if and only if one (or all) left ideals in Σ are left amenable. [Frey proved that if a left ideal of Σ is left amenable, so is Σ. Wilde (1964) shows that if I is a left ideal in Σ then there is a left-invariant μ on Σ with $\mu^{\vee}(I) = 1$, so (3L) applies. Mitchell (1965) has a simpler proof for the existence of such a μ; see Section 7.5].

We can now restate a problem which has gone unsolved since it was first stated in Day (1957, p. 520). We have four ways available to construct good groups from other good groups; (1) subgroups, (2) factor groups, (3) group extensions, and (4) direct limits or expanding unions. Let EG, for elementary groups, be the smallest family of groups which contains all the abelian groups and all the finite groups and is closed under these four processes. Let AG be the family of amenable groups, and let NF be the family of all groups with no free nonabelian subgroups. We have already showed that AG is closed under the four given processes, and it is not difficult to prove the same for NF; also we already have that

$$\mathrm{EG} \subseteq \mathrm{AG} \subseteq \mathrm{NF}.$$

It is not known whether equality holds on either side, though there is some evidence in Rickert's work on connected Lie groups (1965) that it may be true for the second case.

4. The Semigroup Algebra $l_1(\Sigma)$ and Its Second-Conjugate Algebra

Multiplication is defined in $l_1(\Sigma)$ so that the mapping $s \to \delta_s$ is a homomorphism of Σ into the multiplicative semigroup of $l_1(\Sigma)$; in detail, if φ, $\psi \in l_1(\Sigma)$, then $[\varphi * \psi](v) = \sum_{st=v} \varphi(s)\,\psi(t)$. [Since the ordered pairs (s, t) from $\Sigma \times \Sigma$ are not ordered in any natural way, the indicated sum is to be taken over the set of all pairs (s, t) for which $st = v$; the sum converges unconditionally; see, for example, Day (1957, p. 521).]

It is first to be noted that $(\delta_s *)^*$ as an operator in $l_1(\Sigma)^*$ is related to l_s in $m(\Sigma)$; indeed, for each x in $m(\Sigma)$ and s in Σ, $[l_s x]^\vee$ is $[(\delta_s *)^*]\,x^\vee$. (For $[(\delta_s *)^*\, x^\vee](\varphi) = x^\vee(\delta_s * \varphi) = \sum_v x(v) \sum_{st=v} \varphi(t) = \sum_t x(st)\,\varphi(t) = \sum_t [l_s x](t)\,\varphi(t) = [l_s x]^\vee(\varphi)$.)

It follows that each l_s or r_s is continuous in bounded sets in $m(\Sigma)$ in the topology of coordinatewise convergence, since the isometry of $m(\Sigma)$ with $l_1(\Sigma)^*$ carries coordinatewise convergence in bounded sets in $m(\Sigma)$ to w^* convergence in bounded sets in $l_1(\Sigma)^*$.

As we pointed out in Day (1957, Section 6), the scheme invented by Arens for defining a multiplication in B^{**} from that in B, a Banach algebra, specializes here to give a multiplication in $m(\Sigma)^*$. Arens's steps become:

(a) For each x in $m(\Sigma)$ and φ in $l_1(\Sigma)$

$$[x * \varphi]^\vee(\psi) = x^\vee(\varphi * \psi) \qquad \text{for all } \psi \text{ in } l_1(\Sigma).$$

(b) For each μ in $m(\Sigma)^*$ and x in $m(\Sigma)$

$$[\mu * x]^\vee(\varphi) = \mu(x * \varphi) \qquad \text{for each } \varphi \text{ in } l_1(\Sigma).$$

(c) For each ν and μ in $m(\Sigma)^*$

$$[\nu * \mu](x) = \nu(\mu * x) \qquad \text{for each } x \text{ in } m(\Sigma).$$

(4A) The natural mapping Q of $l_1(\Sigma)$ into $m(\Sigma)^*$, defined by $Q\varphi(x) = x^\vee(\varphi)$ for all x in $m(\Sigma)$, is an algebra isomorphism as well as an isometry of $l_1(\Sigma)$ into $m(\Sigma)^*$ and $Q\delta_s * \mu = l^*\mu$ and $\mu * Q\delta_s = r^*\mu$ for all μ in $m(\Sigma)^*$ and s in Σ [Day (1957, p. 528)].

(4B) $*$ is w^* continuous in the first variable but not necessarily in the second (Arens, 1951; Day, 1957, p. 528)].

(4C) The set M of means in $m(\Sigma)^*$ is a subsemigroup of the multiplicative semigroup of $m(\Sigma)^*$ (Day, 1957, p. 527).

(4D) If μ is a left- and ν is a right-invariant mean, then $\mu * \nu$ is a two-sided invariant mean. [This follows from (4C), and the associative law for $*$ in $m(\Sigma)^*$ (Day, 1957, p. 529).]

(4E) If μ is a left-invariant mean, then for every mean ν, $\nu * \mu = \mu$. Hence M is never Abelian if it has more than one element.

For $Q\delta_s * \mu = l^*\mu = \mu$ for all s in Σ, so $Q\varphi * \mu = \mu$ for all finite means φ; use w^* continuity of $* \mu$ and w^* density of QP in M. For an example, the group of integers has many invariant means so (4E) says that M is exceedingly nongrouplike and non-Abelian (Day, 1957, p. 530).

If π is a representation (or antirepresentation) of Σ by uniformly bounded linear operators in some Banach space, then π can be extended to a continuous representation (antirepresentation) of the algebra $l_1(\Sigma)$ by linear operators over B, setting, for φ in $l_1(\Sigma)$, $\pi_\varphi = \sum_{s\in\Sigma} \varphi(s)\, \pi_s$; then $\| \pi_\varphi \| \leqslant \| \varphi \|_1 \sup_{s\in\Sigma} \| \pi_s \|$. In particular, the right- and left- shift operators in $m(\Sigma)$ determine l_φ and r_φ and $\| l_\varphi \| \leqslant \| \varphi \|_1$ [$\| r_\varphi \| \leqslant \| \varphi \|_1$].

(4F) For each φ in $l_1(\Sigma)$, $Q\varphi * \mu = l_\varphi^*(\mu)$ for all μ in $m(\Sigma)^*$; hence $Q\varphi * \mu$ is a w^*-continuous function of μ (Day, 1957, p. 528).

Much of what we have just said for discrete semigroups can be copied in locally compact groups with left Haar measure if we replace l_1 by L_1, l_p by L_p, and m by L_∞. L_1 is a Banach algebra under convolution [see Hewitt and Ross (1963)], and Aren's method then makes a Banach algebra out of L_∞^*. Integrals replace sums so $x^\vee(\varphi)$ becomes $\int \varphi(g)\, x(g)\, dg$. P is the set of nonnegative elements of norm 1 in L_1, and the finite means are replaced by P_0, the elements of P with compact support. We shall be concerned with this in later sections especially in Section 13 on norms and spectra of convolutions (Day, 1968).

A problem still of current interest is to determine which amenable groups are those with symmetric group algebras; i.e., $\delta_u + xx^*$ always has an inverse. Hulanicki (1964) raised this question by stating without proof that amenability suffices for symmetry, but Jenkins (1968) shows that for Hochster's group, among many others, $l_1(G)$ is not symmetric.

5. Strong Amenability and Følner's Conditions.

In Section 5 of Day (1957), I defined strong amenability and proved it equivalent to amenability.

A semigroup Σ is *strongly left* [or *right*] {or *both*} *amenable* if there exists a net φ_n, $n \in \Delta$, (Δ is a directed system) of finite means on Σ such that for each s in Σ

$$\lim_n \| \delta_s * \varphi_n - \varphi_n \|_1 = 0 \qquad [\lim_n \| \varphi_n * \delta_s - \varphi_n \|_1 = 0] \qquad \{\text{both}\}.$$

Theorem 5.1. A semigroup Σ is left amenable [right amenable] {amenable} if and only if it is strongly left amenable [right amenable] {amenable}.

PROOF. Each mean μ is the w^* limit of $Q\varphi_n$ where the φ_n are finite means. We can then show that μ is left [right] invariant if and only if for each s in Σ w $\lim_n(\delta_s * \varphi_n - \varphi_n) = 0$ [w-$\lim_n(\varphi_n * \delta_s - \varphi_n) = 0$]. To replace this by a new net with norm convergence replacing weak, recall a result of Day (1957, p. 523).

Lemma 5.2. If $(c_n, n \in \Delta)$ is a net in a locally convex space L which converges weakly to a point c of L, then there is a net $(d_m, m \in \Delta')$ of finite averages of elements far out in (c_n) such that d_m converges to c in the original topology of L.

We omit this proof; it depends on Mazur's theorem that strongly closed convex sets are weakly closed (Day, 1962, II, 5, 2).

My original application of the lemma to prove 5.1 was somewhat clumsy; Namioka (1964) does it more neatly by letting $L = \prod_{s\in\Sigma} L_s$, where each $L_s = l_1(\Sigma)$. For each n let c_n be the element of L for which $c_n(s) = \delta_s * \varphi_n - \varphi_n$. The assumption on φ_n says that c_n converges to 0 in the product of the w topologies, which is the weak topology of the product of the norm topologies. The lemma asserts the existence of $d_m = \sum_n \lambda_{mn} c_n$ tending to zero in this stronger topology. Setting $\psi_m = \sum_n \lambda_{mn}\varphi_n$, we find that for each s $\| \delta_s * \psi_m - \psi_m \|_1$ goes to 0. Repetition deals with right or two sided.

Følner (1955) has proved that each of the following conditions is equivalent to existence of an invariant mean on a group. Namioka (1967) showed how to get Følner's conditions from strong amenability in left-cancellation semigroups.

Theorem 5.3. For left-cancellation semigroups left amenability is equivalent to each of the conditions below:

(F1) For each number k such that $0 < k < 1$ and for each finite subset γ of Σ, there is a finite subset E of Σ such that (using $|A|$ for the number of elements of A)

$$|E \cap gE|/|E| > k \qquad \text{for each } g \text{ in } \gamma.$$

(F2) There is a k_0 with $0 < k_0 < 1$ such that for each finite sequence (distinct or not) of elements of Σ there is a finite subset E of Σ such that

$$n^{-1} \sum_{i\leqslant n} |E \cap g_i E| > k_0 |E|.$$

PROOF. Obviously (F1) implies (F2).

Følner's (1955) proof that (F2) implies left amenability uses Lemma 2.1. If $h = \sum_{i \leqslant n} (x_i - l_{a_i} x_i)$, set $J = \max_{i<n} \| x_i \|_{m(\Sigma)}$ and let $K(h) = 2nJ$. Then $\sup_s h(s) \geqslant -\| h \|_m \geqslant -K(h)$.

Choose E to satisfy (F2) for $a_1, \ldots, a_n$ and let $h_1 = | E |^{-1} \sum_{t \in E} l_t h$. Then

$$h_1 = | E |^{-1} \sum_{i \leqslant n} \sum_{t \in E} (l_t x_i - l_{a_i t} x_i);$$

(F2) states that at least $k_0 \mid E \mid$ terms cancel out in each inner sum (this is one place left cancellation is needed), so $K(h_1) \leqslant 2(1 - k_0)\, nJ = (1 - k_0)\, K(h)$. Repeating by induction gives $K(h_m) \to 0$ and $\sup_s h_m(s) \leqslant \sup_s h(s)$. It would therefore lead to a contradiction if this latter were negative. Hence Lemma 2.1 says that Σ is left amenable.

Namioka (1967) starts from left amenability of Σ and uses first Theorem 5.1 to get a net φ_n of finite means converging strongly to left invariance.

Now if φ is any finite mean, it can be represented as a finite average of means which are multiplies of characteristic functions, as follows. Let c_1 be the smallest positive value taken by φ and let $E_1 = \{s \mid \varphi(s) \geqslant c_1\}$. Subtract $c_1 \chi_{E_1}$ from φ to get ψ_1. Let c_2 be the smallest positive value taken by ψ_1, etc. to get $\varphi = \sum_{i \leqslant k} c_i \chi_{E_i}$, with $E_1 \supset E_2 \supset \cdots \supset E_k$ and all $c_i > 0$ and $1 = \| \varphi \| = \sum_{i \leqslant k} c_i \mid E_i \mid$. Setting $\varphi_i = | E_i |^{-1} \chi_{E_i}$ and $d_i = c_i \mid E_i \mid$, we get $\varphi = \sum_{i \leqslant k} d_i \varphi_i$, where d_i are all positive and their sum is 1.

Next we need to show that for any s in Σ,

$$\| \delta_s * \varphi - \varphi \|_1 = \sum_{i \leqslant k} d_i \| \delta_s * \varphi_i - \varphi_i \|_1 .$$

Setting $u_i = \delta_s * \varphi_i - \varphi_i$, we need to prove that if $t \in \Sigma$ and $j = j(t)$ is the smallest integer for which $u_j(t) \neq 0$, then for all $i > j$, $u_i(t)$ is zero or has the same sign as $u_j(t)$. For the first case note that $\{t \mid u_j(t) < 0\} = E_j \setminus sE_j$ so $u_j(t) < 0$ implies that $t \notin sE_j$ so $t \notin sE_i$ when $i > j$; hence $u_i(t) \leqslant 0$ if $i \geqslant j$. Starting instead from a point where $u_j(t) > 0$, we see by left cancellation that $t \in sE_j \setminus E_j$, so $t \notin E_i$ if $i > j$ and $u_i(t) \geqslant 0$ if $i \geqslant j$.

Now suppose that $s_1, \ldots, s_m$ in Σ and $\epsilon > 0$ are given; then φ can be chosen by strong left amenability so that $\| \delta_{s_j} * \varphi - \varphi \|_1 < \epsilon/m$ for $j = 1, \ldots, m$. Writing $\varphi = \sum_{i \leqslant k} d_i \varphi_i$ as before, we have

$$\sum_{i \leqslant k} d_i \| \delta_{s_j} * \varphi_i - \varphi_i \|_1 < \epsilon/m \qquad \text{for all} \quad j \leqslant m.$$

Setting

$$A_j = \{i \leqslant k \mid \| \delta_{s_j} * \varphi_i - \varphi_i \|_1 \geqslant \epsilon\}, \qquad \sum_{i \in A_j} d_i < 1/m,$$

so $\sum_j \sum_{i \in A_j} d_i < 1$, so at least one i is in no A_j. For that $i \| \delta_{s_j} * \varphi_i - \varphi_i \|_1 < \epsilon$ for all $j \leqslant m$. But this last norm is exactly $2 \mid E \mid^{-1} \mid E_i \setminus s_j E_i \mid$, which proves (F1).

In case there is some cancellation, Namioka (1967) computes only over the sets $sE_i \setminus E_i$ where the functions u_i are all nonnegative and gets $\| \delta_s * \varphi - \varphi \|_1 \geqslant \sum_i d_i \mid sE_i \setminus E_i \mid$; averaging this as before for $s_1, \ldots, s_m$ he proves a result of Frey (1960).

Theorem 5.4. If Σ is left amenable, then it satisfies the following Følner-Frey condition.

(FF) For each $\epsilon > 0$ and each finite set $\sigma \subseteq \Sigma$ there is a finite set $E \subseteq \Sigma$ such that for each s in σ, $\mid sE \setminus E \mid < \epsilon \mid E \mid$.

Since (FF) holds in every finite semigroup, it is not a sufficient condition for left amenability.

Argabright and Wilde (1967) calculate that for any φ of the form $\mid E \mid^{-1} \chi_E$, $\| \delta_s * \varphi - \varphi \|_1 = 2 \mid E \setminus sE \mid / \mid E \mid$. They then discuss the condition.

(FAW) For each $\epsilon > 0$ and each finite set $\sigma \subseteq \Sigma$ there is a finite set $E \subseteq \Sigma$ such that for each s in σ, $\mid E \setminus sE \mid < \epsilon \mid E \mid$.

(F2) also holds in every finite semigroup, so it too is not sufficient for left amenability. However (F1) is equivalent to (FAW) and Argabright and Wilde (1967) showed, by the norm calculation above, the following.

Theorem 5.5. If Σ is a semigroup satisfying (FAW) [or (F1)], then Σ is left amenable.

In a locally compact group G with left-invariant Haar measure H, recall that P_{00} is the set of continuous elements of P_0. As in the previous case, $Q(P_{00})$ is w^* dense in M, the set of means on $L_\infty(G)$, and if strong left amenability of G is defined to mean that there is a net φ_n of elements of P_{00} such that for each g in G, $\| \delta_g * \varphi_n - \varphi_n \|_1 \to 0$, then the proof of Theorem 5.1 works much as before to prove equivalence of strong left amenability of G and left amenability of G; that is, the existence of a left-invariant mean on $L_\infty(G)$. [Also in Frey (1960)]?

If in Følner's conditions (F1) and (F2) "finite set" is replaced by "compact set" and $\mid E \mid$ is interpreted as Haar measure of E, then all the proofs work as before, including Namioka's proof that strong amenability implies (F1). Hence also for locally compact groups left amenability, strong left amenability, (F1), and (F2) are equivalent.

6. Fixed Point Theorems

Throughout this section K will be a convex subset of a linear space which is compact in some topology for which $A(K)$, the space of real, affine continuous functions on K, separates points of K. Embedding K in $A(K)^*$, we see that (1) this assumption is equivalent to the condition that K be affinely homeomorphic to a compact convex subset of a locally convex linear topological space L, and that, (2) by a theorem of Choquet (Phelps, 1966, p. 31), the vector sum of the constant functions and the elements of L^* reduced to K is dense in $A(K)$ under the topology of uniform convergence on K.

Let $\mathscr{A}(K)$ be the space of all affine continuous maps of K into itself; then $\mathscr{A}(K)$ is a semigroup under composition of mappings, and if the product topology in K^K is used, then it can be checked that the multiplication in $\mathscr{A}(K)$ is separately continuous.

Kakutani-Markov Fixed Point Theorem. If $\mathscr{S}$ is a commutative subset of $\mathscr{A}(K)$, then there is in K a common fixed point of $\mathscr{S}$, that is, a point x such that $Sx = x$ for all S in $\mathscr{S}$.

PROOF. By the Tyhonov fixed point theorem (see Day, 1962, p. 82) each S has a closed nonempty set K_S of fixed points. Since S is affine, K_S is convex. Since S and S' commute, S' carries K_S into itself, so, by Tyhonov again, $K_S \cap K_{S'} \neq \emptyset$. Repeating on $K_S \cap K_{S'}$ with an S'', etc., the K_S have the finite intersection property. By compactness all K_S intersect.

If Σ is a semigroup and M its set of means on $m(\Sigma)$, then, as we saw in Section 2, Σ is left amenable if and only if there is in M an element μ fixed under all l_s^*, $s \in \Sigma$. But if M is given the weak* topology, then each l_s^* is in $\mathscr{A}(M)$; the Kakutani-Markov theorem then provides an elegant proof that each commutative semigroup is amenable. Commutativity is too strong a hypothesis so we are able to prove the theorem of Day (1961).

Theorem 6.1. A semigroup Σ is left [right] amenable if and only if for each compact convex K where $A(K)$ separates points and for each [anti-] homomorphism h of Σ into $\mathscr{A}(K)$ there is in K a common fixed point of all the mappings h_s, $s \in \Sigma$; indeed in this case there is such a fixed point in each K_y, where y is any point of K and K_y is the closed convex hull of the orbit $h(\Sigma)(y)$.

REMARK. It is true that right amenability will not work in the same way here, but only because functional composition is written from the left. The difference between the two forms is due to this accident of notation. We give Argabright's proof of Theorem 6.1 which is somewhat nicer than my original proof, but needs the following.

Lemma 6.2. Each mean μ' on $A(K)$ can be represented by evaluation at some (unique) point x' of K.

PROOF OF LEMMA. By the Hahn-Banach theorem μ' can be extended to a mean μ on $m(K)$. Then there exist finite means φ_n on K such that $f^{\vee}(\varphi_n) \to \mu(f)$ for each f in $m(K)$. Hence if v is in $A(K)$,

$$v^{\vee}(\varphi_n) = \sum_{x \in K} v(x)\, \varphi_n(x) = v\left(\sum_{x \in K} \varphi_n(x)\, x\right) = v(x_n)$$

where x_n in $K = \sum_{x \in K} \varphi_n(x)\, x$. By compactness we can go to a subnet w_m of x_n such that w_m converges to a point x' of K; but $v^{\vee}(\varphi_n)$ had the limit $\mu'(v)$ and $v(w_m)$ has limit $v(x')$ so $\mu'(v) = v(x')$ for all v in $A(K)$.

PROOF OF THEOREM. Take any y in K and map $A(K)$ into $m(\Sigma)$ by $T = T_y$, which is defined for each f in $A(K)$ by $[Tf](s) = f(h_s y)$ for all s in Σ. Then T is linear, nonnegative, and of norm 1, and $Te_K = e_\Sigma$. Hence T^* carries means on $m(\Sigma)$ to means on $A(K)$.

Take a left-invariant mean μ on $m(\Sigma)$, set $T^*\mu = \mu'$, and let x' be the point of K attached to μ' by the lemma. Define H_s in $A(K)$ by $[H_s f](z) = f(h_s z)$ for all z in K; then for all f in $A(K)$

$$\begin{aligned} f(h_s x') = (H_s f)(x') &= \mu'(H_s f) = T^*\mu(H_s f) \\ &= \mu(TH_s f) = \mu(l_s Tf) \\ &= \mu(Tf) = (T^*\mu)(f) = \mu'(f) = f(x'). \end{aligned}$$

Hence x' is fixed under all h_s, $s \in \Sigma$, if Σ is left amenable. To see that x' can be found in K_y we need only observe that once y is chosen, K can be replaced by K_y and x' then lies in K_y.

The converse, of course, is valid because the representation $s \to l_s^*$ over the w^*-compact set M in $m(\Sigma)^*$ is of the kind covered by the fixed point condition.

To make this a topological theorem is fairly easy. If it is assumed that Σ has a topology in which the semigroup multiplication is separately continuous, say that a homomorphism h of Σ into an $\mathscr{A}(K)$, K as before, is *slightly continuous* [*nearly continuous*] {*continuous*} if there is at least one [there is a dense set of] {for all} y in K, $s \to h_s y$ is a continuous function from Σ into K [see Day, 1961; Mitchell, 1966; Argabright, 1968; Huff, 1970]. Then we see that Theorem 6.1 is the discrete case of the following.

Theorem 6.3. There is an left-invariant mean on $C(\Sigma)$, the space of bounded continuous functions on Σ, if and only if every slightly (or every nearly) continuous representation of Σ into $\mathscr{A}(K)$ (K convex, compact and $A(K)$ separates points) has a fixed point. Such a fixed point can always be found in K_y, the closed convex hull of the orbit $h(\Sigma)\, y$, for any y for which $h_s y$ is continuous from Σ into K.

PROOF. If μ_0 is a left-invariant mean on $C(\Sigma)$, let μ be an extension of μ_0 to a mean on $m(\Sigma)$. Then when y is properly chosen, every Tf is in $C(\Sigma)$ so that the proof given above carries through to give a fixed x' in K_y.

Obviously, all nearly continuous representations are good if all slightly continuous ones are. But the representation $s \to l_s^*$ of Σ into $\mathscr{A}(M_0)$, where M_0 is the w^* topologized set of means on $C(\Sigma)$, is nearly continuous, for it is continuous at every $Q_0\varphi$, φ a finite mean.

If G is a locally compact group and M is the set of means on $L_\infty(G)$, the representation $g \to l_g^*$ of G into the w^* topologized M is again nearly continuous; this time we use the $Q\varphi$, where φ is in P_{00}, the continuous, nonnegative elements of norm one in $L_1(G)$. QP_{00} is w^* dense in M. The above proof can be reworked now to give the following:

Theorem 6.4. If G is a locally compact group, then the following conditions are equivalent. (1) There is a left invariant mean on $C(G)$, (2) Every slightly (or nearly) continuous representation of G into suitable $\mathscr{A}(K)$ has a fixed point. (3) There is a left-invariant mean on $L_\infty(G)$.

There is a better proof of the equivalence of (1) with (3) due to Greenleaf (see Section 13), $(la\pi_0)$ equivalent to $(la\pi)$.

Rickert (1965) has investigated locally compact groups with the property that every representation h of Σ in K for which $h_g x$ is a continuous function of both variables together has a fixed point. Namioka (1967) considers fixed points and other properties for representations of Σ into other abstract L spaces than $m(\Sigma)^*$. Mitchell (1970) characterizes certain fixed point properties of representations of a topological semigroup Σ by means of locating the corresponding subspaces of $C(\Sigma)$ on which there must be a left-invariant mean.

7. Stationary Semigroups

Mitchell (1965) observed another property of semigroups which is equivalent to left amenability. For each x in $m(\Sigma)$ define $Z_R(x)$ to be the coordinatewise closure of the convex hull of the right orbit $r(\Sigma)\, x$. [As we remarked in Section 4, this is equivalent to considering the

w^* closure of the convex hull of the orbit of $x^\vee$ under all the conjugate operators in $l_1(\Sigma)^*$ of the operators $* \delta_s$ in $l_1(\Sigma)$.] Σ is called *right stationary* if and only if for each x in $m(\Sigma)$ there is a constant function αe in each $Z_R(x)$.

Theorem 7.1 (Mitchell, 1965). Σ is left amenable if and only if it is right stationary (and dually). More precisely, if μ is a left-invariant mean on $m(\Sigma)$, then for each x in $m(\Sigma)$, $\mu(x)\, e$ is in $Z_R(x)$; if, on the other hand, Σ is right stationary and αe is in $Z_R(x)$, then there is a left invariant mean μ on $m(\Sigma)$ such that $\mu(x) = \alpha$.

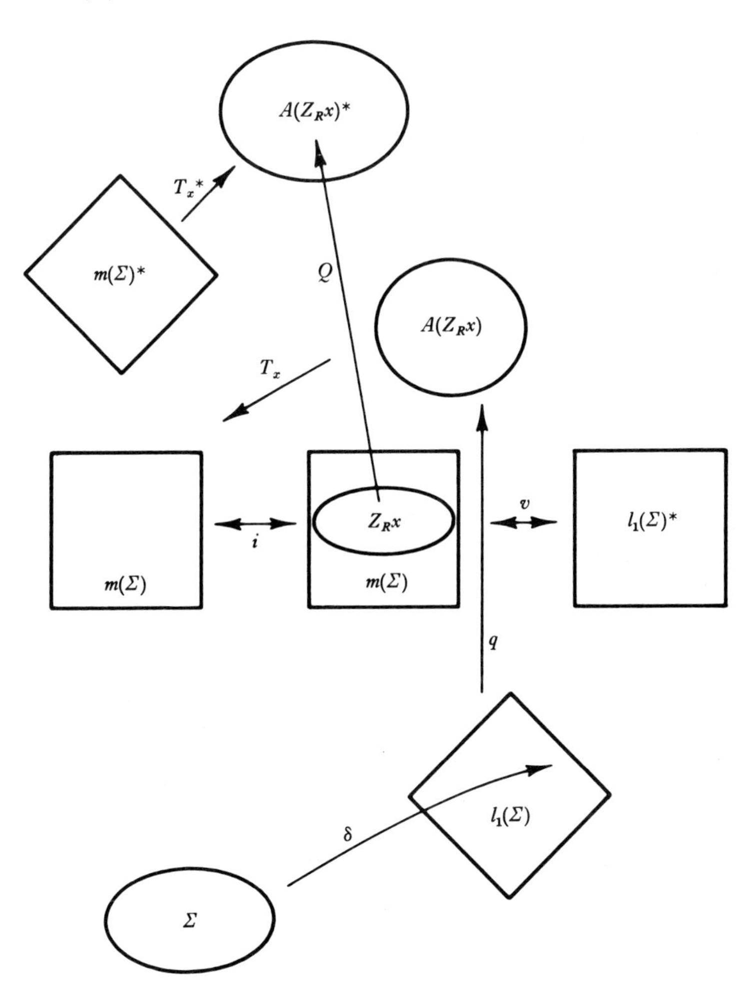

FIGURE 2.

$s \to \delta_s$ is the usual mapping of Σ into $l_1(\Sigma)$. q is defined from $l_1(\Sigma)$ into $A(Z_R x)$ by $q\varphi(y) = y^\vee(\varphi)$ for all y in $Z_R x$.

Q is defined from $Z_R x$ onto the set of means in $A(Z_R x)^*$ by $Qy(F) = F(y)$ for all F in $A(Z_R x)$. $y \to y^\vee$ is the isometry of $m(\Sigma)$ with $l_1(\Sigma)^*$ for which $y^\vee(\varphi) = \sum_{s\in\Sigma} y(s)\,\varphi(s)$ for all φ in $l_1(\Sigma)$. T_x is defined from $A(Z_R x)$ to $C(\Sigma) \subseteq m(\Sigma)$ by $[T_x F](s) = F(r_s x)$ for all s in Σ.

PROOF. Suppose that Σ is right stationary and for each x in $m(\Sigma)$ define $P_R(x) = \sup\{\alpha \mid \alpha e \in Z_R(x)\}$. Then Mitchell showed that P_R is sublinear on $m(\Sigma)$ and dominated by the norm, and

$$\{\alpha \mid \alpha e \in Z_R(x)\} = \{\alpha \mid -P_R(-x) \leqslant \alpha \leqslant P_R(x)\}.$$

Given an x and an α in the last-named interval the Hahn-Banach theorem (Banach, 1932, p. 20) shows that there is a μ in $m(\Sigma)^*$ such that $\mu(x) = \alpha$ and $\mu(y) \leqslant P_R(y)$ for all y in $m(\Sigma)$.

To prove μ left invariant, we need only show that for each y in $m(\Sigma)$ and each s in Σ, $P_R(l_s y - y) = 0$. If $\alpha = P_R(l_s y - y)$, then there exists a net φ_n of finite means such that the net $r_{\varphi_n}(l_s y - y)$ converges coordinatewise to αe. Use the coordinatewise compactness of bounded sets in $m(\Sigma)$ to get a subnet φ_{n_i} for which $r_{\varphi_{n_i}} y$ is coordinatewise convergent to some z in $m(\Sigma)$. But l_s commutes with all r_t, hence with all r_φ, so $\alpha e = \lim_i r_{\varphi_{n_i}}(l_s y - y) = l_s(\lim_i r_{\varphi_{n_i}} y) - \lim_i r_{\varphi_{n_i}} y = l_s z - z$. Hence $l_s z - z = \alpha e$, $l_{s^2} z - l_s z = \alpha e$, and so on. Adding, $l_{s^k} z - z = k\alpha e$ for all $k = 1, 2, \ldots$. Then α must be 0 or this would contradict the boundedness of the sequence $\| l_{s^k} z \|$. Hence $P_R(l_s y - y) = 0$ for each y in $m(\Sigma)$ and s in Σ.

If Σ is left amenable, we replace Mitchell's proof by a use of the fixed point Theorem 6.1, which asserts that there is a common fixed point of all the r_s in each of the compact sets $Z_R(x)$. In any semigroup each fixed element under all r_s is constant on any set $t\Sigma$, $t \in \Sigma$. But left amenability of Σ implies, by (3L″), that each $s\Sigma \cap t\Sigma$ is nonempty; hence each f fixed under all r_s is a constant function. This shows that left amenability implies right stationarity.

To get the last detail of the theorem we need to follow the proof of the fixed point theorem in enough detail to see that if μ is a left-invariant mean, then $\mu(x)\,e$ is precisely the fixed point f in $Z_R(x)$ given by Theorem 6.1; thus

$$f(s) = f^\vee(\delta_s) = [q\delta_s](f) = Qf(q\delta_s) = [T_x^*\mu](q\delta_s)$$

$$= \mu(T_x(q\delta_s)) = \mu(l_s x) = \mu(x).$$

For the next to the last equality we need to show that for each t in Σ

$$[T_x(q\delta_s)](t) = [q\delta_s](r_t x) = [r_t x]^\vee(\delta_s) = [r_t x](s) = x(st) = [l_s x](t)].$$

To topologize this theorem assume that Σ has a topology in which multiplication is separately continuous, then for each f in $C(\Sigma)$ and each s in Σ, $r_s f$ and $l_s f$ are again in $C(\Sigma)$. Even though $C(\Sigma)$ itself is seldom like a conjugate space, we can still use the coordinatewise convergence. If there is a mean μ_0 in $C(\Sigma)^*$ left invariant on $C(\Sigma)$, extend it to a mean μ on $m(\Sigma)$. Then for x in $C(\Sigma)$ the mapping T_x of $A(Z_R(x))$ into $m(\Sigma)$ actually has its range in $C(\Sigma)$. Carefully following the proof above we see that μ has an image f in $Z_R(x)$ and that the left invariance of μ on $C(\Sigma)$ is enough to make $f = \mu_0(x)\, e$, which is a fixed point of all r_s.

The converse proof seems to fail on the proof of subadditivity of P_R; it could be carried through if it could be shown that $x \in C(\Sigma)$ and $y \in Z_R x$, then $C(\Sigma) \cap Z_R y \neq \emptyset$.

Theorem 7.2. Let Σ be a topological semigroup with separately continuous multiplication. Then there is a left-invariant mean on $C(\Sigma)$ only if for each f in $C(\Sigma)$ there is a constant function in the pointwise closed convex hull of $r(\Sigma) f$.

For a locally compact group we no longer have the relation between coordinatewise convergence in $L_\infty(G)$ and w^* convergence in $L_1(G)^*$, so we have to define $L_\infty(G)$ to be right stationary if for each x in $L_\infty(G)$ there is a number α such that $(\alpha e)^\vee$ is in w^* closure of the convex hull of all $[r_g x]^\vee$. If $L_\infty(G)$ is right stationary, we define $P_R(x)$ as the sup of the appropriate α. For φ in $L_1(G)$ we define l_φ on $L_\infty(G)$ by: For each x in $L_\infty(G)$, $l_\varphi x = \int_G \varphi(g)\, l_g x\, dg$. Observe that $[l_\varphi x]^\vee = (\varphi\, *)^*\, x^\vee$ for each x in $L_\infty(G)$. A mean μ on $L_\infty(G)$ is called topologically left invariant (tli) if for each φ in P_{00}, $l_\varphi^* \mu = \mu$. [This is equivalent to $l_\varphi^* \mu = e^\vee(\varphi)\, \mu$ for each φ in $L_1(G)$.] We can show that if $\varphi \in L_1(G)$, then $l_\varphi x$ is left-uniformly continuous, hence continuous.

To adapt the proof of the fixed point Theorem 6.1 requires only to define, for x in $L_\infty(G)$ *a* map T_x on $L_1(G)$ by the following: for each φ in $L_1(G)$, $[T_x \varphi](g) = [r_g x]^\vee(\varphi)$ for each g in G. Note that $T_x \varphi = l_\varphi x$.

Theorem 7.3. Let G be a locally compact group. Then $L_\infty(G)$ is [topologically] left amenable if and only if $L_\infty(G)$ is {topologically} right stationary. More precisely, if μ_0 is a left-invariant mean on $C(G)$, or even on $LUC(G)$ (for this it suffices that $L_\infty(G)$ be left amenable) and if $z^\vee = T_x \mu_0$, then z is a constant function βe and is a fixed point of all r_g which lies in $Z_R x$, so $\beta \leqslant p_R(x)$. Conversely, if $L_\infty(G)$ is right stationary, then p_R is sublinear and every linear functional μ dominated by p_R is a topologically left-invariant mean on $L_\infty(G)$. Hence $\{\alpha | \alpha e \in Z_R x\} = \{\alpha | -p_R(-x) \leqslant \alpha \leqslant p_R(x)\} = \{\beta |$ there is a mean μ_0 on $C(G)$, or on $LUC(G)$ such that $[\beta e]^\vee = T_x^* \mu_0\} = \{\mu(x) | \mu$ a topologically left-invariant mean on $L_\infty(G)\}$.

It may help clarify the proof to note here that $Z_R x$, defined to be the w^* closed convex hull of $\{r_g x | g \in G\}$, is also the w^* closure of $\{r_\varphi x | \varphi \in P_{00}\}$, so that topological right stationarity is equivalent to ordinary right stationarity.

Mitchell (1965) found a useful condition for a subset E of Σ to have $\mu^\vee(E) = 1$ for at least one left-invariant mean μ on $m(\Sigma)$.

Theorem 7.4. Let Σ be a left-amenable semigroup. Then the following conditions on a set $E \subseteq \Sigma$ are equivalent:

(1) There exists a left-invariant mean μ on such that $\mu^\vee(E) = 1$.

(2) For each finite subset σ of Σ there is an s in Σ such that $\sigma s \subseteq E$.

Proof. If (2) holds, let Δ be the directed system of finite subsets of Σ ordered by inclusion; then for each σ in Δ there is an s_σ such that $\sigma s_\sigma \subseteq E$. Then for each s in Σ,

$$[r_{s_\sigma} \chi_E](s) = \chi_E(s s_\sigma) = 1 \qquad \text{as soon as} \quad s \in \sigma.$$

Hence e is the coordinatewise limit of $r_{s_\sigma} \chi_E$, so that

$$1 \geqslant \| \chi_E \| \geqslant P_R(\chi_E) \geqslant 1;$$

Therefore, by Theorem 7.1, there is a left-invariant μ with $\mu(\chi_E) = 1$; that is, $\mu^\vee(E) = 1$.

If (2) fails for some finite $\sigma \subseteq \Sigma$, let $\varphi = | \sigma |^{-1} \chi_\sigma$; then $\| l_\varphi \chi_E \| \leqslant (| \sigma | - 1)/| \sigma |$, so

$$\mu(\chi_E) = \mu(l_\varphi \chi_E) \leqslant P_R(l_\varphi \chi_E) \leqslant (| \sigma | - 1)/| \sigma | < 1.$$

Corollary 7.5 (Wilde, Frey).* If Σ is a left-amenable semigroup and Σ' is a left ideal in Σ, then there is a left-invariant mean μ on $m(\Sigma)$ such that $\mu^\vee(\Sigma') = 1$, so Σ' is left amenable.

Proof. For any s in Σ' and any finite subset σ of Σ we have $\sigma s \subseteq \Sigma'$, so (2) of Theorem 7.4 holds for Σ'. The rest follows from (3L).

Mitchell (1965) also shows that Theorem 7.4 yields many mutually singular invariant means on the integers, because there condition (2) is satisfied by any set E which contains arbitrarily long, finite blocks of consecutive integers, no matter how thinly the blocks are scattered.

We can also use Theorem 7.4 to give a result related to one of Wilde and Witz (1967) but we need some definitions. In a semigroup Σ call a

*Wilde (1964), Frey (1960).

subsemigroup Γ *left seminormal* if for each s in Γ, $s^{-1}\Gamma s \subseteq \Gamma$, i.e., for each s in Γ, $st \in \Gamma s$ implies $t \in \Gamma$. If Γ is a subsemigroup of Σ, then the *left-Γ-order relation in Σ* is defined by letting $\{s\} \cup \Gamma s$ be the set of successors of s. The *left-Γ-equivalence relation in Σ* is the Σ smallest equivalence relation including the left-Γ order.

(7A) Let Γ be a subsemigroup of the semigroup Σ; then s is left-Γ equivalent to a point t if and only if there is a finite chain of elements $s = s_1, \ldots, s_k = t$, and elements $g_1, \ldots, g_{k-1}$ in Γ such that $g_1 s_2 = s_1, g_2 s_2 = s_3, \ldots, g_{2i-1} s_{2i} = s_{2i-1}, g_{2i} s_{2i} = s_{2i+1}, \ldots$.

Theorem 7.6. Let Σ be a left-amenable semigroup and let Γ be (1) a left-seminormal subsemigroup of Σ such that (2) all elements of Σ are in the same left-Γ-equivalence class. Then there is a left-invariant mean μ on $m(\Sigma)$ such that $\mu^{\vee}(\Gamma) = 1$, so Γ is left amenable.

PROOF. In order to use Mitchell's criterion, Theorem 7.4 (2), we let σ be a finite subset of Σ. Then if $s \in \sigma$, by (7A) there is a chain with $s = s_k$, s_1 in Γ, $g_1 s_2 = s_1, g_2 s_2 = s_3, \ldots$, with all g_i in Γ. Let $h_s = g_1 g_3, \ldots$, and let S_σ be the product of the h_s, $s \in \sigma$, in any order. Then we can prove that sS_σ is in Γ for each s in σ.

First, $s_1 \in \Gamma$. g_1 is somewhere in the word S_σ so $S_\sigma = v_1 g_1 w_1$, with v_1 and w_1 words in Γ. Hence $g_1 s_2 S_\sigma = s_1 v_1 g_1 w_1$, but $g_1 s_2 v_1 g_1$ is therefore in Γg_1; hence $s_2 v_1 g_1$ is in Γ so $s_2 S_\sigma = s_2 v_1 g_1 w_1$ is in Γw_1. Hence $s_3 S_\sigma = s_3 v_1 g_1 w_1$ is also in Γw_1. Now $g_3 s_4 = s_3$ and $w_1 = g_3 w_2$ so the first step can be repeated to get $s_4 S_\sigma = s_4 v_1 g_1 g_3 w_2$ in Γw_2. Continuing by induction, sS_σ is in Γ for each s in σ.

In a group G the left-Γ-equivalence class containing Γ is the smallest subgroup of G containing Γ; hence, by (3F) we have the following.

Corollary 7.7. Each left- [right-] seminormal subsemigroup of an amenable group G is left [right] amenable. Hence a left- and right-seminormal subsemigroup of an amenable group is amenable.

REMARK. Normality is automatic for subsemigroups of Abelian groups, so the result which I first tried without the normality hypothesis is true trivially for Abelian G.

Unfortunately Hochster (1968) has just shown that if F is the free group on two generators a and b, and if F'' is the second commutator group $[F', F']$ of F, then the free semigroup on a and b is mapped isomorphically into $F_1 = F/F''$, which is an extension of one Abelian group F/F' by another F'/F'', and therefore is amenable. Hence if μ is any (left or right) invariant mean on F_1, $\mu^{\vee}(\Sigma) = 0$ by (3L).

In locally compact groups Theorem 7.4 takes a somewhat different form.

Theorem 7.8. The following conditions on a measurable subset E of a left-amenable, locally compact group G are equivalent:

(1) There is a mean μ on $L_\infty(G)$ which is topologically left invariant (that is, $l_\varphi^* \mu = \mu$ for all φ in P_{00}) and $\mu(E) = 1$.

(2) For each compact set $K \subset G$, $\sup_{s \in G} H(K \setminus Es) = H(K)$; that is for each $\epsilon > 0$, there is $s = s(\epsilon, K)$ such that $H(K \setminus Es) \geqslant (1 - \epsilon) H(K)$.

Here H is left Haar measure in G. Mitchell's proof (1965) can be adapted to this case, "if" because w^* convergence of bounded nets in $L_1(G)^*$ can be tested using only elements of P_{00}, and "only if" by showing that if (2) fails, for K, then, setting $\varphi = (H(K))^{-1} \chi_K$, we have $\| l_\varphi \chi_E \| \leqslant 1 - \epsilon < 1$. We remark that in a unimodular group $K \setminus Es$ in (2) can be replaced by $Ks \setminus E$, much as in Theorem 7.4.

8. Ergodic Theorems

The mean ergodic theorem originally was due to von Neumann (1932) for one-parameter unitary groups in Hilbert space. The theorem is an operator generalization of a very simple phenomenon: If α is a complex number, then the arithmetic means $s_n(\alpha) = n^{-1} \sum_{i \leqslant n} \alpha^i$ converge or diverge according as $| \alpha | \leqslant 1$ or $| \alpha | > 1$, and for $| \alpha | \leqslant 1$ but $\alpha \neq 1$, $\lim_n s_n(\alpha) = 0$.

If we begin with a bounded linear operator T in a Banach space B we can ask when $A_n = n^{-1} \sum_{i \leqslant n} T^i$ must converge in some sense. Riesz and Yosida gave the first simple proofs that if $\| T \| \leqslant 1$ and B is reflexive, then (1) A_n converges in the strong topology to a projection P; (2) $PT = TP = P$; (3) the range of P is the set of fixed points $\mathscr{F}(T)$ and the null space of P is the closed linear manifold $\mathscr{D}(T)$ spanned by all the elements $x - Tx$, x in B.

Cohen (1940) investigated matrices and averages determined by them, $A_i = \sum_j a_{ij} T^j$. The arithmetic mean matrix is an example of one satisfying the Silverman-Toeplitz conditions (Banach, 1932, p. 91) which are necessary and sufficient that $((a_{ij}))$ transform every convergent real sequence into another sequence with the same limit; these conditions are: (1) $\lim_i a_{ij} = 0$ for each j, (2) $\lim_i \sum_j a_{ij} = 1$, and (3) $\sup_i \sum_j | a_{ij} | < \infty$. Vulich had showed that these conditions were also necessary and sufficient that $((a_{ij}))$ transform every convergent sequence of points in every Banach space B into a sequence in B with the same limit. Cohen showed that if in addition one imposed the condition (4) $\lim_i \sum_j | a_{i,j+1} - a_{ij} | = 0$ (which, of course, is satisfied by the arithmetic mean matrix), then the new A_i also converge in the strong operator topology to exactly the same P as do the arithmetic means of the T^i.

Day (1942) moved from this to the general Abelian semigroup, replacing the matrix by a net of linear functionals (expressed in terms of finitely additive set functions). This paper contains the proof that every bounded Abelian operator semigroup is ergodic, as a consequence of the proof that every Abelian semigroup is amenable.

In a general semigroup $\mathscr{S}$, the elementary arithmetic means are not available. Eberlein showed that the mean ergodic theorem really depended on the existence of a net of averages $\mathscr{A} = (A_n, n \in \Delta)$ of $\mathscr{S}$ satisfying

(A1) $\lim_{n\in\Delta} A_n(S - I) = 0$ for each S in $\mathscr{S}$.

(A2) $\lim_{n\in\Delta} (S - I) A_n = 0$ for each S in $\mathscr{S}$.

(A3) $\limsup_{n\in\Delta} \| A_n \| < \infty$.

The convergence in (A1) and (A2) can be either in the norm, strong, or weak topology for operators in B. One also needs to decide what kind of averages to allow. Eberlein calls the operator semigroup $\mathscr{S}$ *ergodic* if a net $\mathscr{A}$ can be found satisfying (A1, 2, 3) with convergence in the strong topology in (A1, 2) and with each A in $\mathscr{A}$ satisfying the condition.

(A4) For each x in B, each $A_n x$ is in $K(x)$, the closed convex hull of the orbit $\mathscr{S}x$ of x. Finite averages are also useful if available; we shall call an operator semigroup $\mathscr{S}$ *restrictedly ergodic* if the A_n satisfy (A1, 2, 3) and the stronger condition.

(FA4) Each A_n is a finite average of $\mathscr{S}$; that is, there is $\varphi_n \in P_0(\mathscr{S})$ such that $A_n = \sum_S \varphi_n(S)\, S$.

Recall that for a given operator semigroup $\mathscr{S}$ $\mathscr{F}(\mathscr{S})$ is the set of common fixed points of $\mathscr{S}$ and $\mathscr{D}(\mathscr{S})$ is the closed linear set spanned by all $Sx - x$, x in B and S in $\mathscr{S}$; let $\mathscr{E}(\mathscr{S}) = \mathscr{F}(\mathscr{S}) + \mathscr{D}(\mathscr{S})$.

8.1. Ergodic Theorem. Let $\mathscr{S}$ be an ergodic operator semigroup. Then

(1) $\mathscr{F}(\mathscr{S}) \cap \mathscr{D}(\mathscr{S}) = \{0\}$.

(2) $\mathscr{E}(\mathscr{S})$ is closed in B.

(3) $\lim_n A_n x$ exists (in the norm topology of B) if and only if $x \in \mathscr{E}(\mathscr{S})$. If $Px = \lim_n A_n x$ for each x in $\mathscr{E}(\mathscr{S})$, then $\| P \| \leqslant \limsup_n \| A_n \| \leqslant \sup\{\| S \| \mid S \in \mathscr{S}\}$.

(4) For each x in $\mathscr{E}(\mathscr{S})$ and S in $\mathscr{S}$ $PSx = SPx = Px = P^2x$.

(5) $P(\mathscr{E}(\mathscr{S})) = \mathscr{F}(\mathscr{S})$ and $P(\mathscr{D}(\mathscr{S})) = 0$; that is, P is the projection of $\mathscr{E}(\mathscr{S})$ along $\mathscr{D}(\mathscr{S})$ onto $\mathscr{F}(\mathscr{S})$.

(6) When $x \in \mathscr{E}(\mathscr{S})$, Px is the unique point in $K(x) \cap \mathscr{F}(\mathscr{S})$.

(7) If $k(\mathscr{S})$, the convex hull of $\mathscr{S}$, is ordered by left products (that is, $ST > T$ for all S, T in $k(\mathscr{S})$) then the limit, $\lim_\pi$, as π runs out $k(\mathscr{S})$, of πx exists in the sense of Alaoglu-Birkhoff if and only if $x \in \mathscr{E}(\mathscr{S})$; for such x, $\lim_\pi \pi x = Px$.

(8) $x \in \mathscr{E}(\mathscr{S})$ if and only if the net $A_n x$ has a weakly convergent subnet; then $w \lim_i A_{n_i} x = Px$.

Sketch of Proof. (A2) states that if x is such that $Px = \lim_n A_n x$ exists, then $Px \in \mathscr{F}(\mathscr{S})$. Obviously $\lim_n A_n x = x$ if $x \in \mathscr{F}(\mathscr{S})$ and (A1) states that $\lim_n A_n y = 0$ if $y = Sx - x$. (A3) then implies that $\lim_n A_n y = 0$ if $y \in \mathscr{D}(\mathscr{S})$. But if $Px = \lim_n A_n x$ exists, then $x - Px \in \mathscr{D}(\mathscr{S})$. This gives all of (3), and most of the rest is just grinding. [(7) requires the definition of Alaoglu-Birkhoff convergence, which can also be found in Day (1944, p. 207).]

It is pertinent to inquire when $\mathscr{E}(\mathscr{S})$ is all of B. (8) shows that *reflexivity of B is one simple sufficient condition.* From this and the fact that every abelian semigroup is amenable we could get a theorem of Dunford.

Corollary 8.2. A bounded Boolean algebra $\mathscr{B}$ of projections in a reflexive space B can be embedded in a complete Boolean algebra $\mathscr{B}$ of projections in B without increase of bound.

Proof. If $\mathscr{S}$ is the set of infs of finite subsets of a subset $\mathscr{B}_0$ of $\mathscr{B}'$, then $\mathscr{S}$ is an Abelian semigroup under the operation inf; so it is also a directed system, and for any S_1 in $\mathscr{S}$ we have $SS_1 - S = 0 = S_1 S - S$ as soon as S is smaller than S_1, so the semigroup forms a net of averages of itself. The ergodic theorem and reflexivity says that the strong limit of S is a projection P with its norm bounded by that of $\mathscr{S}$. This is the induction step, and an application of the maximum principle shows the existence of $\mathscr{B}$.

Observing that reflexivity was used in the ergodic theorem through weak compactness of the unit ball in B, we may consider compactness to be of enough value to be worth some other trouble [see Day (1942, 1950)]. This suggests that we embed B in the natural way in B^{**} and regard the operators in $\mathscr{S}$ and $\mathscr{A}$ as operators from B into B^{**}. [See Witz (1964) for a way of matching $\mathscr{L}(B, B^{**})$ with $\mathscr{L}(B^*, B^*)$ in order to embed $\mathscr{S}$ in a compact semigroup.] By w^* compactness of the unit ball in B^{**}, there exists a subnet A_{n_i}, $i \in \Delta'$: of $\mathscr{A}$ such that for each x in B, $\Pi x = w^* \lim_i A_{n_i} x$ exists in B^{**}. (That is, $\Pi = w_*\text{-}\lim_i A_{n_i}$, using the product space topology for $\mathscr{L}(B, B^{**})$ with the w^* topology of B^{**} in each factor.) Then $\Pi x = Px$ if $x \in \mathscr{E}(\mathscr{S})$ and $\Pi x \notin B$ if $x \notin \mathscr{E}(\mathscr{S})$.

Also the conditions (A1, 2, 3, 4) imply

(A_*1) $\Pi(S - I) = 0$ for each S in $\mathcal{S}$.

(A_*2) $(S - I)^{**} \Pi = 0$ for each S in $\mathcal{S}$.

(A_*3) $\| \Pi \| < \infty$.

(A_*4) For each x in B, Πx is in the w^*-closed convex hull of the orbit $\mathcal{S}x$ in B^{**}.

Call a semigroup $\mathcal{S}$ *w_* ergodic* if a Π exists satisfying (A_*1, 2, 3, 4). Then we see that if Πx is in B, then Πx is in $\mathcal{F}(\mathcal{S})$ and then $x - \Pi x$ is in $\mathcal{D}(\mathcal{S})$, so x is in $\mathcal{E}(\mathcal{S})$. Then the ergodic theorem conclusions hold with appropriate modifications such as (3_*) Πx is in B if and only if x is in $\mathcal{E}(\mathcal{S})$.

We have just shown that *an ergodic operator semigroup is w_* ergodic*. The *converse is also true*, for we can use (A_*4) to choose a net A_n w_* convergent to Π and make the choice so that the $A_n x$ are averages of $\mathcal{S}x$. We can also keep $\| A_n \| \leqslant \| \Pi \| + 1$, and then ($A_*1$, 2) yield (A1, 2) with w^* convergence. Lemma 5.2 shows that the net A_n thus derived can be replaced by a net A'_m of finite averages far out in A_n so that the A'_m have s^* convergence in (A1, 2). Hence *w_* ergodicity is equivalent to s^* ergodicity*.

Similarly, if $\mathcal{S}$ is restrictedly ergodic in any sense, we find the following:

(FA_*4) Π is in the w_* closure in $\mathcal{L}(B, B^{**})$ of the convex hull of $\mathcal{S}$.

Call $\mathcal{S}$ *restrictedly w_* ergodic* if Π exists in $\mathcal{L}(B, B^{**})$ satisfying (A_*1, 2, 3) and (FA_*4). The proof sketched above shows also that *$\mathcal{S}$ is restrictedly w_* ergodic if and only if it is restrictedly ergodic with s^* convergence in* (A1, 2).

We consider next an abstract semigroup Σ. If B is a Banach space, a *bounded representation* (*antirepresentation*) *of Σ over B* is a bounded homomorphism (antihomomorphism) of Σ into the multiplicative semigroup of $\mathcal{L}(B, B)$.

Theorem 8.3. (Day, 1950, 1957). The following conditions on an abstract semigroup Σ are equivalent:

(1) Σ is amenable (or strongly amenable).

(2) Every bounded representation (or antirepresentation) h of Σ over a Banach space B is ergodic (in any sense).

(3) The right and left representations of Σ over $m(\Sigma)$ are ergodic (in any sense).

Proof. The conditions of (1) are equivalent by Theorem 5.1. Hence if (1) holds, there is a net $(\varphi_n, n \in \Delta)$ of finite means on Σ strongly convergent to invariance; define $h_n = \sum_{s \in \Sigma} \varphi_n(s) h_s$. Then it can be calculated that $\mathscr{S} = h(\Sigma)$ is restrictedly uniformly ergodic under this net $(h_n, n \in \Delta)$ of finite averages of $\mathscr{S}$. Hence (1) implies the strongest form of (2). Obviously each form of (2) implies the corresponding form of (3). If the weakest kind of ergodicity holds in (3), then the left shift is w_* ergodic, and Π reduced to $\mathscr{E}(l(\Sigma))$ is a projection P of norm 1 carrying $\mathscr{D}(l(\Sigma))$ to 0 and leaving the constant functions fixed. Defining ν on $\mathscr{D}(l(\Sigma)) +$ constants to be the value of the constant function, we see that $\| \nu \| = 1$; extend ν by the Hahn-Banach theorem to all of $m(\Sigma)$ to get a mean μ. The condition that μ vanishes on $\mathscr{D}(l(\Sigma))$ is precisely the condition that μ is left invariant.

A dual proof yields a right-invariant μ' from ergodicity of the right shift on $m(\Sigma)$. By (3A) Σ is amenable.

In a general Σ one cannot conclude the amenability of Σ from ergodicity of the right shift representation alone. For an easy example, in semigroups where $st = s$ for all s, t in Σ, $r_s = I$ for all s so $r(\Sigma)$ is ergodic. However, Σ is not left amenable if it has more than one point. However, some special semigroups will work (Day, 1950).

Theorem 8.4. If Σ is a semigroup such that the set of all $l_s x$, x in $m(\Sigma)$, s in Σ, spans $m(\Sigma)$, then $r(\Sigma)$ is restrictedly ergodic if and only if Σ is amenable.

PROOF. If Σ is amenable, it is strongly amenable; then we quote (1) implies (3) from Theorem 8.3: Conversely, if $r(\Sigma)$ is ergodic, then e is at distance 1 from $\mathscr{D}(r(\Sigma))$ so there is a right-invariant mean.

Next, there is a net φ_n of finite means on Σ such that $\| r_t r_{\varphi_n} - r_{\varphi_n} \| \to 0$. We may pass to a subnet such that $Q\varphi_n$ is w^* convergent to some mean μ. Then for all x in $m(\Sigma)$ and s in Σ

$$\begin{aligned} | r_t r_{\varphi_n} x(s) - r_{\varphi_n} x(s) | &= \left| \left[r_t \sum_v \varphi_n(v)\, r_v x \right](s) - \left[\sum_v \varphi_n(v)\, r_v x \right](s) \right| \\ &= \left| \sum_v \varphi_n(v)(x(stv) - x(sv)) \right| = \left| \sum_v \varphi_n(v)[l_t l_s x - l_s x](v) \right| \\ &= |[l_t l_s x - l_s x]^{\vee}(\varphi_n)| \to \mu[(l_t - I)\, l_s x] = [(l_t - I)^* \mu](l_s x). \end{aligned}$$

But the first term in this chain tends to zero; therefore, because the $l_s x$ span $m(\Sigma)$, $l_t^* = \mu$ for all t. A similar proof would have shown also that $r_t^* \mu = \mu$, but we found a right-invariant ν an easier way; (3A) then shows that Σ is amenable.

Of course, some operator semigroups which as abstract semigroups are very bad may be fairly good (for example, compact) semigroups in their actual situations in B, so fixed points may still be present. See Alaoglu and Birkhoff (1940) or Day (1941) for many such cases; in particular, uniformly convex B or strictly convex, reflexive B provide fix points for contraction semigroups, because in that case K_x the closed convex hull of the orbit of an x is w compact and the unique point of K_x nearest the origin is fixed.

9. Almost Convergence

For Σ the Semigroup of Integers, G

G. Lorentz called attention to those functions x in $m(\Sigma)$ which yield the same value $c = \mu(x)$ for all left- [right-] invariant means μ on $m(\Sigma)$; call these x *left- [right-] almost convergent* (to c). Witz (1964) and Granirer (1963) contributed the following result: recall that $\mathscr{D}(l(\Sigma))$ is the closed linear subspace of $m(\Sigma)$ spanned by all the $x - l_s x$, $x \in m(\Sigma)$, $s \in \Sigma$. Let C be the space of constant functions on Σ.

Theorem 9.1. Suppose that Σ is left amenable. Then an x in $m(\Sigma)$ is left-almost convergent (to α) if and only if $x \in C + \mathscr{D}(l(\Sigma))$ (and $x = \alpha e + h$, $h \in \mathscr{D}(l(\Sigma))$.

PROOF. First, if $x \in \mathscr{D}(l(\Sigma))$, then x is lac to 0, for left invariance of μ is equivalent to μ vanishing on $\mathscr{D}(l(\Sigma))$. Conversely, if $x \notin \mathscr{D}(l(\Sigma))$, x cannot be lac to 0, for the Hahn-Banach theorem says that then there is a ν in $m(\Sigma)^*$ vanishing on $\mathscr{D}(l(\Sigma))$ but not vanishing at x. Such a ν is left invariant; Namioka's Lemma 2.2 says that ν^+ and ν^- are left invariant, and one does not vanish at x, so, for example, $\nu^+/\| \nu^+ \|$ is a left-invariant mean not zero at x. Hence x is not lac to 0.

Now if x is lac to α, then $x - \alpha e$ is lac to 0 and hence belongs to $\mathscr{D}(l(\Sigma))$ and $x = \alpha e + h$, h in $\mathscr{D}(l(\Sigma))$. If, on the other hand, $x = \alpha e + h$, then x is clearly lac to α.

Corollary 9.2. If Σ is left amenable and if φ_n is a net of finite means converging strongly to left invariance, then $\lim_n \| l_{\varphi_n} h \| = 0$ if and only if $h \in \mathscr{D}(l(\Sigma))$. Hence there is a constant α such that $\lim_n \| l_{\varphi_n} x - \alpha e \| = 0$ if and only if $x \in C + \mathscr{D}(l(\Sigma))$ and $x = \alpha e + h$, with h in $\mathscr{D}(l(\Sigma))$.

PROOF. For each x in $m(\Sigma)$ and s in Σ,

$$l_{\varphi_n}(x - l_s x)\| = \| l_{\varphi_n - \delta_s * \varphi_n} x \| \leqslant \| \varphi_n - \delta_s * \varphi_n \| \cdot \| x \| \to 0.$$

Also the set where $\| l_{\varphi_n} z \| \to 0$ is closed and linear; hence it contains all of $\mathscr{D}(l(\Sigma))$. But if $\| l_{\varphi_n} z \| \to 0$, then for each left-invariant mean μ, $\mu(z) = \mu(l_{\varphi_n} z) \to 0$, so that z is lac to 0; then by the theorem $z \in \mathscr{D}(l(\Sigma))$.

Next, to say that $\| l_{\varphi_n} x - \alpha e \| \to 0$ says that αe is in the norm-closed convex hull of the left orbit of x. Also $\| l_{\varphi_n} x - \alpha e \| = \| l_{\varphi_n}(x - \alpha e) \| \to 0$ so $x - \alpha e$ is in $\mathscr{D}(l(\Sigma))$ and $x = \alpha e + (x - \alpha e)$ is in $C + \mathscr{D}(l(\Sigma))$. If, on the other hand, $x = \alpha e + h$, h in $\mathscr{D}(l(\Sigma))$, then $l_{\varphi_n} x = \alpha l_{\varphi_n} e + l_{\varphi_n} h \to \alpha e$.

There are various definitions of sublinear functionals p on $m(\Sigma)$ which determine the left- [right-] {two-sided} invariant means as those μ in $m(\Sigma)^*$ which are dominated by p. Lorentz used Banach's functional

$$p(x) = \inf \left[\limsup_{k \to \infty} n^{-1} \sum_{i \leqslant n} x(k + m_i) \right],$$

where the inf is taken over all integers n and $m_1, \ldots, m_n$. Lorentz (1948) and Jerison (1957) proved that

$$p'(x) = \lim_n \left[\limsup_k n^{-1} \sum_{i \leqslant n} x(k + i) \right]$$

is equal to $p(x)$ in m(integers). Følner (1957) went to left-invariant means on groups G and used two functions which for semigroups become

$$p_L(x) = \inf_{\varphi} [\sup_{s \in \Sigma} l_\varphi x(s)],$$

where φ runs over the finite means on Σ;

$$p_L'(x) = \inf_n [\sup_{s \in \Sigma} (x(s) + h(s))],$$

where h is a finite linear combination of $x_i - l_{s_i} x_i$.

Mitchell (1965) used the function defined in Section 7:

$$P_R(x) = \sup\{\alpha |\ \alpha e \in Z_R(x),$$

the pointwise closed convex hull of $r(\Sigma)\, x\}$.

Day (1957) used a two-sided function which for left amenability should be changed to

$$p_L''(x) = \inf\{\mu(y) |\ y \geqslant x \quad \text{and} \quad y \in C + \mathscr{D}(l(\Sigma))\},$$

where μ is one (and by Theorem 9.1, no matter which one) left-invariant mean on $m(\Sigma)$.

Theorem 9.3. If Σ is left amenable, then

$$p_L = p_L' = p_L'' = P_R = \sup\{\mu |\ \mu \text{ a left invariant mean on } m(\Sigma)\}.$$

Hence x is left-almost convergent (to $p(x)$) if and only if for p one (hence any) of the above functions, $-p(-x) = p(x)$.

PROOF. Obviously the last function is sublinear and dominated by the norm. We proved in Section 7 that the last two functions are equal.

Since $l_\varphi x = (l_\varphi x - x) + x$, each $l_\varphi x$ is of the form $x + h$, so $p_L'(x) \leqslant p_L(x)$. Følner's proof of the converse in groups used (F_1), but we can use Result 9.2 instead. If $\eta \geqslant p_L'(x)$, take $\epsilon > 0$ and h so that $(\eta + \epsilon)\, e > x + h$; then for all n, $(\eta + \epsilon)\, e > l_{\varphi_n}(x + h) = l_{\varphi_n} x + l_{\varphi_n} h$, but $l_{\varphi_n} h$ goes to zero by Theorem 9.2 so that there is n with $(\eta + 2\epsilon)\, e > l_{\varphi_n} x$; i.e., $p_L(x) < p_L'(x) + 2\epsilon$ for all $\epsilon > 0$. Therefore $p_L(x) \leqslant p_L'(x)$.

p_L' is obviously sublinear and dominated by the norm and vanishes on $\mathscr{D}(l(\Sigma))$, so any μ it dominates is left invariant. By Theorem 2.1, $p_L'(e) = 1 = -p_L'(-e)$ so a μ under p_L' is also a mean. Clearly p_L' dominates any left-invariant mean, so p_L' is the last function on the list as well.

By the proof of the monotone extension theorem (Day, 1962, p. 20) an element μ of $m(\Sigma)^*$ is a left-invariant mean if and only if p_L'' dominates μ; hence p_L'' is also the last function.

Finally, for any sublinear p, any x and any α in $[-p(-x), p(x)]$, the Hahn-Banach theorem gives a μ in $m(\Sigma)^*$ dominated by p and having the value α at x. Hence the lac elements are precisely those where one (hence all) of the above functions satisfy $-p(-x) = p(x)$.

This is all we do when Σ is only left amenable, dual results hold for right, and a little more can be done when Σ is amenable. For Theorem 7.1 we proved that if Σ is left amenable, then $\mathscr{F}(r(\Sigma)) = C$; hence for amenable Σ, $\mathscr{F}(l(\Sigma)) = C = \mathscr{F}(r(\Sigma))$, and $\mathscr{E}(l(\Sigma)) = C + \mathscr{D}(l(\Sigma))$ and $\mathscr{E}(r(\Sigma)) = C + \mathscr{D}(r(\Sigma))$. By Theorem 8.3 the left- [right-] {two-sided} almost convergent elements are those of $\mathscr{E}(l(\Sigma))$ [$\mathscr{E}(r(\Sigma))$] {$\mathscr{E}(r(\Sigma)\, l(\Sigma))$}. Hence for $i = L$, [R], {2} we can define

$$q_i(x) = \inf\{\mu_i(y) \mid y \geqslant x \quad \text{and} \quad y \in \mathscr{E}(\mathscr{S}_i)\},$$

where μ_i is i invariant and $\mathscr{S}_i = l(\Sigma)$ [$r(\Sigma)$] {$r(\Sigma)\, l(\Sigma)$}.

Theorem 9.4. If Σ is amenable, then

$$q_i = p_i = p_i' = p_i'' = P_{i'}\,,$$

where $L' = R$, $R' = L$, and $2' = 2$. Hence a μ in $m(\Sigma)^*$ is an i-invariant mean if and only if μ is dominated by one of these functions, say p_i. Hence the following conditions on an x in $m(\Sigma)$ are equivalent:

(1) x is i-almost convergent.

(2) $-p_i(-x) = p_i(x)$ (or p_i' or p_i'' or q_i or $P_{i'}$).

(3) There exist in the convex hull of the i orbit of x functions uniformly arbitrarily near to constants.

(4) If φ_n is a net of means on Σ strongly convergent to l [r] {2} invariance, then $\lim_n l_{\varphi_n}x$ [$\lim_n r_{\varphi_n}x$] {$\lim_n r_{\varphi_n}l_{\varphi_n}x$} is a constant where the limits are to be taken in the norm topology of $m(\Sigma)$.

(5) $x \in \mathscr{E}(\mathscr{S}_i)$.

I worked with two-almost convergence, that is, with $\mathscr{E}(r(\Sigma)\, l(\Sigma))$, the closure of $\mathscr{E}(r(\Sigma)) + \mathscr{E}(l(\Sigma))$ (Day, 1957). H. A. Dye needed those elements which are *both* left- *and* right-almost convergent, that is, $\mathscr{E}(r(\Sigma)) \cap \mathscr{E}(l(\Sigma))$.

10. Compact Semigroups

Compactness of a semigroup carries with it so much structure theory analogous to that for finite semigroups that existence of invariant means on $C(\Sigma)$, the space of continuous functions, is fairly easy to test. Numakura (1952) showed that there is a kernel K, that is, a smallest (closed automatically) two-sided ideal in any compact Σ; clearly if a mean μ has any kind of invariance, then $\mu^\vee(K) = 1$. This kernel is the union of the minimal left ideals and of the minimal right ideals. Let U be the set of idempotent elements of K. Then U is closed, hence compact.

Rosen (1956) studied invariant means on $C(\Sigma)$ using this and a little more structure and also the Riesz-Kakutani representation of linear functionals on $C(\Sigma)$ by regular Baire measures on Σ. [See, for example, Hewitt and Ross (1963).]

Theorem 10.1 (Rosen). Let Σ be a compact semigroup; then the following conditions are equivalent:

(1) There is a left-invariant mean μ on $C(\Sigma)$.

(2) There is a left-invariant mean μ on $C(K)$.

(3) There is a regular Baire measure $\mu^\vee$ on Σ (supported on K) such that $\mu^\vee(s^{-1}E) = \mu^\vee(E)$ for all Baire subsets E of Σ and all s in Σ.

(4) There is just one minimal right ideal R in Σ (then $R = K$).

(5) K is homeomorphic and isomorphic to $G \times U$, where G is any one of the minimal left ideals of K, G is a compact group, where U is the set of idempotents in K, and multiplication is defined in U by $uu' = u'$

for all u, u' in U. This isomorphism yields for each measure w on U a left-invariant mean μ on $C(G)$ by the formula

$$\mu(f) = \int_U \int_G f(g, u)\, dg\, dw(u),$$

where dg is normalized Haar measure on G.

PROOF. (1), (2), and (3) are equivalent and imply (4). If (4) holds, and $u \in U$, then $uK = K$, so for each s in K there is t in K with $ut = s$; then $us = u(ut) = ut = s$; that is, each u in U is a left identity in K; in particular, if $u, v \in U$, then $uv = v$. The structure theory shows that Ku is a group for each u in U and that each minimal left ideal of Σ must contain a u of U. Also multiplication on the right by v in U carries Ku isomorphically onto Kv, so, letting G be any one of the groups Ku, we see that K, as a semigroup is isomorphic to $G \times U$ under the mapping $(\infty, u) \rightarrow gu$, and this map is continuous. Compactness makes it a homeomorphism.

If (5) holds, the μ defined there is easily seen to be left invariant no matter what w is chosen; since dg is unique, this means that the set of left invariant means on $C(\Sigma)$ is like the set of all means on $C(U)$.

Because evaluation at u gives for each u a mean on $C(U)$ we also get the following.

Corollary 9.2 (Rosen, 1956). Σ has a unique left-invariant mean if and only if Σ has only one minimal left ideal L and one minimal right ideal R. Then $R = L = K$, K is a compact group, and the unique left or unique right or unique two-sided mean on Σ is given by normalized Haar measure over K.

11. Semigroups with "Few" Invariant Means

We have already pointed out that a finite group has precisely one invariant mean (L, R, or 2). Let $J_i(\Sigma)$ be the linear subspace of $m(\Sigma)^*$ containing just the i-invariant elements; this says that if G is a finite group, then $J_R(G) = J_L(G) = J_2(G)$, and each is of dimension 1. Abelian groups with more than one element have more than one invariant mean [as shown by Day (1957)]. Luthar (1959) proved the following.

Theorem 11.1. Let Σ be an Abelian semigroup; then Σ has only one invariant mean if and only if Σ contains a finite ideal. In this case Σ has a minimal finite ideal K, K is a group, and the only invariant mean on Σ is averaging over K.

Granirer (1963) later asked when any $J_i(\Sigma)$ are finite dimensional. If Σ has a left-invariant mean, then the right ideals have the finite intersection property but the left ideals may be disjoint. If there are any finite left ideals, then there are minimal finite left ideals in Σ; they are groups, and have left cancellation in Σ.

Theorem 11.2 (Granirer, 1963a). (A) If every left ideal of Σ contains a finite left ideal of Σ, then there are disjoint finite subgroups G_α of which are minimal left ideals with left cancellation and the G_α are all isomorphic to each other. If there are n, $0 < n < \infty$, of these G_α, then $\dim J_L(\Sigma) = n$, and the arithmetic means over the G_α form a basis for the vector space $J_L(\Sigma)$. If there are infinitely many G_α, then letting $U = \{u_\alpha | \, u_\alpha$ the idempotent element of $G_\alpha\}$, every mean on U crossed with the unique invariant mean on any fixed G_α determines a left-invariant mean on Σ, so $J_L(\Sigma)$ is isomorphic to $m(U)^*$.

(B) If Σ is a countable semigroup and $\dim J_L(\Sigma) = n$, $0 < n < \infty$, then Σ has exactly n disjoint minimal left ideals with left cancellation and these are isomorphic groups.

We shall not give the proofs here; (B) is much the harder.

Corollary 11.3 (Granirer, 1963). If G is a (left) amenable group, then either G is a finite group or $\dim J_i(G) = \infty$.

Corollary 11.4 (Granirer, 1963). If Σ is a countable amenable semigroup with $\dim J_L(\Sigma) < \infty$, then $J_L(\Sigma) = J_R(\Sigma)$ and $\dim J_L(\Sigma) = 1$, i.e., Σ has only one left- and one right-invariant mean and they are equal.

Replacing countability by a different hypothesis, Granirer (1964) showed the following.

Theorem 11.5. If Σ is an amenable semigroup, and if both $J_L(\Sigma)$ and $J_R(\Sigma)$ are finite dimensional, then they are equal and 1 dimensional and Σ contains a finite group G which is a minimal two-sided ideal; then the arithmetic mean over G is the unique i-invariant mean over $m(\Sigma)$.

Adding a hypothesis of left cancellation instead of countability, Granirer also proved the following:

Theorem 11.6. If Σ is a left-cancellation semigroup, then $\dim J_L(\Sigma) = n$, $0 < n < \infty$, if and only if Σ is the union of n finite disjoint isomorphic groups $G_1, \ldots, G_n$ which are minimal left ideals in Σ, so that Σ is isomorphic to $G_1 \times U$.

To prove this Granirer had to generalize to left-cancellation semigroups the theorem of Day (1957) for groups that when Σ_0 is a subsemigroup of Σ, there is a linear isometry carrying $J_L(\Sigma_0)$ into $J_L(\Sigma)$.

Civin and Yood (1961) worked with second-conjugate algebras of Banach algebras, with some emphasis on the radical.

Granirer (1963) also points out that (4E) shows that large $J_L(\Sigma)$ means that the algebra $m(\Sigma)^*$ has large radical. Granirer and Rajagopalan (1964) characterize those left-amenable, left-cancellation semigroups which have finite-dimensional radical.

Granirer (1965b) extends some of these results, Theorem 11.2(B) for example, to $C(\Sigma)$ on topological semigroups. The main result of that paper is as follows.

Theorem 11.7. If G is a separable topological group amenable as a discrete group, which admits a left-uniformly continuous, unbounded real function (for example, any noncompact locally compact group or any subgroup of a locally convex space), then $LUC(G)$, and hence $C(G)$, has an infinite-dimensional set of left-invariant means.

12. Spectra and Norms of Convolutions by Probability Densities

Discrete Left-Cancellation Semigroups with Left Unit

As we observed in Theorem 5.1, amenability is equivalent to strong amenability of Σ, and this is described inside $l_1(\Sigma)$ by the existence of a net φ_n, $n \in \Delta$, of finite means (more generally one could have used elements of P, the set of probability densities on Σ; that is, the set of nonnegative elements of norm 1 in $l_1(\Sigma)$) such that, considering left amenability for now, we have the following:

($ls a\pi$) $\| \delta_s * \varphi_n - \varphi_n \| \to 0$ for every s in Σ.

From this and the fact that finite means are dense in P it follows that $\| \theta * \varphi_n - (\sum_{s \in \Sigma} \theta(s)) \varphi_n \| \to 0$ for any θ in $l_1(\Sigma)$ so ($lsa\pi$) implies

($lsap$) $\| \alpha * \varphi_n - \varphi_n \| \to 0$ for every α in P.

Because $\theta *$ and $* \psi$ commute (by the associative law in $l_1(\Sigma)$), for every net ψ_n in P, $\varphi_n * \psi_n$ has the same strong convergence to left invariance that φ_n has. Also for every $\alpha \in P$, $\alpha * \varphi_n$ hast he same strong convergence to left invariance because

$$\| \delta_s * (\alpha * \varphi_n) - \alpha * \varphi_n \| \leqslant \|(\delta_s * \alpha) * \varphi_n - \varphi_n \| + \| \varphi_n - \alpha * \varphi_n \| \to 0.$$

We shall deal in this section with groups to prepare for the next section on locally compact groups but (Day, 1964) the results of this section are valid for left cancellation semigroups with left unit.

Throughout this and the next section p will be a (finite) real number greater than 1; that is, L_p will never mean L_1 or L_∞. Then for every measure ν, $L_p(\nu)$ is uniformly convex (Clarkson, 1936; see also Day, 1962, p. 113).

If $\theta \in l_1(G)$ and $p > 1$, define $f = \theta^{(1/p)}$ by $f(g) = |\theta(g)|^{1/p}$ sign $\theta(g)$ for each g in G. Mazur (1929) showed that this determines a homeomorphism between $l_1(G)$ and $l_p(G)$, and Day (1964, 1968) showed the homeomorphism to be uniformly bicontinuous between the unit balls of the two spaces. Observing that $[\delta_g * \theta]^{(1/p)} = \delta_g * [\theta^{(1/p)}]$ for all θ in $l_1(G)$, we see that when φ_n is a net of elements of P, then $\| f_n \|_p = 1$ and $\| \delta_g * \varphi_n - \varphi_n \|_1 \to 0$ if and only if $\| \delta_g * f_n - f_n \|_p \to 0$. This implies for each α in P that $\| \alpha * f_n - f_n \|_p \to 0$. Hence, the following.

Lemma 12.1. If $\varphi_n \in P$ and $f_n = \varphi^{(1/p)}$, then φ_n satisfies ($lsa\pi$) if and only if f_n satisfies the following.

(lkp) For one (or each) $p > 1$ and for each α in P, $\| \alpha * f_n - f_n \|_p \to 0$.

Because this implies that $\alpha * - I$ cannot have a bounded inverse, (lkp) implies the following condition.

(lk) For one (or each) $p > 1$ and each α in P the number 1 is in the spectrum of $\alpha *$ regarded as an operator in $l_p(G)$.

Using the left cancellation in G we can see that the norm of $\theta *$ as an operator in $l_p(G)$ is no greater than $\| \theta \|_1$; hence, the following.

Lemma 12.2. If G satisfies (lk), [(lkp)], then it also satisfies the following.

(ld) For one (or each) $p > 1$ and each $\alpha \in P$, $\alpha *$ as an operator in $l_p(G)$ is of norm 1.

[(ldp) For each (or one) $p > 1$ and each α in P, $\| \alpha * f_n \|_p \to 1$.]

Lemma 12.3. If $p > 1$ and if f_n, $n \in \Delta$, is a net of elements of norm 1 in $l_p(G)$ such that for each α in P, $\| \alpha * f_n \|_p \to 1$, then the following condition holds.

($lk\pi$) For each g in G, $\| \delta_g * f_n - f_n \|_p \to 0$.

Proof. Let u be the identity element of G, so that δ_u is the identity operator in $l_p(G)$. If $g \neq u$, take α to have the weight $\frac{1}{2}$ at g and at u. Then $\| \alpha * f_n \|_p = \| \delta_g * f_n + f_n \|/2$. By uniform convexity of $l_p(G)$ (Clarkson, 1936; Day, 1962, p. 113), $\| \delta_g * f_n - f_n \|_p < \epsilon$ whenever $\| \alpha * f_n \| > 1 - \eta_p(\epsilon)$, so $\| \delta_g * f_n - f_n \|_p \to 0$.

Lemma 12.4. (ld) implies ($lsa\pi$).

PROOF. For any finite subset π of P, define $\alpha_\pi = (\sum_{\alpha\in\pi} \alpha)/|\pi|$, where $|\pi|$ means the number of elements of π. Then $\alpha_\pi \in P$ so, by (ld), an f_π of norm one in $l_p(G)$ can be found so that $\| \alpha_\pi * f_\pi \|_p > 1 - |\pi|^{-2}$. A quick calculation shows then that $\| \alpha * f_\pi \|_p > 1 - |\pi|^{-1}$ for each α in π; hence the net f_π satisfies $\| \alpha * f_\pi \|_p \to 1$ for every α in P. Then $\| \delta_g * f_\pi - f_\pi \|_p \to 0$ by Lemma 12.3; by the uniform continuity of the Mazur homeomorphism, $\| \delta_g * \varphi_\pi - \varphi_\pi \|_1 \to 0$.

If f is a complex-valued function on G, define $f^\sim$ by $f^\sim(g)$ = complex conjugate of $f(g^{-1})$. Then if $p = 2$ and $f \in l_2(G)$, also $l_g f \in l_2(G)$ and

$$[f * f^\sim](g) = (f, \delta_g * f) = (f, l_{g^{-1}} f)$$

for each g in G. (Here (–, –) is the usual inner product in $l_2(G)$.)

Godement (1948, p. 76, Problem 5) studied a property of groups which is now called "type (R)"; for discrete groups this simplifies to the following.

($lg\pi$) For each finite set $\gamma \subseteq G$ there is an f_γ in $l_2(G)$ such that $1 - [f_\gamma * f_\gamma^\sim](g) < 1/|\gamma|$ for all g in γ; equivalently, there is a net f_n of nonnegative elements of norm 1 in $l_2(G)$, each f_n vanishing outside a finite set, and such that $f_n * f_n^\sim$ converges to 1 everywhere in G.

Day (1968) contains the simple proof of the equivalence of these conditions, but we give it while proving

Lemma 12.5. ($lg\pi$) is equivalent to ($lsa\pi$).

PROOF. If $\| \delta_g * \varphi_n - \varphi_n \|_1 \to 0$, then $\| \delta_g * f_n - f_n \|_2 \to 0$; hence $(f_n, \delta_g * f_n) \to 1$ by uniform continuity of (–, –). On the other hand, if $[f_n * f_n^\sim](g) \to 1$ for all g, then in particular $[f_n * f_n^\sim](u) = \| f_n \|^2 \to 1$. Hence we may divide and assume all f_n originally of norm 1; then shifting from f_n to $|f_n|$ these functions still satisfy ($lg\pi$). For any one g in G we have $(f_n, \delta_g * f_n) \to 1$ so, by the uniform convexity of $l_2(G)$, $\| l_{g^{-1}} f_n - f_n \|_2 < \epsilon$ as soon as $(f_n, l_{g^{-1}} f_n) < 1 - \eta_2(\epsilon)$ (Day, 1962, p. 113), so $\| \delta_g * f_n - f_n \| \to 0$ for each g.

From these lemmas we get the theorem for discrete groups which is the pattern, taken basically from Day (1964), for the next section on locally compact groups; as we said before, this still is true in semigroups with left cancellation and left unit.

Theorem 12.6. Let G be a discrete group, let φ_n be a net of finite means on G, and let $f_n = \varphi_n^{1/p}$. Then the following conditions on φ_n and f_n are equivalent:

($lsa\pi$) For each g in G, $\| \delta_g * \varphi_n - \varphi_n \|_1 \to 0$.

($lsap$) For each α in P, $\| \alpha * \varphi_n - \varphi_n \|_1 \to 0$.

($lk\pi$) For each g in G, $\| \delta_g * f_n - f_n \|_p \to 0$
for one (or each) $p > 1$.

(lkp) For each α in P, $\| \alpha * f_n - f_n \|_p \to 0$
for one (or each) $p > 1$.

(ldp) For each α in P, $\| \alpha * f_n \|_p \to 1$
for one (or each) $p > 1$.

($lg\pi$) For $p = 2$ and g in G, $[f_n * f_n^{\sim}](g) \to 1$.

Hence the existence of a net doing any one of these things is equivalent to (left) amenability of G and to each of the following.

(lk) For each α in P, 1 is in the spectrum of $\alpha *$ as an operator in $l_p(G)$ for one (or each) $p > 1$.

(ld) For each α in P, $\alpha *$ is an operator in $l_p(G)$ of norm 1 for one (or each) $p > 1$.

13. Spectra and Norms of Convolutions

Locally Compact Groups

In this section we adapt the results of the preceding section to locally compact groups G with left Haar measure H. Here we lose the automatic equicontinuity which is concealed in the discrete case and with it goes the integral convergence theorems for nets which are not sequences. P becomes the set of probability densities, i.e., the part of $L_1(G)$ containing the nonnegative functions of norm 1; the finite means are replaced by P_0, the part of P consisting of functions supported inside compact sets. Sometimes we will also need P_{00}, consisting of the continuous functions in P_0. $l_p(G)$ is replaced by $L_p(G)$ (using the left Haar measure, H, of course), $l_1(G)$ by $L_1(G)$, and $m(G)$ by $L_\infty(G)$. (See Hewitt and Ross, for example, for the facts about these spaces.) Even though $L_\infty(G)$ is like $L_1(G)^*$ under the isometry $x \to x^\vee$, where now $x^\vee(\varphi) = \int_G \varphi(g)\, x(g)\, dH(g)$, w^* convergence in the unit ball of $L_1(G)^*$ has little to do with pointwise convergence of the corresponding functions in $L_\infty(G)$ (except for sequences).

We shall look for conditions analogous to those of the preceding section and equivalent to the existence of a left-invariant mean on $L_\infty(G)$. We shall consider a net φ_n, $n \in \Delta$, of elements of P or P_0 and the related net $f_n = \varphi_n^{1/p}$. Because the natural analog of a finite set is sometimes a finite set and sometimes a compact set, $lsa\pi$ splits into two conditions.

($lsa\pi$)[($lsau$)] For each g in G [uniformly for g in each compact $K \subseteq G$],

$$\| \delta_g * \varphi_n - \varphi_n \|_1 \to 0.$$

(*lsap*) For each α in P,

$$\| \alpha * \varphi_n - \varphi_n \|_1 \to 0.$$

(*lkπ*)[(*lku*)] For one (or each) $p > 1$ and each g in G [uniformly for g in each compact $K \subseteq G$],

$$\| \delta_g * f_n - f_n \| \to 0.$$

(*lkp*) For one (or each) $p > 1$ and each α in P,

$$\| \alpha * f_n - f_n \| \to 0.$$

(*ldp*) For one (or each) $p > 1$ and for each α in P,

$$\| \alpha * f_n \|_p \to 1.$$

(*lgπ*)[(*lgu*)] For $p = 2$ and for each g in G [uniformly for g in each compact $K \subseteq G$],

$$[f_n * f_n^{\sim}](g) \to 1.$$

REMARK. Since every δ_g is an isometry in every $L_p(G)$, nothing useful comes of conditions like (*ldπ*) or (*ldu*).

Using the proofs from the discrete case, (*lsaπ*), (*lkπ*), and (*lgπ*) are equivalent immediately, as are (*lsau*), (*lku*), and (*lgu*). That each u condition implies its corresponding p and π conditions is also elementary, and it is as easy as before that (*lkp*) implies (*ldp*). Unfortunately, some of the other implications we want may fail until a new net with extra properties is constructed.

The right property, always present in the discrete case, is sometimes available here; say that a net $\varphi_n[f_n]$ is *left equicontinuous in* $L_1(G)$ [*in* $L_p(G)$] if for each $\epsilon > 0$, there is a neighborhood W_ϵ of u in G such that if $s \in W_\epsilon$, then $\| \delta_s * \varphi_n - \varphi_n \|_1 < \epsilon$ [$\| \delta_s * f_n - f_n \|_p < \epsilon$]. The uniform continuity of Mazur's homeomorphism between the unit balls of $L_1(G)$ and $L_p(G)$ [proved in Day (1964, 1968)] shows the following.

(13A) If $\varphi_n \in P$ and $f_n = \varphi_n^{1/p}$, then the net φ_n is left equicontinuous in $L_1(G)$ if and only if f_n is left equicontinuous in $L_p(G)$.

In the next two lemmas it is assumed that φ_n, $n \in \Delta$, *is left equicontinuous in* $L_1(G)$ *net of elements of* P, *and that* $f_n = \varphi_n^{1/p}$.

Lemma 13.1. (*ldp*) implies (*lkπ*).

PROOF. If (*lkπ*) fails, there is s in G with $\| l_s f_n - f_n \|_p > 3\epsilon$ (really for a subnet of f_n). Then in sW_ϵ, $\| l_g f_n - l_s f_n \|_p < \epsilon$ while in W_ϵ,

$\| l_h f_n - f_n \|_p < \epsilon$. Take α_1 in P with its support in sW_ϵ and α_2 in P with its support in W_ϵ and set $\alpha = (\alpha_1 + \alpha_2)/2$. Then $\alpha * f_n = (\alpha_1 * f_n + \alpha_2 * f_n)/2$ while $\| \alpha_1 * f_n - \alpha_2 * f_n \| > \epsilon$. By uniform convexity of $L_p(G)$, $\| \alpha * f_n \| < 1 - \eta_p(\epsilon)$ for all f_n in the subnet, and (ldp) fails for f_n.

Lemma 13.2. $(lsap)$ implies $(lsa\pi)$ implies $(lsau)$.

PROOF. If $(lsau)$ fails for φ_n, there is a subnet φ_{n_i}, a compact K, an $\epsilon > 0$, and points s_i in K such that $\| l_{s_i}\varphi_{n_i} - \varphi_{n_i} \|_1 > 2\epsilon$. Take a subnet for which s_{i_k} converges to some point s of K. Then s_{i_k} eventually enters sW_ϵ so for large k

$$\| l_s\varphi_{n_{i_k}} - \varphi_{n_{i_k}} \|_1 \geqslant \| l_{s_{i_k}}\varphi_{n_{i_k}} - \varphi_{n_{i_k}} \|_1$$

$$-\| l_s\varphi_{n_{i_k}} - l_{s_{i_k}}\varphi_{n_{i_k}} \|_1 > 2\epsilon - \epsilon,$$

so $(lsa\pi)$ fails.

A similar proof disposes of the other implication which proves the first half of the following.

Theorem 13.3. If φ_n is a net left equicontinuous in $L_1(G)$ of elements of P and if $f_n = \varphi_n^{1/p}$, then all the conditions $(lsau)$, (lku), (lgu), $(lsap)$, (lkp), (ldp), $(lsa\pi)$, $(lk\pi)$, and $(lg\pi)$, on φ_n and f_n are equivalent. Hence the existence of one such equicontinuous net φ_n or f_n is equivalent to each of the following conditions.

$(la\pi)$ There is a left-invariant mean on $L_\infty(G)$.

$(la\pi_0)$ There is a left-invariant mean on $UC(G)$.

(lap_0) There is a mean μ_0 on $UC(G)$ such that for each α in P and x in $UC(G)$,

$$\mu_0(\alpha * x) = \mu_0(x)$$

(lap) There is a mean μ on $L_\infty(G)$ such that for each α in P and x in $L_\infty(G)$,

$$\mu(\alpha * x) = \mu(x).$$

(lk) For one (or each) $p > 1$ and each α in P, $\alpha\, *$ as an operator in $L_p(G)$ has 1 in its spectrum.

(ld) For one (or each) $p > 1$ and for each α in P, $\alpha\, *$ as an operator in $L_p(G)$ has norm 1.

Also all of the φ_n and f_n may be chosen to be continuous with compact supports.

PROOF. Without appeal to equicontinuity we see that proofs like those in Section 12 give us the pattern of implications below $(lsap)$ in Fig. 3. To

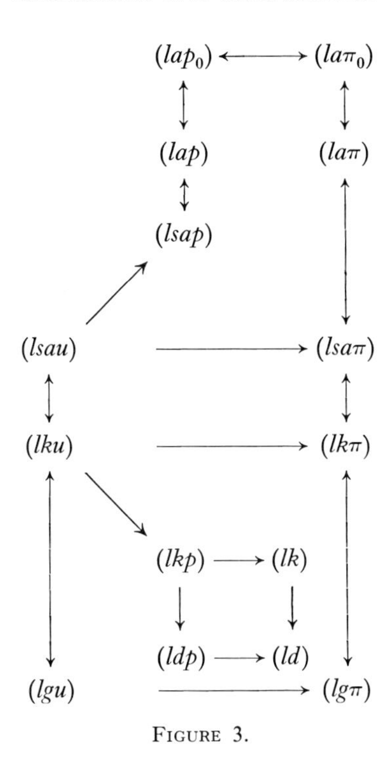

FIGURE 3.

complete the proof we give only sketches for the upper implications, and then use the equicontinuity for the final closing of the pattern.

(1) ($la\pi_0$) implies (lap_0). Greenleaf (1966) showed that if μ_0 is a mean on $UC(G)$, then $\mu_0(l_g v) = \mu_0(v)$ for all v in $UC(G)$ and all g in G if and only if $\mu_0(\alpha * v) = \mu_0(v)$ for all v in $UC(G)$ and all α in P; that is, (lap_0) and ($la\pi_0$) are equivalent. Granirer (1967), in Section 4, has a stronger result.

(2) (lap_0) implies (lap). Hulanicki showed that if μ_0 is a mean on $UC(G)$ such that $\mu_0(\alpha * v) = \mu_0(v)$ for all v in $UC(G)$ and all α in P, and that if β and γ are chosen from P_{00}, and if μ is defined on $L_\infty(G)$ by $\mu(x) = \mu_0(\beta * x * \gamma)$ for all x in $L_\infty(G)$, then $\mu(\alpha * x) = \mu(x)$ for all x in $L_\infty(G)$ and α in P.

We note here that (lap) is equivalent to what was called in Section 7 topological left amenability of $L_\infty(G)$, because (recalling that there is an anti-isomorphic isometry $\alpha \leftrightarrow \alpha^*$ of $L_1(G)$ on itself, where $\alpha^*(g) = \Delta(g^{-1})$ times the complex conjugate of $\alpha(g^{-1})$ for all g in G, and Δ is the modular function of G) we have $l_\varphi x = \varphi^* * x$ for all x in $L_\infty(G)$ and all φ in $L_1(G)$. Note that this equivalence and Theorem 7.3 give a totally new proof that

$(la\pi)$ implies (lap), for that theorem shows that $(la\pi)$ implies topologically right stationary implies topologically left amenable.

(3) (lap) implies $(lsap)$. Hulanicki (1966) and Greenleaf (1966) showed that my proof of equivalence of $(la\pi)$ and $(lsa\pi)$ (Theorem 5.1) works in just the same way to prove equivalence of (lap) and $(lsap)$.

(4) $(lsap)$ implies existence of a net of elements of P_{00} equicontinuous in $L_1(G)$ and satisfying $(lsap)$.

A net from P strongly convergent to left invariance can be replaced by a net ψ_n from P_0, because P_0 is norm dense in P. Take β in P_{00} and set $\varphi_n = \beta * \psi_n$; then φ_n is a net left equicontinuous in $L_1(G)$. It also has $(lsap)$ because

$$\| \alpha * \varphi_n - \varphi_n \| \leqslant \|(\alpha * \beta) * \psi_n - \psi_n \| + \| \psi_n - \beta * \psi_n \| \to 0.$$

Now with these connections added to the diagram, we have shown that the first column, the last column, and the top three places in the middle column are all equivalent and all imply the remaining conditions. All that remains to be done is

(5) (ld) implies the existence of a left-equicontinuous net in $L_p(G)$ of nonnegative elements f_n of norm 1 such that $\| \alpha * f_n \|_p \to 1$ for each α in P.

PROOF. First fix a β in P_{00}. Then for each finite subset $\pi = \{\alpha_1, \ldots, \alpha_k\}$ of P, let $\alpha_\pi = (\alpha_1 + \cdots + \alpha_k) * \beta/k$. Then (ld) implies that there is F_π such that $\| \alpha_\pi * F_\pi \|_p > 1 - 1/k^2$, so for each $i < k$, $\| \alpha_i * \beta * F_\pi \|_p > 1 - 1/k$. Also $\| \beta * F_\pi \|_p \geqslant \frac{1}{2}$ as soon as $\pi \supseteq \pi_0$, a net with two elements, so we can set $f_\pi = | \beta * F_\pi |/\| \beta * F_\pi \|_p$. Since the F_π form a left-equicontinuous net in $L_p(G)$, the f_π, $\pi \supseteq \pi_0$, form a left-equicontinuous net of nonnegative elements of norm 1n $L_p(G)$, and $\| \alpha * f_\pi \| > 1 - 1/| \pi |$ as soon as $\alpha \in \pi$. By the first part of the theorem (ld) implies all the other conditions; hence all are equivalent.

For the origins of the ideas used up to now in this chapter we should name Hulanicki for "topological" left amenability (lap). Dieudonne (1960) studied the groups with (ld) and showed that Reiter's (1952) condition $(lsau)$ implied (lku) implied (ld). Reiter (1965), Stegeman (1965), Namioka (1966), and Leptin (1967) have also proved various of these conditions imply each other. Greenleaf's lecture notes (1966) give a clear picture of the whole field, many of these equivalences included. Godement (1948, p. 47) showed that (lgu) is necessary and sufficient that every continuous positive definite function on G can be approximated uniformly on compact sets by functions $f * f^{\sim}$, f in $L_2(G)$. Fell (1962) studies all the representations of G by unitary operators on inner-product spaces and shows that (lgu) is exactly the condition required on G in order that all the representations be weakly contained in the regular representation of G over $L_2(G)$. Hulanicki also discusses this. Kesten (1959a,b) showed that (lk) is equivalent to $(la\pi)$ in countable discrete groups.

We note here that what has been said for left-sided invariance goes verbatim for right-sided invariance when the group G is unimodular. However, when G is not unimodular, one should not use $x * \varphi$ but the correct operation $r_\varphi x$ in $L_\infty(G)$; it is "correct" because $[r_\varphi x]^\vee = (* \varphi)^* x^\vee$ for all x in $L_\infty(G)$ and φ in $L_1(G)$.

We take the rest of this section to show how the results of Sections 3 and 4 carry to locally compact groups. The construction of an algebra from $L_\infty(G)^*$ works as before and $L_\infty(G)$ is inverse invariant so (matching our labels to these before);

(13B) If G is left amenable, then it is right amenable and amenable.

(Another proof would use Theorem 13.3, $(la\pi_0)$ equivalent to $(la\pi)$, to see that we need only work with $UC(G)$, which is an introverted subspace of $m(G)$, so all the constructions used in $m(G)$ stay in $UC(G)$ if they start there.

(13C) If G_1 is a continuous homomorphic image of an amenable G, then G_1 is amenable.

(13D) If G_α is a family of subgroups of a locally compact group G such that the family is directed by inclusion and such that (1) $\bigcup_\alpha G_\alpha$ is dense in G, and (2) for each α $UC(G_\alpha)$ is left or right amenable, then G_α is amenable.

PROOF. If ν_α is a left-invariant mean on $UC(G_\alpha)$, define $\mu_\alpha(x) = \nu_\alpha(x \mid G_\alpha)$ for all x in $UC(G)$ and take a w^*-convergent subnet of the μ_α with limit μ. It is easy to show $l_s^*\mu = \mu$ for s in any G_α ; then the uniform continuity of the map $s \to l_s x$, for any one x in $UC(G)$, gives $\mu(l_s x) = \mu(x)$ for all s.

(13F) If G is left amenable, so is every closed subgroup of G.

Rickert (1965) did this for second-countable groups. Greenleaf (1968) first did it in the general case. This is the hard one of the discrete construction theorems to generalize to the locally compact case. We omit the proof.

(13G) If H is a closed normal subgroup of G and if H and G/H are amenable, then so is G. (Use the discrete proof on $UC(G)$.)

(13I) Every compact group is amenable with a unique (left- or right-) invariant mean, normalized Haar measure on G.

(13J′) No amenable locally compact group has a free subgroup on two generators as a closed subgroup or as a continuous homeomorphic image.

See Rickert (1965) and Greenleaf (1966) for most of this.

14. Extremely Left-Amenable Semigroups

Mitchell (1966) asked when a semigroup Σ has a *multiplicative* left-invariant mean μ, that is, when $J_L(\Sigma) \cap \beta(\Sigma)$ is not empty. Granirer (1965) called such a semigroup *extremely left amenable* (*ela*).

Theorem 14.1 (Mitchell, 1966). A semigroup Σ is extremely left amenable if and only if for every representation h of Σ by continuous mappings of a compact Hausdorff space K into itself there is a common fixed point of all the mappings in $h(\Sigma)$.

Sufficiency follows by representing Σ by the mappings l_s^* with their domains of definition reduced to $\beta(\Sigma)$, the Stone-Cech compactification of Σ; i.e., the closure in M of $Q\delta(\Sigma)$. Necessity is easier if we prove first a result of Granirer (1965a); see also Granirer (1964).

Theorem 14.2. The following conditions on a semigroup Σ are equivalent:

(1) Σ is extremely left amenable.

(2) There is a net $(s_n, n \in \Delta)$ of points of Σ such that

$$\lim_{n\in\Delta} \| \delta_s * \delta_{s_n} - \delta_{s_n} \| = 0.$$

(3) Every finite subset γ of Σ has a right sink; that is, an s_γ for which $ss_\gamma = s_\gamma$ for all s in γ.

(4) Every two-point set in Σ has a common right sink.

PROOF. (4) implies (3). If γ is any finite subset of Σ, say $\gamma = \{t_1, \ldots, t_k\}$, then there is an s_2 such that $t_i s_2 = s_2$ for $i \leqslant 2$. Then there is s_3 such that $t_i s_2 s_3 = s_2 s_3 = s_3$ for $i \leqslant 3$, etc., so that finally $t_i s_2 s_3 \cdots s_k = s_2 s_3 \cdots s_k = \cdots = s_k$ for all $i \leqslant k$.

(3) implies (2). For each finite subset γ of Σ let s_γ be a right sink for γ, so that $ss_\gamma = s_\gamma$ for all s in γ. Then $\| \delta_s * \delta_{s_\gamma} - \delta_{s_\gamma} \| = 0$ as soon as $s \in \gamma$ so (2) holds for this net on the stack Δ of finite subsets of Σ.

(2) implies (1). Choose any w^*-convergent subnet of $Q\delta_{s_n}$; then the limit μ is both left invariant and in $\beta(\Sigma)$.

(1) implies (4). If μ is a left-invariant element of $\beta(\Sigma)$, the second

property says that there exist s_n in Σ such that $w^*\text{-lim}_{n\in\Delta} Q\delta_{s_n} = \mu$. The invariance of μ says that $w\text{-lim}_{n\in\Delta}(\delta_s * \delta_{s_n} - \delta_{s_n}) = 0$ for each s in Σ.

Now suppose that (4) fails. Then there are s, t such that for no r in Σ do we have $sr = r = tr$, so for no m is $ss_m = s_m = ts_m$. Hence at least one of $\{m \mid ss_m \neq s_m\}$ or $\{m \mid ts_m \neq s_m\}$, say the first, is cofinal in Δ (that is, for each m in Δ there is n in Δ' such that $n \geqslant m$). Hence we may assume from the beginning that the first set is Δ, and for no m is $ss_m = s_m$.

Consider the family of subsets E of Δ, such that (if we set $s(E) = \{s_m \mid m \in E\}$, we have $ss(E) \cap s(E) = \emptyset$. Zorn's lemma shows that there is a maximal such E.

If E is cofinal in Δ, let x be the characteristic function of E; then

$$\mu(x) = \lim_{n\in F} x(s_m) = 1 \neq 0 = \lim_{n\in F} l_s x(s_m) = l_s^* \mu(x),$$

so (1) fails.

If E is not cofinal in Δ, either there is m not in E such that ss_m is not in $s(E)$, or there is not. If such m could exist, it could be added to E and E would not be maximal. Since this contradicts the choice of E, it follows that if m is not in E, then ss_m is in $s(E)$. Because E is not cofinal in Δ, there is m_0 such that $m \geqslant m_0$ implies m not in E. Set $F = \{m \mid m \geqslant m_0\}$. Then $ss(F) \subseteq s(E)$ and $s(E) \cap s(F) = \emptyset$. As F is cofinal in Δ, whenever $\lim_{m\in\Delta} f(m) = a$, then $\lim_{m\in F} f(m) = a$; hence

$$\mu(x) = \lim_{m\in F} x(s_m) = 1 \neq 0 = \lim_{m\in F} l_s x(s_m) = l_s^* \mu(x),$$

so μ is not left invariant, and (1) fails if (4) fails.

The other half of Theorem 14.1 now follows. For if the net s_γ satisfies (3), we can find a fixed point of all the h_s in the orbit of any x by choosing a subnet s_{γ_i} so that $h_{s_{\gamma_i}}$ converges in the compact set K to some y; then $h_s y = h_s(\lim_i h_{s_{\gamma_i}} x) = \lim_i h_s h_{s_{\gamma_i}} x = \lim_i h_{ss_{\gamma_i}} x = \lim_i h_{s_{\gamma_i}} x = y$.

Granirer (1965a) gave a number of other conditions equivalent to ela. In particular, the corollary shows that there are no ela semigroups with right cancellation, hence no ela groups, with more than one element.

Mitchell (1968) and Granirer (1965a) also give constructions of ela semigroups and of large ela subalgebras of certain semigroups.

Granirer (1968) uses Theorem 14.2 to prove his favorite result:

Theorem 14.3. Σ is extremely left amenable if and only if for each representation T of Σ over any normed linear space X by linear operators with $\| T_s \| \leqslant 1$ for all s in Σ, then for all z in X

(G) $\operatorname{dist}(0, T_\Sigma z) = \operatorname{dist}(0, \operatorname{Co} T_\Sigma z)$.

(Here $T_\Sigma z$, the orbit of $z = \{T_s z \mid s \in \Sigma\}$, and Co is convex hull.) It suffices that (G) hold for $X = m(\Sigma)$ and $T_s = l_s$.

15. Invariant Extensions of Linear Operators

In the classical Hahn-Banach theorem real-valued linear functions are extended subject to domination by a real-valued sublinear p. An appropriate attitude toward the definition of invariant means is that it is an extension of the Hahn-Banach theory in which p is assumed to be invariant and it is required that the extended function f also be invariant under some semigroup of operators. A completely different generalization of the Hahn-Banach theorem allows the values of f and p to be in a partially ordered linear space V with a positive cone K. It was probably known to Kantorovič thirty years ago that the Hahn-Banach theorem, with the standard proof of Banach (1932, p. 28), carried through almost verbatim if and only if V is order complete; that is, if every subset of V with an upper bound has a least upper bound. [see Day (1962, p. 105)].

It was natural to combine these two steps from the original Hahn-Banach theorem and its relative the monotone extension theorem, the early version of which is due to Kreĭn (1937).

We consider then a linear space L and an order-complete ordered linear space V (see, for example, Peressini for this subject). p is a sublinear function from L into V, L_0 is a linear subset of L, f_0 is a linear function from L_0 into V dominated by p. Also $\mathscr{S}$ is a semigroup of linear operators in L such that for each S in $\mathscr{S}$, $S(L_0) \subseteq L_0$, $f_0(Sx) = f_0(x)$ for all x in L_0 and $p(Sx) \leqslant Np(x)$ for all x in L. We say that $(V, \mathscr{S}, L, p, L_0, f_0)$ *has the Hahn-Banach extension property*, HBEP, if and only if there exists a linear f from L into V, f an extension of f_0, f dominated by Np, and f invariant under $\mathscr{S}$. If Σ is an abstract semigroup, we say that Σ has the right [left] HBEP if every such $\mathscr{S}$ which is a homomorphic [anti-homomorphic] image of Σ has the HBEP.

Taking $L = m(\Sigma)$, $p = \| \ \|$, $N = 1$, $\mathscr{S} = r(\Sigma)$ [or $l(\Sigma)$], $L_0 = C$, $f_0(\alpha) = \alpha$ for all α, we get the following.

Theorem 15.1 (Silverman, 1956b). Any semigroup with the left [right] HBEP is left [right] amenable.

The converse is not known for all order-complete V, but Silverman proved that amenable semigroups have the HBEP to some degree, that is, when further restrictions are placed on V. Looking at the problem now we can see that we would like to apply the fixed-point Theorem 6.1 (which was not available to Silverman).

Call V *order compact* if V is an order-complete, ordered linear space in which there exists a locally convex topology in which every order interval of V is compact. Say that Σ has the *weaker right- [left-] Hahn-Banach extension property* if $(V, h(\Sigma), L, p, L_0, f_0)$ has the HBEP for all order-compact V and all homomorphisms [antihomorphisms] h of Σ into linear maps from L into L with the other required relations.

Theorem 15.2. Let Σ be a semigroup. Then Σ is left [right] amenable if and only if Σ has the weaker left- [right-] Hahn-Banach extension property.

PROOF. Since the reals are a V in which the usual topology makes intervals compact, the same proof used for Theorem 15.1 shows that the weaker HBEP implies amenability on the same side.

For the other direction, begin with the standard Hahn-Banach theorem for functions with values in V (Day, 1962, p. 105) to get an F linear from L into V and dominated by p and extending f_0.

For each x in L let $I_x = [-Np(-x), Np(x)]$, and let $K = \prod_{x \in L} I_x$. Using the appropriate topology for V, each I_x is compact; by Tyhonov's theorem [see, for example, Kelley (1955, p. 143)], K is also compact.

Now each h_s in $h(\Sigma)$ determines H_s in V^L by $[H_s f](x) = f(h_s x)$ for all x in L. By the hypotheses F and all $H_s F$ are in K, so K', the closed convex hull of $\{H_s F \mid s \in \Sigma\}$, is a compact convex set carried into itself by all the affine continuous mappings H_s.

Finally, if Σ is left [right] amenable, then h is assumed to be an [anti-] homomorphism, so that H is a homomorphism [antihomorphism] of Σ into $\mathscr{A}(K')$. Theorem 6.1 asserts that there is a fixed point f of all H_s in K'. But every element of K' is an extension of f and is dominated by Np. Hence a left- [right-] amenable Σ has the weaker left [right] HBEP.

Silverman (1956b) gives several sufficient conditions on V for the extension theorem to work for every representation of an amenable semigroup; in one of these V is a conjugate space and the w^* topology, a natural source of compactness, is used.

Indeed this is the simplest source we have for compactness of intervals. Referring to Peressini (1967, p. 132), we see that if L is a vector lattice and if L^+ is the linear space of differences of positive linear functionals on L, then the order intervals in L^+ are always w^* compact, that is, compact in the topology of pointwise convergence on L. However the intervals of L are seldom compact in the weak topology induced by L^+.

The space c_0 has w-compact intervals, but this is an accident of the fact that the natural mapping of c_0 into m carries c_0 intervals to coordinatewise closed bounded, hence w^*-compact subsets of m.

If μ is any measure and if V is $L_1(\mu)$ or any abstract L space, Kakutani showed [see Day (1962, p. 107) for references] that V is order complete and that every order interval is w compact.

For an abstract M space V with unit the order completeness is known [see Day (1962, pp. 95, 105), for example] to be equivalent to the property that V is linearly order isometric to some $C(X)$, X compact, Hausdorff, and extremally disconnected. (This means that the closure in X of each open set is again open.) Order intervals here are not always w compact, but if $C(X)$ were isomorphic to a conjugate space, then order intervals in $C(X)$ would be w^* compact. Dixmier (1951) investigated extremally disconnected, compact, Hausdorff spaces (Stonean, in his terminology, in honor of M. H. Stone). He showed that not all $C(X)$, X Stonean, are like conjugate spaces, but that a stronger condition, hyperstonean, is required. When X is hyperstonean, he showed that there is a measure μ defined on a very special locally compact, dense subspace X' of X such that $C(X)$ is like $L_1(\mu)^*$.

REFERENCES

Alaoglu, L., and Birkhoff, G. (1940). General ergodic theorems, *Ann. Math.* [2]**41**, 293–309.

Arens, R. (1951). The adjoint of a bilinear operator. *Proc. Amer. Math. Soc.* **2**, 839–848.

Argabright, L. N. (1968). Invariant means and fixed points, a sequel to Mitchell's paper. *Trans. Amer. Math. Soc.* **130**, 127–130.

Argabright, L. N., and Wilde, C. O. (1967). Semigroups satisfying a strong Følner condition. *Proc. Amer. Math. Soc.* **18**, 587–591.

Banach, S. (1923). Sur la problème de la mesure. *Fund. Math.* **4**, 7–33.

Banach, S. (1932). "Théorie des Opérations Linéaires." Warsaw.

Banach, S., and Tarski, A. (1924). Sur la décomposition des ensembles de points en parties respectivement congruents. *Fund. Math.* **6**, 244–277.

Civin, P., and Yood, B. (1961). The second conjugate space of a Banach algebra as an algebra. *Pacific J. Math.* **11**, 847–870.

Clarkson, J. A. (1936). Uniformly convex spaces. *Trans. Amer. Math. Soc.* **40**, 396–414.

Cohen, L. W. (1940). On the mean ergodic theorem. *Ann. of Math.* [2]**41**, 505–509.

Day, M. M. (1941). Reflexive Banach spaces not isomorphic to uniformly convex spaces. *Bull. Amer. Math. Soc.* **47**, 313–317.

Day, M. M. (1942). Ergodic theorems for abelian semigroups. *Trans. Amer. Math. Soc.* **51**, 583–608.

Day, M. M. (1944). Oriented systems. *Duke Math. J.* **11**, 201–229.

Day, M. M. (1950). Means for the bounded functions and ergodicity of the bounded representations of semigroups. *Trans. Amer. Math. Soc.* **69**, 276–291.

Day, M. M. (1957). Amenable semigroups. *Illinois J. Math.* **1**, 509–544.

Day, M. M. (1961). Fixed point theorems for compact convex sets. *Illinois J. Math.* **5**, 585–590; also Correction, **8**, 713 (1964).

Day, M. M. (1962). "Normed Linear Spaces" (2nd printing corrected). Springer, Berlin.

Day, M. M. (1964). Convolutions, means, and spectra. *Illinois J. Math.* **8**, 100–111.

Day, M. M. (1968). Amenability and equicontinuity. *Studia Math.* **31**, 481–494.

DeLeeuw, K., and Glicksberg, I. (1961). Applications of almost periodic compactifications. *Acta Math.* **105**, 63–67.

Dieudonné, J. (1960). Sur la produit de composition (II). *J. Math. Pures Appl.* [9]**39**, 275–292.

Dixmier, J. (1950). Les moyennes invariantes dans les semigroups et leur applications. *Acta Sci. Math. (Szeged)* **12**, 213–227.
Dixmier, J. (1951). Sur certains espaces considérés par M. H. Stone. *Summa Brasiliensis Math.* **2**, 151–180 (1947–1951).
Dixmier, J. (1964). "Les C^*-algèbres et Leurs Representations." Gauthier-Villars, Paris.
Eberlein, W. F. (1949). Abstract ergodic theorems and weak almost periodic functions. *Trans. Amer. Math. Soc.* **67**, 217–240.
Fell, J. M. G. (1962). Weak containment and induced representations of groups. *Canad. J. Math.* **14**, 237–268.
Følner, E. (1955). On groups with full Banach mean values. *Math. Scand.* **3**, 243–254.
Følner, E. (1957). Note on groups with and without full Banach mean value. *Math. Scand.* **5**, 5–11.
Frey, A. H., Jr. (1960). Studies on amenable semigroups. Thesis. Univ. of Washington.
Godement, R. (1948). Les fonctions de type positif et la théorie des groups. *Trans. Amer. Math. Soc.* **63**, 1–84.
Granirer, E. (1963a). On amenable semigroups with a finite dimensional set of invariant means, I and II. *Illinois J. Math.* **7**, 32–48, 49–58.
Granirer, E. (1963b). On left amenable semigroups which admit countable left-invariant means. *Bull. Amer. Math. Soc.* **69**, 101–105.
Granirer, E. (1964). A theorem on amenable semigroups. *Trans. Amer. Math. Soc.* **111**, 367–379.
Granirer, E. (1965a). Extremely amenable semigroups, I and II, *Math. Scand.* **17**, 177–197; (1967), **20**, 93–113; Also a brief account in (1966). *Bull. Amer. Math. Soc.* **72**, 1028–1032.
Granirer, E. (1965b). On the invariant mean on topological semigroups and on topological groups. *Pacific J. Math.* **15**, 107–140.
Granirer, E. (1966). On the range of an invariant mean. *Trans. Amer. Math. Soc.* **125**, 384–394.
Granirer, E. (1967). On Baire measures on D-topological spaces. *Fund. Math.* **60**, 1–22.
Granirer, E. (1969). Functional analytic properties of semigroups. *Amer. Math. Soc. Transl.* **137**, 53–75.
Granirer, E., and Rajagopalan, M. (1964). A note on the radical of the second conjugate algebra of a semigroup algebra. *Math. Scand.* **15**, 163–166.
Greenleaf, F. P. (1966). Invariant means on topological groups and their applications, lecture notes, Department of Mathematics, Univ. of California, Berkeley, Nov. 1966 (revised).
Hausdorff, F. (1914). "Grundzüge der Mengenlehre." Leipzig, 1914.
Hewitt, E., and Ross, K. A. (1963). "Abstract Harmonic Analysis." Vol. 1. Springer, Berlin.
Hochster, M. (1968). Subsemigroups of amenable groups. *Proc. Amer. Math. Soc.* **21**, 363–364.
Huff, R. E. (1970). Some applications of a general lemma on invariant means. *Illinois J. Math.* (to be published).
Hulanicki, A. (1964). Means and Følner conditions on locally compact groups. *Studia Math.* **27**, 87–104.
Jenkins, J. W. (1968). Symmetry of the group algebra of certain discrete groups. Thesis, Univ. of Illinois, Urbana.
Jerison, M. (1957). The set of all generalized limits of bounded sequences. *Canad. J. Math.* **9**, 79–89.
Kantorovič, L. (1937). Linear operations in semi-ordered spaces. *Mat. Sbornik* [NS] **2**, 121–168.

Kelley, J. L. (1955). "General Topology." Van Nostrand, Princeton, New Jersey.

Kelley, J. L., Namioka, I., *et al.* (1963). "Linear Topological Spaces." New York. 1963.

Kesten, H. (1959a). Full Banach mean values on countable groups. *Math. Scand.* **7**, 146–156.

Kesten, H. (1959b). Symmetric random walks on groups. *Trans. Amer. Math. Soc.* **92**, 336–354.

Kreĭn, M. (1937). Sur les fonctionelles positives additives dans les espaces linéares normés. *Comm. Inst. Sci. Math. et Mecan. Univ. Kharkoff et Soc. Math. Kharkoff IV* **14**, 227–236.

Ljapin, E. S. (1960). "Semigroups" (in Russian). Fizmatgiz, Moscow.

Lloyd, S. P. (1966). A mixing condition for extreme left-invariant means. *Trans. Amer. Math. Soc.* **125**, 461–481.

Lorentz, G. G. (1948). A contribution to the theory of divergent sequences. *Acta Math.* **80**, 167–190.

Luthar, I. S. (1959). Uniqueness of the invariant mean on an abelian semigroup. *Illinois J. Math.* **3**, 28–44.

Markov, A. (1936). Quelques théorèmes sur les ensembles abelians. *Compt. Rend. Acad. Sci. URSS* [NS] **1**, 311–313.

Mazur, S. (1929). Une remarque sur la homéomorphie des champs fonctionelles. *Studia Math.* **1**, 83–85.

Mazur, S. (1933). Über konvexe Mengen in linearen normierten Raümen, *Studia Math.* **4**, 70–84.

Mitchell, T. (1965). Constant functions and left-invariant means on semigroups. *Trans. Amer. Math. Soc.* **119**, 244–261.

Mitchell, T. (1966). Fixed points and multiplicative left invariant means. *Trans. Amer. Math. Soc.* **122**, 195–202.

Mitchell, T. (1968). Function algebras, means, and fixed points. *Trans. Amer. Math. Soc.* **130**, 117–126.

Mitchell, T. (1970). Topological semigroups and fixed points. *Illinois J. Math.* (to be published).

Namioka, I. (1964). Følner's condition for amenable semigroups. *Math. Scand.* **15**, 18–28.

Namioka, I. (1966). On a recent theorem of H. Reiter. *Proc. Amer. Math. Soc.* **17**, 1101–1102.

Namioka, I. (1967). On certain actions of semigroups of L-spaces. *Studia Math.* **29**, 63–77.

Numakura, K. (1952). On bicompact semigroups. *Math. J. Okayama Univ.* **1**, 99–108.

Orlicz, W. (1932). Über eine gewisse Klasse von Raümen von Types. B. *Bull. Internat. Acad. Polon. Sci. Classe Sci. Mat. Nat. Ser. A*, **8**, 207–220.

Peressini, A. L. (1967). "Ordered Topological Vector Spaces." Harper and Row, New York.

Phelps, R. R. (1966). "Lectures on Choquet's Theorem." Van Nostrand, Princeton, N.J.

Reiter, H. (1952). Investigations in harmonic analysis. *Trans. Amer. Math. Soc.* **73**, 401–427.

Reiter, H. (1960). The convex hull of the translates of functions in L_1. *J. London Math. Soc.* **35**, 5–16.

Reiter, H. (1965). On some properties of locally compact groups. *Nederl. Akad. Wetensch. Proc. Ser. A* **68** = *Indag. Math.* **27**, 697–701.

Rickert, N. (1965). Amenable groups and groups with the fixed-point property, thesis, Yale Univ., New Haven.

Riesz, F. (1938). Some mean ergodic theorems. *J. London Math. Soc.* **13**, 274–278.

Rosen, W. G. (1956). On invariant means over compact semigroups. *Proc. Amer. Math. Soc.* **7**, 1076–1082.

Schaefer, H. H. (1966). "Topological Vector Spaces." New York.

Silverman, R. J. (1956a). Invariant linear functions. *Trans. Amer. Math. Soc.* **81**, 411–424.

Silverman, R. J. (1956b). Means on semigroups and the Hahn-Banach extension property. *Trans. Amer. Math. Soc.* **83**, 222–237.

Stegeman, J. D. (1965). On a property concerning locally compact groups. *Nederl. Akad. Wetensch. Proc. Ser.* A **68** = *Indag. Math.* **27**, 702–703.

Sz.-Nagy, B. (1947). On uniformly bounded linear transformations in Hilbert space. *Acta Univ. Szegediensis Sect. Sci. Math.* **11**, 152–157.

Truitt, C. C. B. (1967). An extension to Orlicz spaces of theorems of M. M. Day on convolutions, means, and spectra. Thesis, Univ. of Illinois, Urbana. 1967.

von Neumann, J. (1929). Zur allgemeine Theorie des Masses. *Fund. Math.* **13**, 73–116.

von Neumann, J. (1932). Proof of the quasi-ergodic hypothesis. *Proc. Nat. Acad. Sci. USA* **18**, 70–82.

Wilde, C. O. (1964). On amenable semigroups and applications of the Stone-Čech compactification. Thesis, Univ. of Illinois, Urbana.

Wilde, C. O., and Witz, K. (1967). Invariant means and Stone-Čech compactification. *Pacific J. Math.* **21**, 577–586.

Witz, K. (1964). Applications of a compactification for bounded operator semigroups, *Illinois J. Math.* **8**, 685–696.

Yosida, K. (1939). Mean ergodic theorems in Banach spaces, *Proc. Imp. Acad. (Tokyo)* **14**, 292–294.

*Ternary Operations and Semigroups**

EDWIN HEWITT AND HERBERT S. ZUCKERMAN
University of Washington, Seattle, Washington

0. Introduction

Let $S(\cdot)$ be a semigroup, that is, a nonvoid set S and a mapping $(x, y) \rightarrow x \cdot y$ of $S \times S$ into S that satisfies the associative law. It was noticed long ago that with every semigroup we can associate the ternary operation

$$(x, y, z) \rightarrow x \cdot y \cdot z, \tag{0.1}$$

which obviously maps $S \times S \times S$ into S (see, for example, Dörnte [*1*], Łoś [*2*], and Post [*3*]). There is a large literature dealing with ternary, and indeed, m-ary operations. A selection of papers in this field appears in the bibliography. It is not our purpose to survey the field, and in fact our interest is not in ternary operations as such but in the semigroups (if any) giving rise to them as in (0.1). First, given a ternary operation

$$(x, y, z) \rightarrow x * y * z$$

on S, can we find all of the semigroups $S(\cdot)$ for which (0.1) holds? Second, given a semigroup $S(\cdot)$ and certain properties of triple products $x \cdot y \cdot z$, what can we say about the semigroup itself? Third, given semigroups $S(\cdot)$ and $S(\circ)$ on the same set S such that $x \cdot y \cdot z = x \circ y \circ z$ for all $x, y, z \in S$, we study the relationships that may exist between $S(\cdot)$ and $S(\circ)$.

In studying the first topic, we reproduce in part known facts, although much of our work appears to be new. The second and third topics are new so far as we know.

* Research supported by the National Science Foundation, under Grant No. GP-6729.

In the course of our study, we construct a number of interesting semigroups. Not all are new, but all illustrate one or another facet of our problems. Some of the new examples may be useful to other workers as part of the general catalog of semigroups. We note in particular the semigroup constructed in Lemma 1 (Section 2).

1. Ternary Operations and Their Semigroups

Suppose that we are given a nonvoid set S and a ternary operation, which we write as $x * y * z$, defined for all $x, y, z \in S$. Expressions like $x * y$ and $x * y * z * w$ are *not* defined, but expressions like $x * (y * z * w) * u$ are defined. We wish to find semigroups $S(\cdot)$ such that

$$x \cdot y \cdot z = x * y * z \tag{1.1}$$

for all $x, y, z \in S$. Our first result is simple enough.

Theorem 1. If a semigroup $S(\cdot)$ exists satisfying (1.1), then we have

$$x * y * (z * u * v) = x * (y * z * u) * v = (x * y * z) * u * v \tag{1.2}$$

for all x, y, z, u, v in S.

PROOF. This follows at once from the associative law for $S(\cdot)$.

The next theorem is useful in many situations.

Theorem 2. Let S have a ternary operation $*$ satisfying (1.2), and suppose that S contains an element e such that

$$e * e * x = x \tag{1.3}$$

for all $x \in S$. Then all semigroups $S(\cdot)$ for which (1.1) holds are defined by

$$x \cdot y = u * x * y, \tag{1.4}$$

where u is an element of S such that

$$u * u * e = e \tag{1.5}$$

and

$$u * x * u = x * u * u \tag{1.6}$$

for all $x \in S$. Conversely, if u satisfies (1.5) and (1.6) and $\cdot$ is defined by (1.4), then $S(\cdot)$ is a semigroup and (1.1) holds. If u_1 and u_2 are elements of S that satisfy (1.5) and (1.6), then putting u_1 and u_2 for u in (1.4) yields the same semigroup if and only if

$$u_1 * u_2 * u_2 = u_2 . \tag{1.7}$$

PROOF. First suppose that (1.2) and (1.3) hold and that u is an element of S satisfying (1.5) and (1.6). Then defining $x \cdot y$ as in (1.4), we have, for all x, y, z in S,

$$\begin{aligned}(x \cdot y) \cdot z &= u * (u * x * y) * z = u * u * (x * y * z) \\ &= u * u * (e * e * (x * y * z)) = (u * u * e) * e * (x * y * z) \\ &= e * e * (x * y * z) = x * y * z,\end{aligned}$$

and similarly

$$\begin{aligned}x \cdot (y \cdot z) &= u * x * (u * y * z) = (u * x * u) * y * z \\ &= (x * u * u) * y * z = x * (u * u * y) * z \\ &= x * (u * u * (e * e * y)) * z = x * ((u * u * e) * e * y) * z \\ &= x * (e * e * y) * z = x * y * z.\end{aligned}$$

Thus $S(\cdot)$ is a semigroup and (1.1) holds.

Next suppose that (1.2) and (1.3) hold and that there is some semigroup $S(\cdot)$ for which (1.1) holds. Define u as the element $e \cdot e$. Then we have

$$u \cdot x = e \cdot e \cdot x = e * e * x = x$$

and hence

$$x \cdot y = u \cdot x \cdot y = u * x * y,$$

i.e., (1.4) holds. It is also clear that

$$u * u * e = u \cdot u \cdot e = u \cdot e = e,$$

i.e., (1.5) holds. Next, we write

$$u * x * u = u \cdot x \cdot u = x \cdot u = x \cdot u \cdot u = x * u * u,$$

and this is (1.6).

To prove the last assertion of the theorem, suppose that u_1 and u_2 both satisfy (1.5) and (1.6). If $u_1 * x * y = u_2 * x * y$ for all x, y in S, we have in particular

$$\begin{aligned}u_1 * u_2 * u_2 &= u_2 * u_2 * u_2 = u_2 * u_2 * (e * e * u_2) \\ &= (u_2 * u_2 * e) * e * u_2 = e * e * u_2 = u_2 .\end{aligned}$$

That is, (1.7) holds. Conversely, if (1.7) holds, we have

$$\begin{aligned} u_2 * x * y &= (u_1 * u_2 * u_2) * x * y = u_1 * (u_2 * u_2 * x) * y \\ &= u_1 * (u_2 * u_2 * (e * e * x)) * y = u_1 * ((u_2 * u_2 * e) * e * x) * y \\ &= u_1 * (e * e * x) * y = u_1 * x * y \end{aligned}$$

for all x, y in S. Thus u_1 and u_2 define the same semigroup via (1.4). ▌

NOTE. Theorem 1 has an obvious analog in which every triple $*$-product appearing in (1.3)–(1.6) is written in reversed order. For example, (1.3) becomes $x * e * e = x$ for all $x \in S$.

We now give some examples.

EXAMPLE 1. Let S be the real numbers, let k be a fixed real number, and let $x * y * z = k + x + y + z$. It is easy to see that the binary operation $x \cdot y = (k/2) + x + y$ is associative and that (1.1) holds. By Theorem 1, (1.2) holds. The number $e = -k/2$ satisfies (1.3). There is only one u satisfying (1.5) and (1.6), namely, $u = -k/2$. Theorem 2 shows that $x \cdot y = (k/2) + x + y$ is the only semigroup operation for which (1.1) holds.

EXAMPLE 2. Again let S be the real numbers, and let $x * y * z = xyz$. Clearly the semigroup operation $x \cdot y = xy$ satisfies (1.1), and so (1.2) holds, by Theorem 1. The number 1 can be taken for e in Theorem 2. Plainly the elements u for which (1.5) and (1.6) hold are just the numbers ± 1. Since $1(-1)(-1) \neq -1$, (1.7) is not satisfied, the two semigroup operations xy and $-xy$ are distinct and yield the same ternary operation xyz.

EXAMPLE 3. Let S be the integers and let $x * y * z = k + x + y + z$, where k is an integer. If k is even, the results duplicate those of Example 1. If k is odd, on the other hand, no integer e satisfies (1.3), so that Theorem 2 is not applicable. Even so, assume that (1.1) holds for some semigroup operation $\cdot$ on S, and let $u = 0 \cdot 0$. Then we have $u \cdot u \cdot u = u * u * u = k + 3u$, and also

$$\begin{aligned} u \cdot u \cdot u &= 0 \cdot 0 \cdot u \cdot u = k + 0 + 0 + (u \cdot u) = k + (0 \cdot 0 \cdot u) \\ &= 2k + 0 + 0 + u = 2k + u, \end{aligned}$$

an evident contradiction, since k is odd. Plainly the associative law (1.2) holds for all choices of k, although for k odd, no semigroup exists satisfying (1.1). Several other writers have given examples of this phenomenon. The first we know is Dörnte [*1*], who showed that the odd integers under addition admit no semigroup for which (1.1) holds. Łoś [*2*, p. 53] asserts that S. Banach had an example which was never published. A rather complicated example was published by Monk and Sioson [*4*].

EXAMPLE 4. Let S be any nonvoid set, let a be a fixed element of S, and let $x * y * z = a$ for all $x, y, z \in S$. Suppose that $S(\cdot)$ is a semigroup satisfying (1.1). Let $A = S \cdot S$ and let $B = S \cap A'$. Plainly a is in A. For $x \in A$ and $y \in S$, we have $x = u \cdot v$ for some $u, v \in S$ and therefore, $x \cdot y = u \cdot v \cdot y = u * v * y = a$, and likewise $y \cdot x = a$. If $x \in B$ and $y \in B$, we know nothing about $x \cdot y$ except that it lies in A.

Conversely, let A and B be any two complementary subsets of S such that $a \in A$. Define $x \cdot y$ as a if either x or y is in A, and define $x \cdot y$ as any element c of A if x and y are in B (c may vary with x and y). Then $x \cdot y$ is in A for all x, y in S, and so

$$(x \cdot y) \cdot z = x \cdot (y \cdot z) = a$$

for all x, y, z in S. Thus $S(\cdot)$ is a semigroup satisfying (1.1). Plainly $S(\cdot)$ is not unique if S contains more than two elements. If S contains at least four elements, then both A and B can be chosen to contain at least two elements, and $S(\cdot)$ can be commutative or noncommutative, just as we please.

EXAMPLE 5. We here give a set and a ternary operation for which there is an e as in Theorem 2, but for which there is no u as in Theorem 2. Let

$$S = \left\{ \begin{pmatrix} \alpha & \beta \\ \gamma & \delta \end{pmatrix} : \ \alpha, \beta, \gamma, \delta \text{ are real, } \alpha\delta - \beta\gamma = -1 \right\},$$

and let $x * y * z = xyz$ [matrix product] for $x, y, z \in S$. Since matrix multiplication is associative, (1.2) holds. Plainly $\left(\begin{smallmatrix} 1 & 0 \\ 0 & -1 \end{smallmatrix}\right)$ can be taken for e in (1.3). Assume that there is a matrix $u = \left(\begin{smallmatrix} \alpha & \beta \\ \gamma & \delta \end{smallmatrix}\right)$ in S for which (1.5) and (1.6) hold, that is, for which $u = u^{-1}$ and $ux = xu$ for all $x \in S$. Since $u^{-1} = \left(\begin{smallmatrix} -\delta & \beta \\ \gamma & -\alpha \end{smallmatrix}\right)$, we have $\alpha = -\delta$. Setting $x = \left(\begin{smallmatrix} 1 & 0 \\ 1 & -1 \end{smallmatrix}\right)$ in the equality $ux = xu$, we find $\beta = 0$ and $\gamma + \delta = \alpha - \gamma$, so that $\gamma = \alpha$. Setting $x = \left(\begin{smallmatrix} 1 & 1 \\ 0 & -1 \end{smallmatrix}\right)$, we find $\gamma = 0$. Thus u is $\left(\begin{smallmatrix} 0 & 0 \\ 0 & 0 \end{smallmatrix}\right)$, and therefore there is no u in S satisfying (1.5) and (1.6). Theorem 2 shows that the ternary operation on S has the form (1.1) for no semigroup $S(\cdot)$.

EXAMPLE 6. Let S be any nonvoid set, and let $x * y * z = x$ for all x, y, z in S. Plainly the semigroup operation $x \cdot y = x$ satisfies (1.1). Now suppose that $S(\cdot)$ is any semigroup satisfying (1.1). Then we have

$$\begin{aligned} x \cdot y &= (x \cdot y) * (x \cdot y) * z = (x \cdot y) \cdot (x \cdot y) \cdot z \\ &= (x \cdot y \cdot x) \cdot y \cdot z = (x * y * x) * y * z = x. \end{aligned}$$

That is, there is a unique semigroup $S(\cdot)$ satisfying (1.1).

EXAMPLE 7. Let S contain at least two elements, and let $x * y * z = y$. For distinct a, b in S we have $a * a * (a * b * a) = a$ and $(a * a * a) * b * a = b$, so that (1.2) is violated. Theorem 1 shows that (1.1) holds for no semigroup $S(\cdot)$.

EXAMPLE 8. We modify Example 6. Let S be the real numbers, and let $x * y * z = [x]$, where $[x]$ is the greatest integer not exceeding x. We will exhibit many distinct semigroups $S(\cdot)$ and $S(\circ)$ satisfying (1.1). [There are others.] Let $x \cdot y = [x]$. Plainly $S(\cdot)$ is a semigroup and (1.1) holds. Next, let

$$x \circ y = \begin{cases} [x] & \text{if } x \text{ or } y \text{ is an integer or an integer plus } \alpha, \text{ where } \alpha \text{ is a fixed number in }]0, 1[, \\ [x] + \alpha & \text{otherwise.} \end{cases}$$

Since $x \circ y$ is an integer or an integer plus α, we have $(x \circ y) \circ z = [x \circ y]$. Since $x \circ y$ is $[x]$ or $[x] + \alpha$, we have $[x \circ y] = [[x]] = [x]$ or $[[x] + \alpha] = [x]$. Thus we have $(x \circ y) \circ z = [x]$. Also, $y \circ z$ is an integer or an integer plus α, so that $x \circ (y \circ z) = [x]$. Thus $S(\circ)$ is a semigroup for which (1.1) holds.

EXAMPLE 9. Let S be a set containing at least three elements, and let a and b be elements of S [not necessarily distinct]. Let

$$x * y * z = \begin{cases} y & \text{if } x = z = a, \\ b & \text{otherwise.} \end{cases}$$

Let c be in S, where $c \neq a$, $c \neq b$. Then we have

$$(a * c * a) * a * a = c * a * a = b,$$

while

$$a * c * (a * a * a) = a * c * a = c.$$

Hence (1.2) is violated, and so there is no semigroup $S(\cdot)$ for which (1.1) holds. If $a = b$, the same argument works even if S contains but two elements.

EXAMPLE 10. Let $S = \{a, b\}$, where $a \neq b$, and define $x * y * z$ as in Example 9. Let

$$x \cdot y = \begin{cases} a & \text{if } x = y = a, \\ b & \text{otherwise.} \end{cases}$$

Then $S(\cdot)$ is a semigroup for which (1.1) holds. The corollary to

Theorem 23 *infra* shows that no other semigroup will do, because $S(\cdot)$ is idempotent.

EXAMPLE 11. Let S be any set containing at least two elements, let a and b be distinct elements of S, and define

$$x * y * z = \begin{cases} x & \text{if } y = z = a, \\ b & \text{otherwise.} \end{cases}$$

If $S(\cdot)$ is a semigroup for which (1.1) holds, then we have $a \cdot a \cdot a = a$ and $(x \cdot y) \cdot a \cdot a = x \cdot y$. If $a \cdot a \neq a$, then we have $x \cdot y \cdot (a \cdot a) = b$, so that $x \cdot y = b$ for all $x, y \in S$. This violates the equality $(a \cdot a) \cdot a = a$. We thus have $a \cdot a = a$, and also

$$x \cdot y = (x \cdot y) \cdot a \cdot a = x \cdot y \cdot a = x * y * a = \begin{cases} x & \text{if } y = a, \\ b & \text{if } y \neq a. \end{cases}$$

Conversely, let us define $x \cdot y$ by

$$x \cdot y = \begin{cases} x & \text{if } y = a, \\ b & \text{if } y \neq a. \end{cases}$$

Then we have $(x \cdot y) \cdot a = x \cdot y$ and $x \cdot (y \cdot a) = x \cdot y$. For $z \neq a$, we have $(x \cdot y) \cdot z = b$ and $x \cdot (y \cdot z) = x \cdot b = b$. Hence $S(\cdot)$ is a semigroup. It is easy to see that (1.1) holds.

EXAMPLE 12. As another application of Theorem 2, consider together the sets $S = \{0, 1, 2, \ldots, m - 1\}$ and $S = \{x: x \text{ is an integer}, 1 \leqslant x \leqslant m - 1, (x, m) = 1\}$, $m > 2$. Let $x * y * z \equiv xyz \pmod{m}$. Plainly (1.2) holds. We may take $e = 1$ in (1.3). Condition (1.5) becomes $u^2 \equiv 1 \pmod{m}$ and (1.6) always holds. Defining $x \cdot y$ by $x \cdot y \equiv uxy \pmod{m}$ for any u such that $u^2 \equiv 1 \pmod{m}$, we obtain a semigroup for which (1.1) holds. For m prime, there are exactly two u's; for composite m, there may be many. Condition (1.7) becomes $u_1 \equiv u_2 \pmod{m}$, and so distinct u's modulo m yield distinct semigroups.

EXAMPLE 13. Part of Example 12 admits an evident generalization. Let S be any nonvoid set, and let $S(\circ)$ be an Abelian group. Let $x * y * z = x \circ y \circ z$. Then $S(\cdot)$ is a semigroup for which (1.1) holds if and only if $x \cdot y = u \circ x \circ y$, where u is the group identity or an element of order 2. Distinct such elements yield distinct semigroups. All this follows directly from Theorem 2.

EXAMPLE 14. Let S be the set $\{x: x \text{ is a real number}, x \geqslant \alpha_0\}$, where α_0 is any nonnegative number. Let a be a fixed positive element of S, and define $x * y * z = \min\{x + y + z, a\}$. We will exhibit two semigroups, of some interest in themselves, for which (1.1) holds.

First, let $x \cdot y = \min\{x + y, a\}$. Then we have

$$(x \cdot y) \cdot z = \min\{\min\{x + y, a\} + z, a\} = \min\{\min\{x + y + z, a + z\}, a\}$$
$$= \min\{x + y + z, a + z, a\} = \min\{x + y + z, a\},$$

since $a + z \geqslant a$. Similarly, we find that $x \cdot (y \cdot z) = \min\{x + y + z, a\}$. Thus $S(\cdot)$ is a semigroup and (1.1) holds.

Second, define $S(\circ)$ by the following rules:

$$x \circ y = x + y \quad \text{if} \quad x + y \leqslant a;$$
$$(2a) \circ (2a) = (3a);$$
$$x \circ y = a \quad \text{if} \quad x + y > a \text{ and not both } x \text{ and } y \text{ are equal to } 2a.$$

We compute as follows. If $x + y + z \leqslant a$, then $(x \circ y) \circ z = (x + y) \circ z = x + y + z$. If $x + y \leqslant a$ and $x + y + z > a$, then

$$(x \circ y) \circ z = (x + y) \circ z = a.$$

If $x = y = 2a$, then $(x \circ y) \circ z = (3a) \circ z = a$. If $x + y > a$ and not both x and y are $2a$, then $(x \circ y) \circ z = a \circ z = a$. The last four sentences show that

$$(x \circ y) \circ z = \min\{x + y + z, a\}.$$

Since $u \circ v = v \circ u$, we have

$$x \circ (y \circ z) = (y \circ z) \circ x = \min\{y + z + x, a\} = (x \circ y) \circ z.$$

Hence $S(\circ)$ is a semigroup satisfying (1.1).

EXAMPLE 15. Let $S = \{a, a + 1, a + 2, \ldots\}$, where a is a positive integer, and define

$$x * y * z = x + y + z.$$

Plainly Theorem 2 cannot be applied, but we may still look for the semigroups $S(\cdot)$ satisfying (1.1). If $S(\cdot)$ is such a semigroup, we have

$$(x \cdot y) + (x \cdot y) + a = (x \cdot y) * (x \cdot y) * a = (x \cdot y) \cdot (x \cdot y) \cdot a$$
$$= (x \cdot y \cdot x) \cdot y \cdot a = (x * y * x) * y * a = 2x + 2y + a.$$

It follows that $x \cdot y = x + y$. Since $S(+)$ plainly satisfies (1.1), there is exactly one semigroup $S(\cdot)$ satisfying (1.1).

EXAMPLE 16. Let T be any nonvoid set, and let S be the set of all functions with domain T and range contained in T. Define $x * y * z$ by the rule

$$x * y * z(\alpha) = x(y(z(\alpha))).$$

Evidently (1.2) holds. The function e such that $e(\alpha) = \alpha$ for all $\alpha \in T$ satisfies (1.3). Condition (1.5) becomes $u(u(\alpha)) = \alpha$ for all $\alpha \in T$, and (1.6) reduces to $u(x(u(\alpha))) = x(\alpha)$. If x is a constant function $[x(\alpha) = \beta$ for all $\alpha \in T]$, then the last equality becomes $u(\beta) = \beta$. Since β is arbitrary, u must be e. Since e satisfies (1.5) and (1.6), we find from (1.4) that $S(\cdot)$, where $x \cdot y(\alpha) = x(y(\alpha))$, is the only semigroup satisfying (1.1).

EXAMPLE 17. Let T be a nonvoid set, S the family of all subsets of T, and define

$$x * y * z = \{\alpha \in T : \alpha \text{ is in exactly one or three of the sets } x, y, z\}.$$

The symmetric difference $x \cdot y = (x \cap y') \cup (x' \cap y)$ makes S a semigroup satisfying (1.1). By Theorem 1, (1.2) holds. We may take $e = \emptyset$ in (1.3) (any element x will do just as well). It is easy to see that (1.5) and (1.6) hold for *all* $u \in S$, and that (1.7) holds if and only if $u_1 = u_2$. The operation $x \cdot y = u * x * y$ is thus a semigroup operation on S satisfying (1.1), for all $u \in S$, and distinct u's yield distinct semigroups. There are $2^{\mathfrak{a}}$ such semigroups, $\mathfrak{a}$ being the cardinal number of T. All of them are groups in which every element has order 2. The element u is the identity, and it is clear that $x \cdot x = u$. Plainly all of these groups are isomorphic [see also Corollary 2 to Theorem 22].

The reader may find it amusing to work out what happens if "one or three" is replaced by "one," "two," "three," "one or two," "two or three," or "one or two or three" in the description of $x * y * z$, in Example 17.

2. Properties of Semigroups Expressible in Terms of xyz

Throughout this section, we will be dealing with one or another semigroup. For simplicity's sake, we will write all products as $xy, xyz, x^4, \ldots$. The symbol "S" in this section will always denote a semigroup.

Theorem 3. If $a \in S$ and $axy = a$ for all $x, y \in S$, then a is a left zero for S.

PROOF. Since $a^3 = a$, we have also $a^2 = a^4 = aa^2a = a$, and so $ax = a^2x = aax = a$.

Theorem 4. If $xay = a$ for all $x, y \in S$, then a is a two-sided zero for S.

PROOF. Since $a^3 = a$, we also have $a^2 = a^4 = a^2aa = a$, and so $ax = a^2x = aax = a$; similarly $xa = a$.

Theorem 5. If $axb = x$ for all $x \in S$, then ab is a two-sided identity in S.

PROOF. We have $abx = a(abx)\,b = (aab)\,xb = axb = x$; similarly $xab = x$.

Theorem 6. Suppose that $xyx = y$ for all $x, y \in S$. Then S is an Abelian group such that $x^2 = e$ for all $x \in S$, where e is the identity element of S. The converse also holds.

PROOF. By Theorem 5, x^2 is a two-sided identity for all $x \in S$. Such identities are unique, so we call it e and have $x^2 = e$ for all $x \in S$. It follows at once that S is a group all elements of which have order 2. Also we have $xy = x(xyxy)\,y = x^2yxy^2 = yx$. The converse is obvious.

An identity slightly different from the one in Theorem 6 leads to a markedly different result. Given two nonvoid sets A and B, consider the Cartesian product $A \times B$ and in it the product $(a, b) \circ (a', b') = (a, b')$. It is easy to see that $A \times B$ is the direct product of semigroups A and B with $xy = x$ in A and $xy = y$ in B. This is the *rectangular band on* $A \times B$.

Theorem 7. Suppose that $xyx = x$ for all $x, y \in S$. Then there are nonvoid sets A and B such that S is isomorphic with $A \times B$, multiplication in $A \times B$ being defined as in the preceding paragraph. The converse also holds.

PROOF. It is plain that $x^3 = x$, that $xyxy = xy$, and that

$$x^2 = x^3x^3 = (xx^2x)\,x^2 = xx^2 = x.$$

It is also clear that $xyz = xy(zxz) = (x(yz)\,x)\,z = xz$.

Let the elements of A be the *sets* xS, as x runs through all of S, and let B consist of all sets Sx. It is clear that $xy \in (xS) \cap (Sy)$. Now let u be any element of $(xS) \cap (Sy)$; that is, $u = xv = wy$ for some $v, w \in S$. Then we have $xy = xvy = (xv)\,y = (wy)\,y = wy = u$. Thus $(xS) \cap (Sy)$ consists of the single element xy.

Now for $a \in A$ and $b \in B$, consider the element x such that $\{x\} = a \cap b$, and map x into $\varphi(x) = (a, b) \in A \times B$. Let us first show that φ is well defined. Since $x = x^2$, we have $x \in (xS) \cap (Sx)$. If u and v are elements of S such that $x \in (uS) \cap (Sv)$, then we have $x = uv$, and consequently $xS = uvS \subset uS$ and $Sx = Suv \subset Sv$. We also have $xu = uvu = u$, so that $uS = xuS \subset xS$. Similarly we find $vx = vuv = v$, and so $Sv = Svx \subset Sx$. That is, there is just one pair of sets (uS, Sv) with intersection $\{x\}$, and so $\varphi(x)$ is well defined. It is evident that φ is a one-to-one mapping of S onto $A \times B$.

Now we have $\varphi(x) = (xS, Sx)$, $\varphi(y) = (yS, Sy)$, $\varphi(xy) = (xyS, Sxy)$. Since $xyv = xv$ and $vxy = vy$, (xyS, Sxy) is the pair (xS, Sy). The definition of multiplication in $A \times B$ shows that φ is an isomorphism.

The converse is obvious. ▮

NOTE. Let S be a semigroup such that $xy \neq yx$ unless $x = y$. Since $x^2x = xx^2$, we have $x^2 = x$ and also $x(xyx) = xyx = (xyx)x$. It follows that $xyx = x$, and hence S has the form given in Theorem 7. Semigroups $A \times B$ as in Theorem 7 plainly have this "anticommutative" property. Thus semigroups of the form $A \times B$ are just those in which $xy \neq yx$ unless $x = y$.

Theorem 8. Suppose that $xxy = x$ for all $x, y \in S$. Then we have $xy = x$ for all $x, y \in S$.

PROOF. We have $xy = (xxy)\,y = xxy^2 = x$.

Theorem 9. Suppose that $xxy = y$ for all $x, y \in S$. Then S is isomorphic with the direct product of a group G all of whose elements have order 2 and a semigroup T with the multiplication $x \circ y = y$. The converse also holds.

PROOF. Let b be any element of S, and let $a = b^2$. Let G be the set $\{x \in S\colon x^2 = a\}$, and let multiplication in G be inherited from S. For $x, y \in G$ we have $xyxy = xyxyyy = (xy)(xy)\,yy = yy = a$. Thus G is a subsemigroup of S. For x in G, we have $xa = xxx = x$ and similarly $ax = x$. Thus G is a group whose identity is a, and all of whose elements have order 2.

Let $T = \{x^2\colon x \in S\}$. For u, v in T, define $u \circ v = v$. Obviously T is a semigroup.

For $x \in S$, we have $(xa)(xa) = x(bbx)\,a = xxa = a$, and so xa is in G. We define $\varphi(x)$ as the element $(xa, x^2) \in G \times T$. To see that φ is one-to-one, suppose that $\varphi(x) = \varphi(y)$. Then we have

$$x = xxx = xbbxx = xaxx = yaxx = yayy = ybbyy = yyy = y.$$

To show that $\varphi(S) = G \times T$, let u be any element of G and v be any element of S. Let $x = uv^2$. Then we have

$$xa = uv^2a = ua = uu^2 = u$$

and

$$x^2 = uv^2uv^2 = u(vv(uv^2)) = uuv^2 = v^2,$$

i.e., $\varphi(x) = (u, v^2)$.

To show that φ is an isomorphism, note that

$$xyxy = xyx(yyy) = (xy)(xy)\,yy = y^2.$$

Then we have

$$\varphi(x)\,\varphi(y) = (xa, x^2)(ya, y^2) = (xaya, y^2) = (xbbya, y^2)$$
$$= (xya, y^2) = \varphi(xy).$$

The converse is obvious. ∎

We now take up a different class of relations involving triple products.

Theorem 10. If S contains a unique element a such that $axa = x$ for all $x \in S$, then a is a two-sided identity element in S.

PROOF. We have $a^2xa^2 = a(axa)\,a = axa = a$, and so $a^2 = a$. We then have

$$ax = a(ax)\,a = a^2xa = axa = x$$

and similarly $xa = x$.

Theorem 11. If there is a unique element a in S such that $aax = x$ for all x in S, then a is the unique left identity in S.

PROOF. We have $a^2a^2x = a^2aax = a^2x = x$, and so $a^2 = a$. We then have $ax = aax = x$. If b is any left identity, then $bbx = b(bx) = bx = x$, and so $a = b$.

Theorem 12. If there is a unique element $a \in S$ such that $axa = a$ for all $x \in S$, then a is a two-sided zero in S.

PROOF. For $x, y \in S$, we have

$$(ay)\,x(ay) = (a(yx)\,a)\,y = ay,$$

and so $ay = a$. Similarly we see that $ya = a$.

Theorem 13. If there is a unique element $a \in S$ such that $axy = a$ for all $x, y \in S$, then a is a two-sided zero in S.

PROOF. For all $x, y, z \in S$, we have $(za)\,xy = z(axy) = za$, and so $za = a$. That is, a is a right zero in S. Note that $a^2 = a$, and so $ax = a^2x = aax = a$. That is, a is also a left zero.

The next theorem does not involve triple products, but it is interesting and also seems to fit in here.

Theorem 14. If S has a unique left zero a, then a is a two-sided zero for S.

PROOF. For all $x, y \in S$, we have $(xa)y = x(ay) = xa$, so that xa is a left zero, and so $xa = a$.

The analog of Theorem 14 with "zero" replaced by "identity" does not hold, as the following example shows.

EXAMPLE 18. Let $S = \{a, b, c\}$, where a, b, c are distinct, and let $ax = x$, $bx = cx = c$ for all $x \in S$. It is easy to check that this operation makes S a semigroup, that a is the only left identity, and that a is not a right identity.

Theorem 15. Suppose that xyz is one of the elements x or z for each triple x, y, z of elements of S. Then either $xy = x$ for all $x, y \in S$ or $xy = y$ for all $x, y \in S$.

PROOF. If $xy = x$ for all $x, y \in S$, there is nothing to prove. Suppose then that $ab \neq a$ for some pair of elements a, b in S. In this case, we have

$$abbxy = a(bbx)y = a \quad \text{or} \quad y \tag{2.1}$$

and

$$abbxy = (ab)(bx)y = ab \quad \text{or} \quad y. \tag{2.2}$$

If $abbxy = a$, then (2.2) shows that $abbxy = y$. If $abbxy \neq a$, then (2.1) shows that $abbxy = y$. Thus we always have $abbxy = y$. Similarly, we may write

$$abbxy = a(bb)(xy) = a \quad \text{or} \quad xy,$$

$$abbxy = (ab)\,b(xy) = ab \quad \text{or} \quad xy.$$

These equalities show that $abbxy = xy$, and so $xy = y$.

Theorem 16. Suppose that xyz is one of the elements x or y for each triple x, y, z of elements of S. Then $xy = x$ for all $x, y \in S$.

PROOF. We have $x = xxx$ and $xy = (xxx)y = xx(xy) = x$.

Our next theorem describes completely the semigroups in which every product xyz is equal to one of the elements x, y, z. We begin with two lemmas.

Lemma 1. Let Λ be a nonvoid set completely ordered by a relation $<$ ($x < y$ implies $x \neq y$). Let f be a mapping of Λ into a two-element set $\{l, r\}$. Let $\{S_\lambda\}_{\lambda \in \Lambda}$ be a family of nonvoid, pairwise disjoint sets indexed by Λ, and let $S = \bigcup_{\lambda \in \Lambda} S_\lambda$. For $x, y \in S$, let λ_1 and λ_2 be the elements of Λ such that $x \in S_{\lambda_1}$, and $y \in S_{\lambda_2}$. We define multiplication in S by the following rules:

(i) if $\lambda_1 = \lambda_2$ and $f(\lambda_1) = l$, then $xy = x$;
(ii) if $\lambda_1 = \lambda_2$ and $f(\lambda_1) = r$, then $xy = y$;
(iii) if $\lambda_1 < \lambda_2$, then $xy = y$;
(iv) if $\lambda_2 < \lambda_1$, then $xy = x$.

Then S is a semigroup in which xy is either x or y for all $x, y \in S$.

Proof. It is a routine matter to check that multiplication is associative; we omit the details. It is obvious that xy is either x or y.

The next lemma is less trivial.

Lemma 2. Let S be a semigroup in which xy is either x or y for all $x, y \in S$. Then S is isomorphic with a semigroup of the sort described in Lemma 1.

Proof. Consider three elements x, y, z of S such that

$$y \neq z, \qquad xy \neq yx, \qquad xz \neq zx. \tag{2.3}$$

It is plain that $x \neq y$ and $x \neq z$. There are exactly four possibilities:

$$\text{(a)}\quad \begin{matrix} xy = x, & yx = y \\ xz = z, & zx = x; \end{matrix} \qquad \text{(b)}\quad \begin{matrix} xy = y, & yx = x \\ xz = x, & zx = z; \end{matrix}$$

$$\text{(c)}\quad \begin{matrix} xy = x, & yx = y \\ xz = x, & zx = z; \end{matrix} \qquad \text{(d)}\quad \begin{matrix} xy = y, & yx = x \\ xz = z, & zx = x. \end{matrix}$$

We will show that (a) cannot occur. If (a) holds, then we have

$$x(yz) = (xy)\,z = xz = z.$$

If $yz = y$, then $x(yz) = xy = x \neq z$. Hence yz must be z. We also have

$$(yz)\,x = y(zx) = yx = y.$$

If $yz = z$, then $(yz)\,x = zx = x \neq y$. Hence yz must be y. Thus (a) cannot occur. Similarly, (b) cannot occur.

Both cases (c) and (d) can occur. Suppose that (c) occurs. Then we have

$$yz = (yx)(zx) = y(xz)\,x = yxx = yx = y \tag{2.4}$$

and

$$zy = (zx)(yx) = z(xy)\,x = zxx = zx = z. \tag{2.5}$$

In like manner, we have in case (d)

$$yz = z$$

and

$$zy = y.$$

Thus if xy and xz multiply "on the left," so do yz and zy; and similarly for "on the right."

We now define some subsets of S. For each $x \in S$, let

$$T_x = \{x\} \cup \{y \in S: xy \neq yx\}.$$

Each T_x is a subsemigroup of S, and in each T_x we have either $uv = u$ for all $u, v \in T_x$ or $uv = v$ for all $u, v \in T_x$. To prove this, let u and v be elements of T_x such that $u \neq v$. The elements x, u, v satisfy the requirements on x, y, z respectively, in (2.3). Thus case (c) or case (d) above must occur. In case (c), (2.4) applies to show that $uv = u$ and $vu = v$. In case (d), (2.5) shows that $uv = v$, $vu = u$. The products ux, xu, vx, xv are taken care of by cases (a) and (b) themselves.

We next show that any two subsemigroups T_x are either disjoint or identical. Consider any elements x_1 and x_2 of S such that $T_{x_1} \cap T_{x_2} \neq \emptyset$. If $x_1 = x_2$, T_{x_1} and T_{x_2} are trivially identical. Suppose from now on that $x_1 \neq x_2$. If $x_1 \in T_{x_2}$, then

$$x_2x_1 \neq x_1x_2,$$

so that $x_2 \in T_{x_1}$. Now let y be any element of T_{x_1} such that $y \neq x_2$. Thus we have

$$yx_1 \neq x_1y.$$

The elements x_1, y, and x_2 satisfy the requirements on x, y, and z, respectively, in (2.3). Thus either case (c) or case (d) occurs. If case (c) occurs, (2.4) and (2.5) tell us that $yx_2 = y$ and $x_2y = x_2$. Since $x_2 \neq y$, we see that $yx_2 \neq x_2y$, and so $y \in T_{x_2}$. If case (d) occurs, we have a similar proof that $y \in T_{x_2}$. This proves the inclusion

$$T_{x_1} \subset T_{x_2}$$

under the hypothesis that $x_1 \in T_{x_2}$. Since we also have $x_2 \in T_{x_1}$, the reversed inclusion can be proved similarly.

Now suppose that there is a z such that $z \neq x_1$, $z \neq x_2$, and $z \in T_{x_1} \cap T_{x_2}$. This means that the elements z, x_1, x_2 satisfy the requirements on x, y, z respectively, in (2.3). If case (c) occurs, (2.4) and (2.5) show that $x_1x_2 = x_1$ and $x_2x_1 = x_2$. Thus we have $x_1x_2 \neq x_2x_1$ and so x_1 is in T_{x_2}. The argument is similar if case (d) occurs. We thus have $x_1 \in T_{x_2}$ if $T_{x_1} \cap T_{x_2} \neq \emptyset$, and the preceding paragraph shows that $T_{x_1} = T_{x_2}$.

Now let $\{S_\lambda\}_{\lambda \in \Lambda}$ be the family of all distinct (and hence disjoint) sets T_x: Λ is simply an index set. We know that each S_λ is a semigroup and that $xy = x$ for all $x, y \in S_\lambda$ or $xy = y$ for all $x, y \in S_\lambda$. In the first case, we define $f(\lambda) = l$, and in the second we define $f(\lambda) = r$. This agrees with rules (i) and (ii) of Lemma 1.

For $\lambda \neq \mu$ and $x \in S_\lambda$, $z \in S_\mu$, it is easy to see that $xz = zx$. Pick $x_0 \in S_\lambda$ and $z_0 \in S_\mu$. Suppose that $x_0z_0 = x_0$. We will prove that $xz = x$ for all $x \in S_\lambda$ and $z \in S_\mu$. In S_μ, we have either $z_0z = z_0$ and $zz_0 = z$ or $z_0z = z$ and $zz_0 = z_0$. In the first case, we may write

$$zx_0 = x_0z = (x_0z_0)\, z = x_0(z_0z) = x_0z_0 = x_0 . \tag{2.6}$$

In the second case, we have

$$x_0z = zx_0 = z(z_0x_0) = (zz_0)\, x_0 = z_0x_0 = x_0 . \tag{2.7}$$

Finally we compute xz. In S_λ, we have either $x_0x = x_0$ and $xx_0 = x$ or $x_0x = x$ and $xx_0 = x_0$. In the first case, (2.6) and (2.7) show that

$$zx = xz = (xx_0)\, z = x(x_0z) = xx_0 = x.$$

In the second case, (2.6) and (2.7) again show that

$$xz = zx = z(x_0x) = (zx_0)\, x = x_0x = x.$$

We now produce a complete ordering in Λ. For $\lambda, \mu \in \Lambda$ where $\lambda \neq \mu$, choose any $x \in S_\lambda$ and $z \in S_\mu$. If $xz = x$, we write $\lambda > \mu$. The preceding paragraph shows that the relation $>$ depends only on λ and μ and not on the particular choice of x and z. For $\lambda > \mu$ and $\mu > \nu$, choose $x \in S_\lambda$, $y \in S_\mu$, and $z \in S_\nu$. Then we have $xy = x$ and $yz = y$, so that $xz = (xy)\, z = x(yz) = xy = x$. Thus $>$ is transitive.

It is now clear that rules (iii) and (iv) of Lemma 1 apply to elements of S_λ and S_μ. ∎

Theorem 17. Suppose that xyz is one of the elements x, y, or z for all $x, y, z \in S$. Then S is a semigroup of one of the three following types.

(I) Multiplication in S is defined as in Lemma 1.

(II) The semigroup S is a two-element group $\{a, b\}$, with identity b.

(III) Let $\bar{S}$ be any semigroup of type (I), let a, b be elements not in $\bar{S}$, and let $S = \bar{S} \cup \{a, b\}$. Multiplication in $\bar{S}$ and in $\{a, b\}$ are as in (I) and (II) respectively, and $xa = xb = ax = bx = x$ for all $x \in \bar{S}$.

The converse also holds.

PROOF. Suppose that $x^2 = x$ for all $x \in S$. Then $xy = xxy$ is either x or y, and Lemma 2 shows that S is of type (I).

Otherwise, let a be an element of S such that $a^2 \neq a$. For every $x \in S$, we have

$$a^2x = aax = (aaa)\,ax = a^2a^2x,$$

which is either a^2 or x. We also have

$$a^2x = aax,$$

which is either a or x. If $a^2x \neq x$, then a^2x is both a^2 and a, an impossibility. Hence we have $a^2x = x$, and we can prove similarly that $xa^2 = x$. That is, a^2 is a two-sided identity in S. Since identities are unique, we see that if $y \in S$ and $y^2 \neq y$, then $y^2 = a^2$.

It is clear that $\{a, a^2\}$ forms a two-element subgroup of S. Let $\bar{S} = S \cap \{a, a^2\}'$, and let x be any element of $\bar{S}$. We have

$$xa = xaaa = xaa^2,$$

which is x or a or a^2. If $xa = a$, then we have

$$x = xa^2 = xaa = a^2.$$

If $xa = a^2$, then we have

$$x = xa^2 = xaa = a^2a = a.$$

Both of these are impossible by our choice of x, and so we have $xa = x$ for all $x \in \bar{S}$. The identities $ax = x$ can be proved similarly.

Let x be an element of $\bar{S}$ and assume that $x^2 \neq x$. As noted above, we have $x^2 = a^2$ and

$$(xx)\,a = a^2a = a, \qquad x(xa) = xx = a^2.$$

Since $a^2 \neq a$, we have a contradiction, and so $x^2 = x$.

Finally, let x, y be any elements of $\bar{S}$. We have

$$xy = xxy,$$

which is either x or y, and so xy is in $\bar{S}$. Thus $\bar{S}$ is a subsemigroup of S such that xy is either x or y for all $x, y \in \bar{S}$. Thus $\bar{S}$ is of type (I). If $\bar{S}$ is void, then S is of type (II), with $b = a^2$. If $\bar{S}$ is nonvoid and S is not of type (I), it is clear from the foregoing that S is of type (III), and that $xa = xb = ax = bx = x$ for all $x \in \bar{S}$.

The converse is obvious. ▌

We close this section with some examples suggested by Theorems 15–17.

EXAMPLE 19. Consider a four-element set $S = \{a, b, c, d\}$ and the multiplication table

	a	b	c	d
a	a	a	a	a
b	b	b	b	b
c	c	c	c	c
d	a	a	b	a

For $r \in \{a, b, c\}$ and $y, z \in S$, we have

$$r(yz) = r, \qquad (ry)\,z = rz = r;$$

$$d(rz) = dr, \qquad (dr)\,z = dr \quad \text{since } dr \text{ is } a \text{ or } b;$$

$$d(dz) = a \quad \text{since } dz \text{ is } a \text{ or } b, \qquad (dd)\,z = az = a.$$

Thus we have a semigroup in which xyz is independent of z. Since $daz = a$ and $dcz = b$, xyz is *not* independent of y.

NOTE. Other cases in which triple products are independent of some of their variables are the following. If $xy = x$, then $xyz = x$ is independent of y and z. If $xy = a$, then $xyz = a$ is independent of x, y, and z. If xyz is independent of x and z, then we have $xyz = f(y)$. It follows that

$$(xy)\,uv = f(u), \qquad xy(uv) = f(y),$$

and so $f(y)$ is a constant, say a. That is, if xyz is independent of x and z, it is also independent of y. All the semigroups with this property are given in Example 4.

3. Semigroups with the Same Triple Products

In this section, we revert to the notation $x \cdot y$ and $x \circ y$ to denote products. The symbols $S(\cdot)$ and $S(\circ)$ will always denote semigroups on the set S.

Definition. If $x \cdot y \cdot z = x \circ y \circ z$ for all $x, y, z \in S$, then we write $S(\cdot) \mathscr{R} S(\circ)$, and we say that $S(\cdot)$ and $S(\circ)$ are in *the relation* $\mathscr{R}$ *to each other.*

Clearly $\mathscr{R}$ is an equivalence relation. We will explore properties of $\mathscr{R}$, finding that it shares some properties of isomorphisms, but is actually incomparable with isomorphism. Our first four theorems show that $\mathscr{R}$ is a little like isomorphism.

Theorem 18. If $S(\cdot)$ has a two-sided identity e and if $S(\cdot) \mathscr{R} S(\circ)$, then $S(\circ)$ also has a two-sided identity.

PROOF. For all $x \in S$, we have $e \circ x \circ e = e \cdot x \cdot e = x$. By Theorem 5, $e \circ e$ is a two-sided identity for $S(\circ)$.

Theorem 19. If $S(\cdot)$ has a two-sided zero a and if $S(\cdot) \mathscr{R} S(\circ)$, then a is also a two-sided zero for $S(\circ)$.

PROOF. For all $x, y \in S$, we have $x \circ a \circ y = x \cdot a \cdot y = a$. Theorem 4 implies that a is a two-sided zero for $S(\circ)$.

Theorem 20. If $S \cdot S = S$ and $S(\cdot) \mathscr{R} S(\circ)$, then we also have $S \circ S = S$.

PROOF. For each $x \in S$, there are $u, v, r, s \in S$ such that $x = u \cdot v = u \cdot r \cdot s = u \circ (r \circ s)$.

Theorem 21. Let $I(S(\cdot))$ denote the cardinal number of the set of idempotents in $S(\cdot)$, and define $I(S(\circ))$ similarly. If $S(\cdot) \mathscr{R} S(\circ)$, then $I(S(\cdot))$ and $I(S(\circ))$ are equal.

PROOF. If $a \cdot a = a$, then we have $a \circ a \circ a = a \cdot a \cdot a = a$, so that $(a \circ a) \circ (a \circ a) = a \circ a$; that is, $a \circ a$ is idempotent in $S(\circ)$. If a, b are idempotents in $S(\cdot)$ and if $a \circ a = b \circ b$, then we may write

$$a = a \cdot a \cdot a = a \circ a \circ a = b \circ b \circ a = b \cdot b \cdot a = b \cdot a$$

and

$$b = b \cdot b \cdot b = b \circ b \circ b = b \circ a \circ a = b \cdot a \cdot a = b \cdot a,$$

so that $a = b$. Therefore distinct a and b determine distinct $a \circ a$ and $b \circ b$, which implies that $I(S(\circ)) \geqslant I(S(\cdot))$. Similarly we have $I(S(\cdot)) \geqslant I(S(\circ))$ and therefore $I(S(\cdot)) = I(S(\circ))$.

REMARK. If $S(\cdot)\,\mathscr{R}\,S(\circ)$, then $S(\cdot)$ and $S(\circ)$ have the same number of left identities and the same number of right identities. The proof is like the proof of Theorem 21 and is omitted.

On the other hand, Example 4 shows that we can have $S(\cdot)\,\mathscr{R}\,S(\circ)$ with $S(\cdot)$ commutative, $S(\circ)$ noncommutative, and hence with $S(\cdot)$ and $S(\circ)$ nonisomorphic. We will now give two additional examples of this sort.

EXAMPLE 20. Let $G(\star)$ be a commutative group with identity e and containing an element a such that $a \neq e$ and $a \star a = e$. Let $e^\dagger$ be any element not in G and let $S = G \cup \{e^\dagger\}$. For $x \in S$, let

$$\bar{x} = \begin{cases} x & \text{if } x \in G, \\ e & \text{if } x = e^\dagger. \end{cases}$$

We define $\cdot$ and $\circ$ on S by the rules

$$x \cdot y = \bar{x} \star \bar{y}, \qquad x \circ y = a \star \bar{x} \star \bar{y}.$$

For $x, y, z \in S$, it is clear that

$$x \cdot (y \cdot z) = x \cdot (\bar{y} \star \bar{z}) = \bar{x} \star \overline{(\bar{y} \star \bar{z})} = \bar{x} \star (\bar{y} \star \bar{z});$$

$$(x \cdot y) \cdot z = (\bar{x} \star \bar{y}) \cdot z = (\bar{x} \star \bar{y}) \star \bar{z};$$

$$x \circ (y \circ z) = x \circ (a \star \bar{y} \star \bar{z}) = a \star \bar{x} \star (a \star \bar{y} \star \bar{z}) = \bar{x} \star (\bar{y} \star \bar{z});$$

$$(x \circ y) \circ z = (a \star \bar{x} \star \bar{y}) \circ z = a \star (a \star \bar{x} \star \bar{y}) \star \bar{z} = (\bar{x} \star \bar{y}) \star \bar{z}.$$

It follows that $S(\cdot)$ and $S(\circ)$ are semigroups and that $S(\cdot)\,\mathscr{R}\,S(\circ)$.

To show that $S(\cdot)$ and $S(\circ)$ are nonisomorphic, we first show that e is the only idempotent of $S(\cdot)$. It is plain that $e \cdot e = \bar{e} \star \bar{e} = e \star e$. Also if $x = x \cdot x$, then we have $x = \bar{x} \star \bar{x}$, so that $x \in G$, $x = \bar{x}$, and $x = x \star x$. This implies that $x = e$.

Note next that $a \circ a = a \star \bar{a} \star \bar{a} = a \star a \star a = a$, i.e., a is an idempotent in $S(\circ)$. By Theorem 21, a is the only idempotent in $S(\circ)$.

Now assume that there is an isomorphism τ carrying $S(\cdot)$ onto $S(\circ)$. Plainly we must have $\tau(e) = a$. Furthermore, $e^\dagger$ is the only element in $S \cap (S \cdot S)'$ and also the only element in $S \cap (S \circ S)'$. Thus we also have $\tau(e^\dagger) = e^\dagger$, and also

$$\tau(e \cdot e^\dagger) = \tau(e \star e) = \tau(e) = a,$$

but

$$\tau(e) \circ \tau(e^\dagger) = a \circ e^\dagger = a \star \bar{a} \star \overline{e^\dagger} = a \star a \star e = e.$$

This is a contradiction.

A special case of Example 20 is given by $S = \{0, 1, 2\}$,

$\cdot$	0	1	2
0	0	1	0
1	1	0	1
2	0	1	0

,

$\circ$	0	1	2
0	1	0	1
1	0	1	0
2	1	0	1

.

EXAMPLE 21. Let $S = \{a, a^2, a^3, \ldots, a^k\}$ be a semigroup of order k, where $a^{k+1} = a^3$ and $a^i \cdot a^j = a^{i+j-n(k-2)}$, n being determined by the conditions $3 \leqslant i + j - n(k-2) \leqslant k$. For $3 \leqslant j \leqslant k$, our rule gives

$$a^{k-2} \cdot a^j = a^{k-2+j-(k-2)} = a^j.$$

Now let $x \circ y = a^{k-2} \cdot x \cdot y$. Then we have

$$\begin{aligned}(x \circ y) \circ z &= (a^{k-2} \cdot x \cdot y) \circ z = a^{k-2} \cdot (a^{k-2} \cdot x \cdot y) \cdot z \\ &= a^{k-2} \cdot a^{k-2} \cdot (x \cdot y \cdot z) = x \cdot y \cdot z,\end{aligned}$$

because $x \cdot y \cdot z$ is a power a^j, with $3 \leqslant j \leqslant k$. The equality $x \circ (y \circ z) = x \cdot y \cdot z$ is proved similarly. Thus $S(\circ)$ is a semigroup and $S(\cdot) \mathscr{R} S(\circ)$. Since

$$S \cdot S = \{a^2, a^3, \ldots, a^k\} \quad \text{and} \quad S \circ S = \{a^3, a^4, \ldots, a^k\},$$

$S(\cdot)$ and $S(\circ)$ are nonisomorphic.

EXAMPLE 22. It is possible to have $S(\cdot)$ not in the relation $\mathscr{R}$ to $S(\circ)$ even though $S(\cdot)$ and $S(\circ)$ are isomorphs. For example, $S = \{0, 1, 2\}$,

$\cdot$	0	1	2
0	0	1	2
1	1	2	0
2	2	0	1

,

$\circ$	0	1	2
0	2	0	1
1	0	1	2
2	1	2	0

.

Plainly $S(\cdot)$ and $S(\circ)$ are three-element groups and so are isomorphs. Since $0 \cdot 0 \cdot 0 = 0$ and $0 \circ 0 \circ 0 = 1$, the relation $\mathscr{R}$ does not hold.

We now show that $\mathscr{R}$ does imply isomorphism under certain additional hypotheses.

Definition. Suppose that the equalities $z \cdot a = z \cdot b$ and $a \cdot z = b \cdot z$

for all $z \in S$ imply that $a = b$, for any two elements a, b of S. Then we say that $S(\cdot)$ has the *weak cancellation property*.

Theorem 22. Suppose that $S(\cdot) \mathscr{R} S(\circ)$, that $S \cdot S = S$, and that $S(\cdot)$ has the weak cancellation property. Then $S(\cdot)$ and $S(\circ)$ are isomorphic.

PROOF. Since $S \cdot S = S$, we can choose for each $x \in S$ a pair of elements r_x, s_x in S such that $r_x \cdot s_x = x$. We define u_x as $r_x \circ s_x$ and consider the mapping τ of S into S defined by $\tau(x) = u_x$.

To prove that τ is one-to-one, suppose that $u_x = u_y$. Then we have

$$z \circ r_x \circ s_x = z \circ r_y \circ s_y, \qquad r_x \circ s_x \circ z = r_y \circ s_y \circ z$$

for all $z \in S$, so that

$$z \cdot r_x \cdot s_x = z \cdot r_y \cdot s_y, \qquad r_x \cdot s_x \cdot z = r_y \cdot s_y \cdot z.$$

It follows that

$$z \cdot x = z \cdot y, \qquad x \cdot z = y \cdot z,$$

and so $x = y$.

We next show that $S(\circ)$ has the weak cancellation property. If $z \circ a = z \circ b$ and $a \circ z = b \circ z$ for all $z \in S$, then we have

$$w \circ z \circ a = w \circ z \circ b, \qquad a \circ w \circ z = b \circ w \circ z,$$

$$w \cdot z \cdot a = w \cdot z \cdot b, \qquad a \cdot w \cdot z = b \cdot w \cdot z,$$

for all $w, z \in S$. Since $S \cdot S = S$, the last line implies that

$$v \cdot a = v \cdot b, \qquad a \cdot v = b \cdot v$$

for all $v \in S$, so that $a = b$.

Also Theorem 20 implies that $S \circ S = S$.

We will now show that $\tau(S) = S$. For $x \in S$, we may write $x = v \circ w$. For $z \in S$, we have

$$x \circ z = v \circ w \circ z = v \cdot w \cdot z = r_{v \cdot w} \cdot s_{v \cdot w} \cdot z = r_{v \cdot w} \circ s_{v \cdot w} \circ z = u_{v \cdot w} \circ z$$

and similarly

$$z \circ x = z \circ u_{v \cdot w}.$$

Since $S(\circ)$ has the weak cancellation property, we have $x = u_{v \cdot w} = \tau(v \cdot w)$.

Finally let us show that τ is an isomorphism. For $x, y, z = S$, we write

$$z \circ u_{x \cdot y} = z \circ r_{x \cdot y} \circ s_{x \cdot y} = z \cdot r_{x \cdot y} \cdot s_{x \cdot y} = z \cdot (x \cdot y)$$

and similarly

$$u_{x \cdot y} \circ z = (x \cdot y) \cdot z.$$

Also we write

$$u_x \circ y = r_x \circ s_x \circ y = r_x \cdot s_x \cdot y = x \cdot y$$

and

$$y \circ u_x = y \cdot x.$$

From this we have

$$(z \circ u_x) \circ u_y = (z \cdot x) \circ u_y = (z \cdot x) \cdot y$$

and similarly

$$u_x \circ (u_y \circ z) = x \cdot (y \cdot z).$$

From the above it follows that

$$z \circ u_x \circ u_y = z \circ u_{x \cdot y} \qquad \text{and} \qquad u_x \circ u_y \circ z = u_{x \cdot y} \circ z$$

for all $x, y, z \in S$. The weak cancellation property for $S(\circ)$ shows that $u_x \circ u_y = u_{x \cdot y}$, that is, $\tau(x) \circ \tau(y) = \tau(x \cdot y)$. ∎

Corollary 1. If $S(\cdot) \mathscr{R} S(\circ)$ and $S(\cdot)$ has a one- or two-sided identity, then $S(\cdot)$ and $S(\circ)$ are isomorphic.

Corollary 2. If $S(\cdot) \mathscr{R} S(\circ)$ and $S(\cdot)$ is a group, then $S(\circ)$ is also a group.

REMARK. For a given S and ternary operation $x * y * z$ as in Section 1, the semigroups $S(\cdot)$ produced by Theorem 2 are all isomorphic to each other.

PROOF. If Theorem 2 produces any semigroup $S(\cdot)$, then by (1.2) there is an element e such that $e * e * x = x$ for all x in S. Then we have $(e \cdot e) \cdot x = e * e * x = x$ for all x in S, and so $e \cdot e$ is a left identity. The preceding corollary shows that all other semigroups produced by Theorem 2 are isomorphic to $S(\cdot)$.

EXAMPLE 23. To illustrate further the nature of $\mathscr{R}$, consider $S = \{0, 1\}$ and the multiplication tables

$\cdot$	0	1
0	0	1
1	1	$\circ$

,

$\circ$	0	1
0	1	0
1	0	1

.

Plainly $S(\cdot)$ and $S(\circ)$ are isomorphic groups and also $S(\cdot)\,\mathscr{R}\,S(\circ)$. Note that the operations $\cdot$ and $\circ$ are actually different.

We do not know whether both of the conditions $S \cdot S = S$ and the weak cancellation law for $S(\cdot)$ are essential in order to prove Theorem 22. Thus one would like to exhibit nonisomorphic semigroups $S(\cdot)$ and $S(\circ)$ such that $S \cdot S = S$ and $S(\cdot)\,\mathscr{R}\,S(\circ)$, and another pair such that $S(\cdot)$ has the weak cancellation property and $S(\cdot)\,\mathscr{R}\,S(\circ)$. We have not succeeded in finding any such semigroups. It is simple enough to find semigroups $S(\cdot)$ with the weak cancellation property such that $S \cdot S \neq S$. Example 15 provides such a semigroup, with the strong cancellation property $a \cdot b = a \cdot c$ implies $b = c$. There is also a semigroup $S(\cdot)$ of order 4 with the weak cancellation property such that $S \cdot S \neq S$.

EXAMPLE 24. Let $S = \{0, 1, 2, 3\}$, and define $\cdot$ by the following rules:

$\cdot$	0	1	2	3
0	0	0	0	0
1	0	0	0	2
2	2	2	2	2
3	3	3	3	3

It is a routine matter to verify that $S(\cdot)$ is a semigroup, and obvious that $S(\cdot)$ has the weak cancellation property and that $S \cdot S \neq S$. This semigroup sheds no new light on Theorem 22, however, since it can be shown that $S(\cdot)\,\mathscr{R}\,S(\circ)$ implies that $S(\cdot)$ and $S(\circ)$ are identical. We omit the proof of this fact.

It seems difficult to find semigroups $S(\cdot)$ such that $S \cdot S = S$ and which lack the weak cancellation property. A check of semigroups of orders 2, 3, 4 shows that no semigroup in this class can exhibit this phenomenon. In view of this, the following example may be of interest.

EXAMPLE 25. Let T be any set containing at least three distinct elements a, b, c. Let Z be an element *not* in $T \times T$, and let $S = T \times T \cup \{Z\}$. We define multiplication in S by the following rules:

$$(x, y) \cdot (u, v) = \begin{cases} (x, v) & \text{if } y = u = a; \\ Z & \text{otherwise;} \end{cases}$$

$$Z \cdot (x, y) = (x, y) \cdot Z = Z \cdot Z = Z.$$

We have

$$((x, y) \cdot (u, v)) \cdot (r, s) = \begin{cases} (x, v) \cdot (r, s) = (x, s) & \text{if } y = u = v = r = a, \\ Z \quad \text{otherwise,} \end{cases}$$

and

$$(x, y) \cdot ((u, v) \cdot (r, s)) = \begin{cases} (x, y) \cdot (u, s) = (x, s) & \text{if} \quad v = r = y = u = a, \\ Z & \text{otherwise.} \end{cases}$$

Any product of three elements of S, at least one of which is Z, is equal to Z no matter how the terms are grouped. Therefore $S(\cdot)$ is a semigroup.

To show that the weak cancellation property fails, note that

$$(x, y) \cdot (b, b) = Z = (x, y) \cdot (b, c), \qquad Z \cdot (b, b) = Z = Z \cdot (b, c)$$

and

$$(b, b) \cdot (x, y) = Z = (b, c) \cdot (x, y), \qquad (b, b)\, Z = Z = (b, c)\, Z,$$

for all $(x, y) \in T \times T$. Since $(b, b) \neq (b, c)$, the weak cancellation property is violated. For all $(x, y) \in T \times T$, we have $(x, y) = (x, a) \cdot (a, y)$, and also $Z = Z \cdot Z$. Thus $S = S \cdot S$.

The smallest S in Example 25 has order 10. However, by taking $S = \{a, b\} \times \{a, b, c\} \cup \{Z\}$ in Example 25, we can find an example of order 7.

Example 25, like Example 24, sheds no new light on Theorem 22. In fact, if $S(\cdot)$ is as in Example 25 and if $S(\circ)\, \mathscr{R}\, S(\cdot)$, then $S(\cdot)$ and $S(\circ)$ are identical. Again we omit the proof.

The conditions in Theorem 22 are far from being necessary, as our next example shows.

EXAMPLE 26. Let $S = \{0, 1, 2\}$, and define multiplication by

$\cdot$	0	1	2
0	0	0	0
1	0	0	0
2	2	2	2

It is evident that $S(\cdot)$ is a semigroup, that $S \cdot S \neq S$, and that the weak cancellation property fails. Suppose that $S(\cdot)\, \mathscr{R}\, S(\circ)$, and let $u_x = x \circ x$. Then we have

$$u_x \circ y = x \circ x \circ y = x \cdot x \cdot y = \begin{cases} x & \text{if} \quad x = 0 \quad \text{or} \quad x = 2, \\ 0 & \text{if} \quad x = 1. \end{cases}$$

Now suppose that x is 0 or 2. Then we have

$$x \circ z = u_x \circ 0 \circ z = u_x \cdot 0 \cdot z = u_x \cdot 0.$$

and so $x \circ z = x \circ x$ for all $z \in S$. Also we have

$$x = x \cdot x \cdot x = x \circ (x \circ x) = x \circ x,$$

and so

$$x \circ z = x = x \cdot z.$$

Also we have

$$1 \circ x = 1 \circ u_x \circ y = 1 \cdot u_x \cdot y = 0 = 1 \cdot x.$$

Finally, to deal with $1 \circ 1$, we write

$$(1 \circ 1) \circ 2 = 1 \cdot 1 \cdot 2 = 0.$$

Since $2 \circ 2 = 2 \cdot 2 = 2$, $1 \circ 1$ cannot be 2. If $1 \circ 1 = 1$, we would have $1 = 1 \circ 1 = 1 \circ 1 \circ 1 = 1 \cdot 1 \cdot 1 = 0$. Hence $1 \circ 1$ must be 0, which is also $1 \cdot 1$. Thus $S(\cdot)$ and $S(\circ)$ are identical.

Theorem 23. Suppose that $S(\cdot) \mathscr{R} S(\circ)$ and that $x \cdot x = y \cdot y$ implies $x = y$ for all $x, y \in S$. Then $S(\cdot)$ and $S(\circ)$ are identical.

PROOF. Clearly if $x \cdot x \cdot x \cdot x = y \cdot y \cdot y \cdot y$, then $x = y$. The proof is now a long rearrangement of dots and circles:

$$\begin{aligned}
(x \circ y) \cdot (x \circ y) \cdot (x \circ y) \cdot (x \circ y) &= (x \circ y) \cdot (x \circ y) \cdot ((x \circ y) \cdot (x \circ y)) \\
&= (x \circ y) \circ (x \circ y) \circ ((x \circ y) \cdot (x \circ y)) \\
&= (x \circ y \circ x) \circ y \circ ((x \circ y) \cdot (x \circ y)) \\
&= (x \cdot y \cdot x) \cdot y \cdot ((x \circ y) \cdot (x \circ y)) \\
&= (x \cdot y \cdot x \cdot y) \cdot (x \circ y) \cdot (x \circ y) \\
&= (x \cdot y \cdot x \cdot y) \circ (x \circ y) \circ (x \circ y) \\
&= (x \cdot y \cdot x \cdot y) \circ (x \circ y \circ x) \circ y \\
&= (x \cdot y \cdot x \cdot y) \cdot (x \cdot y \cdot x) \cdot y \\
&= (x \cdot y) \cdot (x \cdot y) \cdot (x \cdot y) \cdot (x \cdot y). \quad \blacksquare
\end{aligned}$$

Corollary. If $S(\cdot)$ is idempotent and $S(\cdot) \mathscr{R} S(\circ)$, then $S(\cdot)$ and $S(\circ)$ are identical.

PROOF. This corollary is immediate from Theorem 23. A second proof is the following. It is also easy to check that $S \cdot S = S$ and that S has the weak cancellation property. By Theorem 22, $S(\cdot)$ and $S(\circ)$ are isomorphic and so $S(\circ)$ is also idempotent. Thus we have

$$x \circ y = x \circ x \circ y = x \cdot x \cdot y = x \cdot y.$$

NOTE. The preceding corollary cannot be proved under the weaker hypothesis that $x \cdot x \cdot x = x$ for all $x \in S$. See Example 23.

We close by applying some theorems of the present section to ternary operations of the kind studied in Section 1.

EXAMPLE 27. Let a be a nonnegative integer, let

$$S = \{a, a + 1, a + 2, \ldots\},$$

and define a ternary operation by $x * y * z = xyz$ (ordinary multiplication). Plainly xy is a semigroup operation on S that reproduces $*$ as in (1.1). Since $x^2 = y^2$ implies $x = y$, Theorem 23 shows that no other semigroup operation will do this.

EXAMPLE 28. Let S be a nonvoid completely ordered set, and let $x * y * z = \max\{x, y, z\}$. There may or may not be an element e as in (1.3). However, the binary operation $x \cdot y = \max\{x, y\}$ obviously is a semigroup operation satisfying (1.1), and the corollary to Theorem 23 implies that this is the only semigroup operation doing so.

EXAMPLE 29. Let T be a nonvoid set, $S = T \times T$, and

$$(x, y) * (u, v) * (z, w) = (x, w).$$

Then $(x, y) \cdot (z, w) = (x, w)$ satisfies (1.1) and the corollary to Theorem 23 shows that no other semigroup operation will do.

EXAMPLE 30. Let S be a nonvoid set, a a fixed element of S. We define

$$x * y * z = \begin{cases} x & \text{if } x = y = z, \\ a & \text{otherwise.} \end{cases}$$

Plainly

$$x \cdot y = \begin{cases} x & \text{if } x = y, \\ a & \text{otherwise,} \end{cases}$$

is a semigroup operation on S satisfying (1.1). The corollary to Theorem 23 shows that there are no others.

EXAMPLE 31. Let S be any nonvoid set, and T a subset of S (possibly void). Define

$$x * y * z = \begin{cases} x & \text{if } x \in T, \\ y & \text{if } x \notin T \text{ and } y \in T, \\ a & \text{if } x \notin T \text{ and } y \notin T. \end{cases}$$

Define

$$x \cdot y = \begin{cases} x & \text{if } x \in T, \\ y & \text{if } x \notin T. \end{cases}$$

It is easy to check that $S(\cdot)$ is a semigroup satisfying (1.1). By the corollary to Theorem 23, there are no others.

Finally, we look at the relation $\mathscr{R}$ and its connection with semicharacters. A *semicharacter of a semigroup* $S(\cdot)$ is a complex-valued function χ on S such that $\chi(x \cdot y) = \chi(x)\,\chi(y)$ for all $x, y \in S$. The function χ may be identically zero, and it need not be bounded. The set of all semicharacters of $S(\cdot)$ is denoted by $\hat{S}(\cdot)$. It is clearly a commutative semigroup under ordinary multiplication: $\chi_1\chi_2(x) = \chi_1(x)\,\chi_2(x)$ for all $x \in S$.

Theorem 24. If $S(\cdot)\,\mathscr{R}\,S(\circ)$, then $\hat{S}(\cdot)$ and $\hat{S}(\circ)$ are isomorphic.

PROOF. Let χ be an element of $\hat{S}(\cdot)$ not identically zero: choose $a \in S$ such that $\chi(a) \neq 0$. Then we have

$$(x \circ y) \cdot (a \circ a) \cdot a = x \circ y \circ a \circ a \circ a = x \circ y \circ a \circ a \circ a)$$
$$= x \cdot y \cdot (a \cdot a \cdot a) = x \cdot y \cdot a \cdot a \cdot a,$$

so that

$$\chi(x \circ y)\,\chi(a \circ a)\,\chi(a) = \chi(x)\,\chi(y)\,\chi(a)^3.$$

In particular we have

$$\chi(a \circ a)^2\,\chi(a) = \chi(a)^5 \neq 0,$$

and hence $\chi(a \circ a) \neq 0$. Now we may write

$$\chi(x \circ y) = [\chi(a)^2/\chi(a \circ a)]\,\chi(x)\,\chi(y).$$

Setting $\alpha_\chi = [\chi(a)^2/\chi(a \circ a)]$, we see at once that $\alpha_\chi\chi = \varphi_\chi$ is a semicharacter of $S(\circ)$ not vanishing at a.

Although α_χ appears to depend upon a, it actually does not. For, suppose that α and β are nonzero complex numbers such that both $\alpha\chi$ and $\beta\chi$ are semicharacters of $S(\circ)$. Then we have

$$\alpha^2\chi(x)\,\chi(y) = \alpha\chi(x)\,\alpha\chi(y) = \alpha\chi(x \circ y) = (\alpha/\beta)\,\beta\chi(x \circ y)$$
$$= (\alpha/\beta)\,\beta\chi(x)\,\beta\chi(y) = \alpha\beta\chi(x)\,\chi(y).$$

It follows that $\alpha^2 = \alpha\beta$ and $\alpha = \beta$, since $\chi(a) \neq 0$.

Consider now the mapping φ defined by $\chi \to \varphi_\chi = \alpha_\chi\chi$, which carries nonzero elements of $\hat{S}(\cdot)$ into $\hat{S}(\circ)$. We first show that this mapping is one-to-one. If $\varphi_{\chi_1} = \varphi_{\chi_2}$, so that

$$\chi_1 = (\alpha_{\chi_2}/\alpha_{\chi_1})\,\chi_2\,,$$

then we have

$$(\alpha_{\chi_2}/\alpha_{\chi_1})\,\chi_2(x)\,\chi_2(y) = (\alpha_{\chi_2}/\alpha_{\chi_1})\,\chi_2(x\cdot y) = \chi_1(x\cdot y) = \chi_1(x)\,\chi_1(y)$$
$$= (\alpha_{\chi_2}/\alpha_{\chi_1})^2\,\chi_2(x)\,\chi_2(y).$$

Since χ_2 is not identically zero, we infer that $\alpha_{\chi_2} = \alpha_{\chi_1}$ and hence $\chi_1 = \chi_2$.

We next show that the mapping $\chi \to \varphi_\chi$ is onto. If ψ is in $\hat{S}(\circ)$ and $\psi \neq 0$, then as above there is a constant $\beta_\psi \neq 0$ such that $\beta_\psi\psi$ is in $\hat{S}(\cdot)$. Write $\beta_\psi\psi$ as χ, so that $\psi = \beta_\psi^{-1}\chi$. By the second preceding paragraph, we have $\varphi_\chi = \psi$.

Now extend φ to the zero semicharacter by the natural definition $\varphi_0 = 0$, and let α_0 be 1. Thus φ on all of $\hat{S}(\cdot)$ is defined by $\varphi_\chi = \alpha_\chi\chi$. We will show that φ is an isomorphism, by verifying the identity

$$\alpha_{\chi_1}\alpha_{\chi_2}\chi_1(x)\,\chi_2(x) = \alpha_{\chi_1\chi_2}\chi_1(x)\,\chi_2(x) \tag{3.1}$$

for all $\chi_1, \chi_2 \in \hat{S}(\cdot)$ and $x \in S$. If $\chi_1(x)\,\chi_2(x) = 0$ for all $x \in S$, (3.1) is trivially satisfied. Otherwise there is an $a \in S$ for which $\chi_1(a) \neq 0$, $\chi_2(a) \neq 0$, and $\chi_1\chi_2(a) \neq 0$. We obtain

$$\alpha_{\chi_1} = \frac{\chi_1(a)^2}{\chi_1(a\circ a)}, \qquad \alpha_{\chi_2} = \frac{\chi_2(a)^2}{\chi_2(a\circ a)}, \qquad \alpha_{\chi_1\chi_2} = \frac{\chi_1\chi_2(a)^2}{\chi_1\chi_2(a\circ a)},$$

and so

$$\alpha_{\chi_1}\alpha_{\chi_2} = \alpha_{\chi_1\chi_2}.$$

Therefore, (3.1) is satisfied. ▌

REFERENCES

1. Dörnte, W., Untersuchungen über einen verallgemeinerten Gruppenbegriff, *Math. Z.* **29**, 1–19 (1929).
2. Łoś, J., On the extending of models (I), *Fund. Math.* **42**, 38–54 (1955).
3. Post, E. L., Polyadic groups. *Trans. Amer. Math. Soc.* **48**, 208–350 (1940).
4. Monk, D. and Sioson, F. M., *m*-Semigroups, semigroups, and function representations. *Fund. Math.* **59**, 233–241 (1966).
5. Sioson, F. M., Cyclic and homogeneous *m*-semigroups. *Proc. Japan Acad.* **39**, 444–449 (1963).
6. Sioson, F. M., Ideals in $(m+1)$-semigroups. *Ann. Mat. Pura Appl.* [4] **68**, 161–200 (1965).
7. Vagner, V. V. Predstavlenie obobščennyh grud. *Ukrain. Mat. Ž.* **11**, 231–242 (1959).
8. Vagner, V. V., Teoriya obobščennyh grud i obobščennyh grupp. *Mat. Sb.* (NS) **32** [**74**], 545–632 (1953).

Problems about Compact Semigroups

KARL HEINRICH HOFMANN*,‡ AND PAUL S. MOSTERT†,‡

Tulane University
New Orleans, Louisiana
and
The Institute for Advanced Study
Princeton, New Jersey

The collection of problems about compact topological semigroups which we are about to present is considered to be a preliminary one. We hope that the interest of researchers in this field to have a comprehensive list of problems is keen and their cooperation strong enough so that the present catalog can be implemented, expanded, discussed more thoroughly, and perhaps published in expanded form at a later date. Such a collection of unsolved problems should then have a wide range of interest and comprise problems of varying degrees of difficulty, from hopefully tractable ones to others which have resisted repeated and concerted efforts to solve them.

Some of the problems listed below have circulated among workers interested in compact semigroups for more than ten years while others have occurred to us only recently and have not yet been propagated. There is a fairly large and important block of problems which we started to popularize in our book [*4*]. Of these problems only two have been solved in the meantime. On some occasions, we have made an attempt to comment on the difficulty and some of the implications of the problems, and in certain instances we ventured to guess the methods which may lead to solutions.

It is not easy to organize a collection of problems; even though we group them according to certain criteria, we decided to number them

* Fellow of the Alfred P. Sloan Foundation.

† National Science Foundation Senior Postdoctoral Fellow.

‡ Present address of both authors: Tulane University, New Orleans, Louisiana.

consecutively, regardless of their grouping. This may be even more excusable insofar as we cannot make a very strong point in favor of our particular preference in grouping and selecting the problems.

I

In this section we discuss problems concerning compact connected not necessarily Abelian semigroups with identity.

The first block of problems seems to us to center around the most important problem left in a general structure theory for compact connected semigroups with identity. We deem it to be a very difficult one. Even partial results and answers to the more special problems which we will formulate would be important contributions.

1. Let S be a compact connected semigroup with identity and zero and G a compact group of automorphisms (with the topology of uniform convergence). Let T be the semigroup of points left fixed by G. Is T connected?

The basic significance of this problem is perhaps better understood in a formally different, but nevertheless equivalent formulation:

1a. Let S be a compact connected semigroup, with identity, zero, and group of units H. Let T be the centralizer of H, i.e., the set of all elements $s \in S$, with $hs = sh$ for all $h \in H$. Is T connected?

The significance of a positive answer to Problem 1a would lie in a deepened insight into the local structure of S near 1, since then HT would be a subsemigroup and if T' were an irreducible subsemigroup (existing in T by the second fundamental theorem, which also guarantees its commutativity), then HT' would be a hormos whose local and global structure is very well understood. The equivalence of Problem 1 with Problem 1a is easy to see; the group of units H acts on S under inner automorphisms; on the other hand, if G is an automorphism group of S and one forms the splitting extension of S by G, it will contain G as a group of units, and the fixed point set of G will contain the intersection of the centralizer of the group of units with S.

It is useful to keep a third formulation of the same problem in mind. If G is a topological group and S a topological semigroup, we will call S a G *semigroup* if there is a continuous transformation group action $(g, s) \to g \cdot s$: $G \times S \to S$ such that $g \cdot st = (g \cdot s)(g \cdot t)$. A compact G semigroup S is called G *irreducible* if there is no proper G subsemigroup T in S which is connected, contains the identity, and meets the minimal ideal. A $\{1\}$-irreducible semigroup is just called irreducible, as usual. It is not hard to see that if an irreducible semigroup is a G semigroup for a compact group G, then G must act trivially by fixing every element.

1b. Let G be a compact group and S a compact connected G semigroup with identity. If S is G irreducible, is it irreducible?

Here are some specialized versions of Problem 1. Possibly some of them may have to be solved on the way to a general solution of Problem 1.

2. Let S be a compact connected semigroup, with $E(S) = \{1, 0\}$ (i.e., with identity and zero and no other idempotents). Is there a one parameter semigroup in the centralizer of $H(1)$? Is there one at least in the centralizer of the identity component $H(1)_0$ of $H(1)$?

If $S/\mathscr{D}$ is totally ordered, then we showed this problem to have a positive answer. But the only proof we know is hard [*4*, p. 177]. It would be even valuable to have a simpler proof of this case.

3. Is the answer to Problem 2 positive at least if

(1) $H(1)$ is a Lie group,

(2) $H(1)$ is a finite group,

(3) $H(1) \cong SO(3)$ or $H(1) \cong SU(2)$?

4. Let G be a compact monothetic group, and S a G-irreducible semigroup. Is S irreducible?

If G does not have a direct factor which is isomorphic to some p-adic group, or if $E(S) = \{1, 0\}$, or if S is a semilattice, then the answer to this question is yes [*4*, pp. 63, 117, 135]. This problem is likely to be attackable. The tools involved in the cases in which a solution has been given uses the Conner-Borel fixed point theorem for circle group actions on rationally acyclic spaces and the Smith fixed point theorem for cyclic p groups acting on spaces which are acyclic modulo p.

The following problem would be trivially solved by a positive answer to Problem 1a, but its solution is unknown.

5. Let S be a compact connected semigroup. Does there exist an invariant semigroup wedge T, i.e., a closed connected subsemigroup invariant under inner automorphisms satisfying $T \cap M(S) \neq \emptyset$ and $T \cap H(1) = \{1\}$?

The following questions are related to Problem 5. If $K \subset H(1)$ is a subgroup of the group of units and T a subsemigroup of the compact connected semigroup S, we call T *irreducible about* K if it is a compact subsemigroup with connected Rees quotient $T/M(T)$, contains K and meets $M(S)$, and is, in addition, minimal with respect to these properties. It is called *completely irreducible* about G if it is not contained in $H(1)$, is irreducible about G in $S/SM(T)S$, and is minimal relative to this property.

6. If S is a compact connected semigroup with identity which is completely irreducible about $H(1)$, is it cylindrical?

Clearly if the answer to Problem 1 is yes, so is the answer to Problem 6.

7. Let S be a compact connected semigroup with identity which is irreducible about some closed group $G \subset H(1)$ of units. Is $G = H(1)$?

The preceding remark applies with Problem 7 in place of Problem 6.

8. Let S be a compact connected semigroup with identity. Is there a hormos T in S containing $H(1)$ and all H classes, which it passes through, and which meets $M(S)$?

A positive answer to Problem 1 would provide one for this problem.

9. Let S be a compact connected semigroup with identity. Is there a closed connected subsemigroup containing $D(1) = H(1)$, $M(S)$, all D classes which it passes through, and such that $T/\mathscr{D}$ is totally ordered?

If $\mathscr{D}$ is a congruence, then the answer is easily seen to be yes. This applies in particular to the case of Clifford semigroups. Otherwise the answer to the problem is unknown and would not be settled by a solution of Problem 1.

10. Let S be a compact connected semigroup such that $S/\mathscr{D}$ is totally ordered and all D classes are regular. Does there exist a Koch's arc meeting all D classes?

This problem does not belong to the context of Problem 1, but into the vicinity of the preceding problem. It should be more elementary than the preceding ones, and one is tempted to start by looking for a counterexample.

While one mentions problems involving cross sections for the $\mathscr{D}$ relation, one has to observe the following problem whose solution has not been found yet.

11. Let S be a compact Clifford semigroup. Is there a cross-section morphism to $S \to S/\mathscr{D}$?

If $S/\mathscr{D}$ is totally ordered, then any Koch's arc defines such a cross section. If, in addition, the set of idempotents in each D class is finite dimensional, then there is only one such Koch's arc. Thus Problem 11 is really concerned with a generalization of the results of Hofmann and Mostert [*4*, C-1].

12. Let S be a compact connected semigroup with identity. Let T be the smallest closed subsemigroup containing all irreducible subsemigroups. Can one somehow characterize T?

This problem is difficult, even in its formulation, which in the presence of the undefined term "somehow" necessarily remains vague. We shall try to examine some of the rather formidable difficulties that probably have to be cleared out of the way of a solution.

From a categorical standpoint, it is fairly routine to show that the category of compact semigroups with identity and identity-preserving morphisms is not only complete, but also cocomplete. (The completeness is virtually trivial, since products and equalizers are immediately seen to exist. Cocompleteness is a little more difficult to check.) In particular, coproducts exist, especially the coproduct of two element families.

We recall that the coproduct of a family $\{S_i: i \in I\}$ of objects is a diagram $S_i \xrightarrow{\text{copr}_i} C$ such that for any family of morphisms $f_i: S_i \rightarrow T$ there is a unique morphism $F: C \rightarrow T$ with $F \text{ copr}_i = f_i$ for all $i \in I$. If now, with the notation of Problem 12, $\{S_i: i \in I\}$ is the family of irreducible subsemigroups of S, we obtain a natural morphism from their coproduct C onto T. An understanding of the coproduct would therefore seem, if not indispensable, nevertheless highly desirable. Coproducts in the category of compact semigroups with identity have not been considered thus far. The answers to some very natural questions in relatively simple special cases seem to be hard to obtain.

13. Let S and T be compact semigroups with identity and $S \amalg T$ their coproduct in the category of compact semigroups with identity. There is a natural morphism $HS \amalg HT \rightarrow H(S \amalg T)$ by the property of the coproduct, where $HS = H_S(1)$, etc.

(1) Is this map surjective?

(2) Is this map an isomorphism?

(3) Is this map surjective if S is a group and T is the unit interval [0, 1] under multiplication?

(4) Let $\pi: (S \amalg T) \rightarrow T$ be the natural map defined via the coproduct property by the map $S \rightarrow T$ sending all of S onto $\{1\}$ and by the identity map $T \rightarrow T$. If S is a group and $HT = \{1\}$, is $\pi^{-1}(1) = H(S \amalg T)$?

(4a) Is the answer in (4) positive if $T = \mathbb{H}^*$, where $\mathbb{H}^*$ is the one point compactification of the nonnegative half-line under addition?

As an example of some of the possible consequences, we indicate that an affirmative answer to 13(1) if S is a group and T an irreducible semigroup would settle Problem 5. The argument would be as follows. In this case, the inclusions $HS \to S$ and $HT \to T$ trivially are coretractions. Thus $HS \amalg HT \to S \amalg T$ and therefore $HS \amalg HT \to H(S \amalg T)$ are coretractions; in particular, they are monics and thus injective. By 13(1), we then may identify $S = HS \cong HS \amalg HT$ with $H(S \amalg T)$. Define $p\colon S \amalg T \to S$ by the diagram

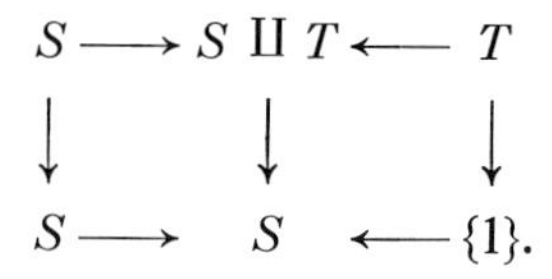

$$\begin{array}{ccccc} S & \longrightarrow & S \amalg T & \longleftarrow & T \\ \downarrow & & \downarrow & & \downarrow \\ S & \longrightarrow & S & \longleftarrow & \{1\}. \end{array}$$

Let $W = p^{-1}(1)$. Then W is an invariant wedge semigroup in $S \amalg T$. Now let A be an arbitrary compact connected semigroup. We set $S = H_A(1)$ and let T be an irreducible subsemigroup of A. Then there is a natural morphism $\varphi\colon S \amalg T \to A$ whose image is the smallest subsemigroup generated by S and T. Then $\varphi(W)$ is an invariant wedge semigroup in A.

14. Let S and T be compact semigroups with identity and $S \amalg T$ their coproduct as before. Suppose that the minimal ideals MS and MT are groups.

(1) Is $M(S \amalg T)$ a group?

(2) If the answer in (1) is no, can one say anything about $EM(S \amalg T)$?

(3) Is the answer in (1) yes if S is a group and T an Abelian hormos?

Although questions concerning the coproduct are elementary in their formulation, and perhaps in their treatment, they may very well be quite difficult. Were we forced into making a conjecture about any of the questions in Sections 13 and 14, we would be inclined to guess that the answer to each is likely to be no. If one would understand a coproduct of the form $G \amalg \mathbb{H}^*$ with a compact group, one would certainly have made substantial progress toward a solution of Problem 2.

We now turn to an entirely different block of problems, namely the problems involving the peripheral position of the identity in a compact semigroup. Hofmann and Mostert [*4*, B-7] described and collected from the literature a number of concepts which were introduced to formulate in one way or another when a point of a compact space was a "boundary" point in some intrinsic sense. The most elegant of these concepts in our opinion is the cohomological one introduced by Wallace, and it deserves further attention [*4*, p. 168]. Unfortunately it did not suffice for all purposes involving compact semigroups; thus the important Theorem VI [*4*, p. 177], a partial solution to Problem 2, used a different concept of peripherality. We do not advocate the search for another proof involving the more elegant concept of peripherality; however, we think that progress in the following problem would be very valuable.

15. Find a concept of peripherality for compact connected spaces satisfying the following two conditions:

(a) If S is a compact connected semigroup with identity 1, then 1 is peripheral.

(b) Every compact finite dimensional space contains at least one nonperipheral point.*

If such a concept of peripherality were to be found, we would have an immediate and most appropriate proof of the fact that a topological semigroup with identity on a finite dimensional homogeneous compact connected space is a group. This conclusion remains valid for certain infinite dimensional continua, notably the homogeneous spaces of compact groups (Madison [*8*]). Thus one might phrase the following somewhat vague problem.

16. Find a category of compact connected homogeneous spaces satisfying the following condition.

* Since this was written, the authors have observed that every compact finite dimensional connected space has at least one nonperipheral point, where a point is called peripheral if it has a basis of open neighborhoods U, with $H_c(U) = 0$ (cohomology with compact supports relatively to a fixed anonymous principal ideal domain as coefficient ring). This solves Problem 15. As a corollary one has the following.

Let S be a compact connected semigroup with identity. Suppose that any two points of S have neighborhoods which are homeomorphic under a map sending one of the points onto the other and that S is finite dimensional. Then S is a group.

In particular, this sharpens and provides a new proof of a result of Hudson and Mostert (see Hofmann and Mostert [4, p. 169]). Such a proof has been called for by Hofmann and Mostert [4, p. 174].

Problem 15 above was phrased by Hofmann and Mostert [**4**] as Problem 7 on p. 173. The above concept of peripherality was called marginality by Hofmann and Mostert [4]; see p. 168 in this reference.

If S is a topological semigroup with identity and the space $|S|$ underlying S is an object of the category, then S is a group.

The following question is still open.

17. Let S be a compact connected semigroup with identity, and suppose that the underlying space is the homogeneous space of a locally compact topological group. Is then S a group?

The following fairly old problem (posed by Corson) is worth restating in the context of peripherality.

18a. Let S be a compact connected semigroup with identity. Let B be the set of peripheral points relative to some suitable sense of peripherality. If every element in S has a square root, does then every element of B have a square root in B?

This may be a very good test problem for the usefulness of the methods applied to treat the concept of peripherality.

A very good test class of compact connected semigroups with identity is the one containing all semigroups having only one more idempotent, a zero. Even in the case of Abelian semigroups, one is far from understanding the structure of the semigroups in this class completely.

18b. Let S be a compact connected semigroup, with $E(S) = \{1, 0\}$. Is it possible to define on the space $\mathrm{Hom}(\mathbb{H}, S)$ the structure of a Lie (semi-) algebra, where $\mathrm{Hom}(\mathbb{H}, S)$ is the space of all one parameter semigroups with the compact open topology?

For compact groups there is the structure of a Lie algebra on $\mathrm{Hom}(\mathbb{R}, G)$, and for Abelian semigroups with trivial groups Problem 18 has been carefully discussed by Keimel [6]. In the case of an Abelian semigroup, the space $\mathrm{Hom}(\mathbb{H}, S)$ has trivially the structure of an additive commutative semigroup and a trivial Lie product. But even in that case the structure of the semigroup $\mathrm{Hom}(\mathbb{H}, S)$ has not been investigated.

We will return to related questions when we discuss problems about Abelian semigroups.

19 (J. Day). Let S be a compact connected semigroup, with $E(S) = \{1, 0\}$. Suppose that every element has a square root in S. If $H(1)$ is connected, is the union of one parameter semigroups dense in S? If $H(1)$ is arcwise connected, does every element lie on a one parameter semigroup?

If $Hs \subset sH$ or $sH \subset Hs$ for all $s \in S$, then the answer is yes on both counts. If every element has arbitrary roots, the answer again is yes to the first question. It should be pointed out in this context that there are comparatively simple semigroups on a three cell with $E(S) = \{1, 0\}$, $H(1) = \{1\}$ in which the union K of all one parameter subsemigroups has the following properties:

(a) K is the set of elements with square roots.

(b) K is closed.

(c) $S \backslash K$ is connected and not empty.

(d) $\bigcup K^n = \text{interior } S \cup \{1, 0\}$.

The existence and characterization of irreducible semigroups [*4*, B-5] gives us a great deal of information about the semigroups in many cases. However, there may be many different irreducible semigroups in a semigroup S. One would like to have some means of choosing the "best" ones. For example, one might ask the following question.

20. Let S be a compact arcwise connected semigroup with identity. Is there an arcwise connected irreducible semigroup in S?

One should note that this problem reveals some strange aspects even in very primitive special cases. Let $S = \mathbb{R}/\mathbb{Z} \times \mathbb{H}^*$. Then among the infinite number of irreducible semigroups, there is exactly one arcwise connected one. Even in this simple example it seems very difficult to characterize this distinguished one in any other terms than the very property of being arcwise connected.

The field of linear representations of compact semigroups is still wide open to research.

21. Which classes of compact semigroups with identity are characterized by the property that the representations by semigroups of linear contractions on some Hilbert space separate points?

This problem generalizes the problem of unitary representations of compact groups. The indications speak for a preference of operator representations on Banach spaces when semigroups are involved. The class outlined in Problem 21 may be comparatively small.

22. Which subclass of the class in Problem 21 is singled out by the requirement that the finite dimensional linear representations separate points?

Problems 21 and 22 remain valid, interesting, and apparently nontrivial in the case of Abelian semigroups. It would in fact still be valuable to describe the representation theory of some quite specialized classes of semigroups which comprise groups but still show significant features of semigroup pathology. An example is stated in the following problem.

23. Describe all linear representations of cylindrical semigroups [*4*, B-2].

Some work in this direction for the Abelian case goes back to Hunter and Rothman [*5*].

Another type of problem has not received any attention at all, in spite of the fact that it promises interesting information and seems tractable, at least for special classes of compact semigroups.

24. Let S be a compact connected semigroup with identity. Determine its automorphism group.

In this form the problem is problably too general. Therefore we formulate the following.

25. Solve Problem 24 for the class of all the following:

(1) cylindrical semigroups [*4*, B-2],
(2) I semigroups [*4*, B-3, 4, 5],
(3) irreducible semigroups [*4*, B-5],
(4) paragroups [*4*, A].

For what other classes can one solve the problem of determining the automorphism group?

Problem 25 is certainly tractable. For part (3) one needs parts (1) and (2), and if parts (3) and (4) are solved, then the first and second fundamental theorems have worthwhile additions. The algebraic counterpart of part (4) is already developed to some extent (see Clifford and Preston [*3*, Vol. I, p. 104]).

II

In this section, we formulate a number of problems about compact Abelian semigroups. We believe that this part of the theory of compact connected semigroups may receive increasing attention by the workers in the area. Although there are some apparently difficult problems even for very special compact Abelian semigroups, the questions in this area generally seem to be more accessible than most of the general problems cited in the first section. Commutativity adds a few significant simplifications in the structure of a compact semigroup. In particular, all Green's relations collapse to $\mathscr{H}$, and this one is a congruence relation. Thus every compact Abelian semigroup carries functorially the natural morphism $S \to S/\mathscr{H}$. The semigroup $S/\mathscr{H}$ contains no groups. Thus the theory of compact Abelian semigroups presents two overruling problems, each of which creates a variety of subproblems.

26. Characterize as completely as possible the structure of compact, connected Abelian semigroups in which all groups are trivial.

27. Describe as completely as possible how a compact, connected Abelian semigroup S is built up in terms of the semigroup $S/\mathscr{H}$ and the fibering $S \to S/\mathscr{H}$.

Let us turn to Problem 26 first. If S has an identity, then one can be sure that the greatest divisible subsemigroup S_d is large enough to contain the identity and the zero. It is still connected and compact. Thus in view of the premise that S_d describes an essential part of the structure of S, we are led to the following problem.

28. Characterize the structure of a compact, connected, divisible Abelian semigroup with identity and trivial groups.

Essential progress toward a complete solution of this problem has been made by Keimel [*6*], Brown and Friedberg [*2*], and Lawson [*7*], although some significant questions remain open, particularly in the case of infinite dimensional semigroups. Every compact Abelian semigroup carries along a natural transformation $\exp\colon LS \to S$, where LS is the compact semigroup $\mathrm{Hom}(\mathbb{H}, S)$ (in the pointwise topology, which turns out to be equal to the compact open one, at least in the case of trivial groups), and $\exp X = X(1)$. In the case of trivial groups, Keimel [*6*] has investigated the exponential function quite carefully. The "Lie algebra" LS there turns out to have interesting universal properties; notably, it is uniquely divisible. In the case of the presence of perhaps nontrivial groups, the pointwise topology has to be replaced by the compact open, and LS is no longer generally compact, as the example of compact groups shows, where LS is a topological vector space over the reals which is finite dimensional if and only if S is finite dimensional. This then leads to the following problem, which may provide one of the links between Problems 26 and 27.

29. Study the exponential function $\exp\colon LS \to S$ on the category of all Abelian compact (connected) semigroups with identity.

A first test class which should be tried is spelled out in the following.

30. Study the exponential function $\exp\colon LS \to S$ on the category of all Abelian compact connected semigroups with $E(S) = \{1, 0\}$. (Compare the more general Problem 18.)

The Lie algebra $LH(1)$ is a subvector space of LS in this case.

31. In Problem 30, under what circumstances is $LH(1)$ a direct summand of LS?

This problem, whose answer is positive in the case of finite dimensionality of $S/\mathscr{H}$, is intimately connected with the following question, which is a typical subquestion of Problem 27.

32. If S is a compact, connected Abelian semigroup with $E(S) = \{1, 0\}$, does $S \to S/\mathscr{H}$ allow a cross-section morphism?

In the case where $S/\mathscr{H}$ is finite dimensional, Brown and Friedberg [2] have shown the answer to be positive.

However, even in the study of compact, connected, divisible Abelian semigroups with trivial groups, a series of very interesting problems are left. If $e \in E(S)$, then Keimel [6] defines the *e component* $C(e)$ of LS to be the subsemigroup of all $X \in LS$, with $X(0) = e$. He shows that for any such component $C(e)$, there is an additively written semigroup T which satisfies the following conditions:

(a) There is a real vector space V in which T is a convex cone, and there is a bijection of Abelian semigroups $C(e) \to T$. In particular, T has a natural scalar multiplication.

(b) T has a topology relative to which addition and scalar multiplication are continuous maps $T \times T \to T$ and $\mathbb{H} \times T \to T$, and relative to which $C(e) \to T$ is an isomorphism of topological semigroups.

(c) The subspace $\{(t, t')\colon t' \in t + T\}$ is closed in $T \times T$.

Semigroups T satisfying (a)–(c) are called *ordered topological cone semigroups*.

If $e \subset E(S)$ is isolated in $E(eSe)$, then $C(e)$ is locally compact.

33 (Keimel). Let S be an Abelian compact semigroup with trivial groups. Is the e component $C(e)$ of LS always locally compact, provided there is a neighborhood U of e such that $X(\mathbb{H}) \not\subset U$ for all $X \in C(e)$? Test this problem on $S = \mathbb{H}^{*I}$ for an infinite set I, where $C(1)$ is not locally compact.

We draw attention to the fact that in the definition of an ordered topological cone semigroup, the embedding vector space did not carry a vector space topology which induced the topology of the cone. It is a rather crucial problem whether such a vector space topology exists.

34. Let T be a locally compact, ordered topological cone semigroup. Is there a topological vector space V and an embedding of topological semigroups $T \to V$?

If T is finite dimensional or has an order unit [*6*], then the answer to this problem is affirmative.

35. Let T be a locally compact ordered topological cone semigroup. Is there a surjective morphism $T \to \mathbb{H}$?

An equivalent formulation (according to Keimel's results [*6*]) is the following.

35a. Let S be a uniquely divisible compact Abelian semigroup, with $E(S) = \{0, 1\}$ and with trivial groups. Is there a co-one-parameter semigroup $S \to \mathbb{H}^*$? If the answer is positive, what happens when "uniquely divisible" is replaced by "divisible" or by "connected"?

Problem 35 is undecided even in the case where T is a cone in a topological vector space (unless the embedding space is locally convex, in which case the existence is secured). (Some recent contributions by Backer and Baker may be found in this area [*12*].)

36. Let T be a locally compact, ordered topological cone semigroup. Describe the structure of the universal (almost periodic) compactification $K(T)$ of T. [Certainly $K(T)$ exists and there is an isomorphism i of T onto an open subsemigroup of $K(T)$ such that for any continuous morphism f of T into a compact semigroup S, there is a unique morphism $F: K(T) \to S$ of compact semigroups such that $f = Fi$.] Describe $K(T)/\mathscr{H}$, and $EK(T) \cong E(K(T)/\mathscr{H})$.

It seems to be a good exercise to start looking at the examples $T = \mathbb{H}^3$, $T = \{(x, y, z) \in \mathbb{R}^3: x^2 + y^2 \leqslant z^2\}$.

There are other important questions left, even after an improved understanding of the exponential function. All of Keimel's e components may in fact be singleton, which is the case if S is a semilattice. Lawson has improved the knowledge of semilattices substantially [7]. Yet the following general question remains open.

37. Let S be a compact semilattice. Do the morphisms into the unit interval [0, 1] endowed with the min multiplication separate points?

Lawson [7] proved that this is the case iff S has small subsemilattices. Recently he showed that locally connected finite dimensional semilattices have this property and found an example of a one-dimensional semilattice with identity on which all morphisms into [0, 1] are constant [*7a*, *7b*].

This question is in some sense parallel to Problem 35a. The dual question, which in the analogous situation has already proved to be successful, apparently was not studied in the present context.

38. Let I be the unit interval with the min multiplication. If S is a compact semilattice (or, more generally, a compact Abelian semigroup), what is the structure of $\mathrm{Hom}(I, S)$, given the pointwise (respectively, the compact open) topology?

Only a closer inspection can reveal whether or not Problem 38 is indeed feasible.

A general approach to Problem 27 is missing and is badly needed. It seems virtually certain that any solution must generalize classical duality theory for groups, some of the investigations that have been performed on special classes of compact semigroups such as Clifford semigroups [*1*], and the theory of Abelian hormoi [*5*]. (Carruth and Mislove noticed that the construction of $\mathrm{Irr}(X)$ by Hunter and Rothman [*5*] contains a gap.)

39. Let B be a fixed Abelian semigroup with identity and trivial groups. Develop a structure theory (perhaps a duality theory) for the category, whose objects are compact Abelian semigroups S together with a morphism $f_S\colon S \to B$ whose fibers are exactly the $\mathscr{H}$ classes of S; the morphisms of the category are morphisms $\varphi\colon S \to T$ of compact semigroups such that $\varphi f_T = f_S$.

It is not at all clear what kind of theory one is looking for. We are inclined to think that certain sheaf theoretic concepts will play an important role in any future theory of the kind postulated in Problem 39.

III

In this section we mention a few problems which are typical for the category of compact semigroups without identity. This category is not likely to yield equally general structure theorems as did the first and second fundamental theorems in the case of compact semigroups with identity. Thus it is feasible to turn to special classes which are restricted by strong assumptions about the topological nature of the underlying space, or, on the other hand, by strongly restrictive algebraic hypotheses.

Recently it was shown [*3*a] that there is no semigroup on the disk such that $E(S)$ is the boundary of the disk. One may phrase the old problem, to which this is a solution, in more general terms.

40. Suppose that S is a topological semigroup on a compact manifold with regular boundary B. If $B = E(S)$, under what circumstances does S necessarily have the trivial right or left zero multiplication?

For instance, is this the case if S is an n cell, $n > 2$?

If cohomological arguments should lead toward a solution of this question, then it is not implausible to surmise that the hypothesis $E(S) = B$ may be relaxed to read: $B \subset E(S)$ and the inclusion induces an isomorphism $H(E(S)) \to H(B)$ of the cohomology ring.

Another question along similar lines, which has resisted a complete solution despite partial progress, is the following.

41. Let S be a compact semigroup with $SS = S$ on an n sphere. If S does not have right- or left-zero multiplication, is $\dim S = 0, 1, 3$?

There is an algebraic characterization for Clifford semigroups, with $\mathscr{H} = \mathscr{D}$. In the topological case the situation has been handled under the hypothesis that $S/\mathscr{H}$ is totally ordered, in which case S is a hormos [*4*, Theorem 5, p. 178]. But even in that case the topology imposes nontrivial complications which have to be overcome. The following problems relate to these ideas.

42. Characterize compact (connected) Clifford semigroups S with $\mathscr{D} = \mathscr{H}$ in terms of $S/\mathscr{H}$ and the groups in S (compare Problem P5 of Hofmann and Mostert [*4*, p. 160]).

43. Are there construction techniques which enable one to construct connected compact semigroups from a compact semilattice X and a collection of cylindrical semigroups $\{S_x: x \in X\}$ with suitable properties in a way analogous to the construction of the hormos?

REFERENCES

1. Austin, C. W., Duality theorems for some commutative semigroups. *Trans. Amer. Math. Soc.* **109**, 245 (1963).

1a. Backer, A. C., and Baker, J. W., Duality of topological semigroups with involution, *J. London Math. Soc.* **44**, 251–260 (1969); A note on duality of topological semigroups, *ibid.* **44**, 261–264 (1969).

2. Brown, D., and Friedberg, M., Representation theorems for uniquely divisible semigroups, *Duke Math. J.* **35**, 341–352 (1968).

3. Clifford, A. H., and Preston, G. B., "The Algebraic Theory of Semigroups." Vols. I and II (Math. Surveys No. 7). Amer. Math. Soc., Providence, Rhode Island, 1961, 1967.

3a. Ferguson, E. N., Semigroups on the two cell with idempotent boundary, *Notices Amer. Math. Soc.* **14**, 511 (1967).

4. Hofmann, K. H. and Mostert, P. S., "Elements of Compact Semigroups", Chas. E. Merrill Books, Columbus, Ohio, 1966.

5. Hunter, R. P., and Rothman, N., Characters and cross sections for certain semigroups. *Duke Math. J.* **29**, 347 (1962).

6. Keimel, K., Eine Exponentialfunktion für kompakte abelsche Halbgruppen. *Math. Z.* **96**, 7 (1967); Lokal kompakte Kegelhalbgruppen und deren Einbettung in topologische Vektorräume, *Math. Z.* **99**, 405 (1967).
7. Lawson, J. D., Vietoris mappings and embeddings of topological semilattices, dissertation, University of Tennesee, 1967.
7a. Lawson, J. D., Topological semilattices with small semilattices (to be published).
7b. Lawson, J. D., Lattices with no interval homomorphisms (to be published).
8. Madison, B. L., Semigroups on coset spaces. *Abstract Notices Amer. Math. Soc.* **14**, No. 5, 636 (1967); *Proc. Amer. Math. Soc.* (to be published).

A Survey of Results on Threads[†]

R. J. KOCH
Louisiana State University
Baton Rouge, Louisiana

In this note we present a summary of results dealing with threads and local threads in compact semigroups. It is hoped that this collection of results together with the bibliography may be of use to researchers in the area. A *standard thread* (briefly thread) is a topological semigroup on a closed real interval in which the endpoints act as zero and identity. A local semigroup S is a Hausdorff space in which there is an open set V and a function m: $V^* \times V^* \to S$ which is continuous, associative insofar as is meaningful, and there exists $1 \in V$ with $m(1, x) = x = m(x, 1)$ for each $x \in V$. A local subsemigroup T of a local semigroup S is a subset T of S with $1 \in T$, and $(T \cap V)^2 \subset T$. A local thread is a local semigroup in which the associated V^* is a real interval.

I. Structure

The structure of threads is well known through the work of Clifford [*7*], Faucett [*10*], and Mostert and Shields [*26*]. Briefly, the set E of idempotents is closed, $S \setminus E$ is the countable disjoint union of open intervals I_j. Each I_j^* is a semigroup with zero, identity, and no other idempotents, and is isomorphic to either [0, 1] under usual multiplication, (called *usual*), or $[\frac{1}{2}, 1]$ under the multiplication $a * b = \max(\frac{1}{2}, ab)$ (called *nilpotent*). For $x \in I_i$, $y \in I_j$, $i < j$, we have $xy = x = yx$. For $e \in E$, e acts as identity on $[0, e]$, and as zero on $[e, 1]$.

This analysis can be carried through in case the underlying space is a generalized arc (continuum with exactly two noncutpoints). If the

† This work was supported by NSF Grant GP9022.

underlying space S is a continuum irreducible between zero and 1, then S must be an arc (Koch and Wallace [*23*]). The structure of local threads has not been discussed in the literature. However, it seems to be known that a compact local thread is isomorphic to a compact neighborhood of the identity of a thread.

II. Existence of Local Threads; Extensions to Full Threads

If S is a compact semigroup with maximal group $H(1)$ not isolated, and if there is a neighborhood of 1 free of other idempotents, then there is a local usual thread L with $1 \in L \subset V$. This result is due to Mostert and Shields, and was actually proved in a local setting. A similar result was obtained later by Hofmann [*14*]. If there are idempotents arbitrarily close to 1, then there may be no arc at 1 (Hunter, [*19*]) and even if S is locally connected, there may be no local thread at 1 [*18*].

In case there are sufficiently many idempotents near 1 in the sense that there is a neighborhood V of f in which no idempotent is a local minimum of the relation $e \leqslant f \leftrightarrow ef = fe = f$, then there exists a min thread from 1 to $Bd\ V$ [*20*]. This result yields the existence of local threads in any neighborhood of the identity of a compact connected semigroup. Also, it yields threads from zero to identity in a compact connected semilattice.

A result of the author provides local threads in partially ordered local semigroups [*21*], extending a result of Gleason [*12*]. In case S is compact connected and normal, then $S/\mathscr{D}$ is partially ordered*; thus threads exist in $S/\mathscr{D}$, and these can be lifted (near 1) to S (Hunter [*18*]). The most useful result to date is the existence of threads from minimal ideal to identity in compact connected semigroups in which each subgroup is totally disconnected [*22*]. The author's proof uses all of the above theorems, and involves knowing the extensions of local threads in a compact semigroup. This information is well known [*25*] (see also Mostert and Shields [*27*] and Hofmann and Mostert [*15*]). The possible extensions are (1) usual thread, (2) nilpotent thread, (3) nonnegative reals under addition, with reals $\geqslant C$ identified mod 1, and (4) a half-way winding densely on a compact, connected, separable Abelian group (the general example is given in Koch and Wallace [*23*]).

If an element p of a compact semigroup S has an infinite sequence of square roots, then there is a local usual thread in the closure of the

* Here $x \mathscr{D} y$ iff $SxS = SyS$.

semigroup of dyadic powers of p (Hudson [*16*]). Further results on threads in uniquely divisible semigroups are given by Hildebrant [*13*]. Hunter [*18*] has shown the existence of a local usual thread at the identity of any compact connected semigroup embeddable in the plane. This extends a result on lattices by Anderson [*1*].

III. Mapping Properties

By a basic result of Phillips [*28*], each closed congruence on a standard thread has connected cosets. This yields the fact that a translate of a thread is an arc. The homomorphic image of a thread is again a thread; Cohen and Krule [*8*] have described homomorphic images of semigroups with identity and zero (not necessarily at an end point) on an interval, and they are at worst triods. Along these lines Clark [*6*] has shown that the homomorphic image of a product of a min thread with a usual thread is a cyclic chain in which each true cyclic element is a two cell. He also gives other results of this nature. There is the extension theorems of Shields [*30*] in which homomorphisms defined on the boundary of a product of threads are shown to be extendable to the n cell. Anderson and Hunter [*2, 3*] have shown that idempotent threads can be lifted through open homomorphisms of compact semigroups, but usual or nilpotent threads do not enjoy this property. However, any standard thread can be lifted through light open homomorphisms. An example of Ursell furnishes a compact Abelian semigroup which does not admit a homomorphism onto a standard thread, and hence does not admit a homomorphism onto a one-dimensional semigroup: let $I = [0, 1]$ (usual), $M = [0, 1]$ (min), $S = I \times M/[(I \times 0) \cup (0 \times M)]$. However, any compact connected semigroup with 1 contains an algebraically irreducible semigroup T (from K to 1), and T is Abelian (Hofmann and Mostert [*15*]); thus T admits a homomorphism onto the thread $T/\mathscr{D}$. Lawson [*24*] has shown that if S is a compact connected semilattice with upper sets connected, then S admits enough homomorphisms to a min thread to separate points.

IV. Internal Position

A thread in a compact semigroup can meet a $\mathscr{D}$ class in at most one point (Anderson and Hunter [*3*]). A recent result of Tymchatyn [*32*] shows that a usual thread may "bump" through a regular $\mathscr{D}$ class.

The following example shows that only one local thread may exist at the identity: $I = [0, 1]$ (usual), $M = [0, 1]$ (min), $S \subset I \times M$, $S = \{(x, g): x \leqslant y\}$. This simple example points up the difficulty in attempting to control the construction in the small of a local thread. The unsettled problem of Hofmann and Mostert [*15*] is of this nature —does there exist a local thread in the centralizer of the group of units? They give an affirmative answer in case $S/\mathscr{D}$ is totally ordered. The notion of independent threads at 1 has been introduced by Clark [*6*]: the family $T_1, \ldots, T_u$ of threads each containing 1 is called locally algebraically independent if there exists a neighborhood W of 1 such that for each partition of the integers $[1, \ldots, n]$ into nonempty sets A and B, $\prod_{i \in A} T_i \cap \prod_{i \in B} T_i \cap W = \{1\}$. If S is compact and commutative, and $\{T_i\}$ are independent, then the map $(t_1, t_2, \ldots, t_n) \to t_1 t_2 \cdots t_n$ is a homomorphism, and is 1–1 on some neighborhood of $(1, 1, \ldots, 1)$.

V. Miscellaneous

There are several interesting examples (Hofmann and Mostert [*15*]) of splitting extensions of semigroups by special threads. The more general question as to the ability of a thread to act as a semigroup of transformations on a continuum has been considered by Stadtlander [*31*]. Related work on semigroup actions is due to Day and Wallace [*9*].

An interesting result on the existence of arcs in one-parameter semigroups of compact sets is given by Hofmann and Mostert [*15*]. A result of Radstrom [*29*] shows that a one-parameter semigroup $A(\delta)$ of compact sets in a locally convex Hausdorff linear space is of the form $A(\delta) = f(\delta) + \delta K$, where $f(\delta)$ is a one-parameter semigroup of points and K is a compact convex set.

VI. Applications

One of the main conceptual applications of threads is the possibility of using them to introduce coordinates (this line of thought is more hopeful with algebraically irreducible semigroups replacing threads). This has been successfully applied by Mostert and Shields [*26*], and by Hudson [*16*] in characterizing certain semigroups on two cells. Ferguson [*11*] has made full use of threads in showing that there is no semigroup on a two cell with $E =$ boundary. The existence of a thread T from zero to identity implies arcwise connectedness, and this technique was used by Hunter [*17*] in showing that one-dimensional, compact, connected semigroups with 0 and 1 are generalized trees. Compact connected semigroups S with 0 and 1 are acyclic (Wallace [*33*]); in case the subgroups of S are totally disconnected, then S is contractible [*22*]. This technique was used by Brown [*4*] in showing that compact connected semigroups of nonnegative matrices are contractible. Brown and Friedberg [*5*] used the results of Clark and Hildebrant in their investigation of representation spaces for divisible semigroups.

REFERENCES

1. Anderson, L. W., The existence of continuous lattice homomorphisms, *J. London Math. Soc.* **37**, 60–62 (1962).
2. Anderson, L. W. and Hunter, R. P., Homomorphisms and dimension. *Math. Ann.* **147**, 248–268 (1962).
3. Anderson, L. W. and Hunter, R. P., Certain homomorphisms of a compact semigroup onto a thread, unpublished paper.
4. Brown, D. R., On clans of non-negative matrices. *Proc. Amer. Math. Soc.* **15**, 671–674 (1964).
5. Brown, D. R. and Friedberg, M., A new notion of semicharacters. Unpublished paper.
6. Clark, C. E., Locally algebraically independent collections of subsemigroups of a semigroup, unpublished paper.
7. Clifford, A. H., Naturally totally ordered commutative semigroups. *Amer. J. Math.* **56**, 631–646 (1954).
8. Cohen, H., and Krule, I. S., Continuous homomorphic images of real clans with zero. *Proc. Amer. Math. Soc.* **10**, 106–108 (1959).
9. Day, J. M. and Wallace, A. D., Semigroups acting on continua. *J. Australian Math. Soc.* **7**, 327–340 (1967).
10. Faucett, W. M., Compact semigroups irreducibly connected between two idempotents. *Proc. Amer. Math. Soc.* **6**, 741–747 (1955).
11. Ferguson, E. N., Semigroups on the two-cell with idempotent boundary. Dissertation, Univ. of Oregon, 1967.
12. Gleason, A. M., Arcs in locally compact groups. *Proc. Math. Acad. Sci.*, **36**, 663–667 (1950).
13. Hildebrant, J. A., On compact unithetic semigroups. *Pacific J. Math.* **21**, 265–273 (1967).
14. Hofmann, K. H., Topologische Halgruppen mit dichter Submonogener Unterhalbgruppen. *Math. Z.* **74**, 232–276 (1960).
15. Hofmann, K. H. and Mostert, P. S., "Elements of Compact Semigroups." Merrill Books, Columbus, Ohio, 1966.
16. Hudson, A. L., Some semigroups on the two-cell. *Proc. Amer. Math. Soc.* **10** 648–655 (1959).
17. Hunter, R. P., On the semigroup structure of continua. *Trans. Amer. Math. Soc.* **93**, 356–368 (1959).
18. Hunter, R. P., Certain upper semi-continuous decompositions of a semigroup. *Duke Math. J.* **27**, 283–290 (1960).
19. Hunter, R. P., Note on arcs in semigroups. *Fund. Math.* **49**, 233–245 (1961).

20. Koch, R. J., Arcs in partially ordered spaces. *Pacific J. Math.* **9**, 723–728 (1959).
21. Koch, R. J., Ordered semigroups in partially ordered semigroups. *Pacific J. Math.* **10**, 1333–1336 (1960).
22. Koch, R. J., Threads in compact semigroups. *Math. Z.* **86**, 312–316 (1964).
23. Koch, R. J. and Wallace, A. D., Admissibility of semigroup structures on continua. *Trans. Amer. Math. Soc.* **88**, 277–287 (1958).
24. Lawson, J. D., Vietoris mappings and embeddings of topological semilattices. Dissertation, Univ. of Tennessee, 1967.
25. Lecture Notes, Univ. of Kentucky, 1965.
26. Mostert, P. S. and Shields, A. L., On the structure of semigroups on a compact manifold with boundary. *Ann. Math.* **65**, 117–143 (1957).
27. Mostert, P. S. and Shields, A. L., One-parameter semigroups in a semigroup. *Trans. Amer. Math. Soc.* **96**, 510–517 (1960).
28. Phillips, R. C., Interval Clans with non-degenerate kernel. *Proc. Amer. Math. Soc.* **14**, 396–400 (1963).
29. Radstrom, H., One-parameter semigroups of subsets of a real linear space. *Ark. Mat.* **4**, 87–97 (1959).
30. Shields, A. L., The n-cube as a product semigroup. *Michigan Math. J.* **4**, 165–166 (1957).
31. Stadtlander, D., Thread Actions. *Duke Math. J.* **35**, 483–490 (1968).
32. Tymchatyn, E. D., An example of a one-parameter semigroup which meets several regular $\mathscr{D}$-classes." *Canad. J. Math.* (to be published).
33. Wallace, A. D., The structure of topological semigroups. *Bull. Amer. Math. Soc.* **61**, 95–112 (1955).

Some Recent Results on the Structure of Inverse Semigroups

W. D. MUNN
University of Stirling
Stirling, Scotland

One of the most rapidly developing areas of the algebraic theory of semigroups has been that concerned with the structure of inverse semigroups of various special types. My aim in this lecture is to give a self-contained account of some recent results on bisimple and simple inverse semigroups. The former class of semigroups, in particular, has been extensively studied during the past few years.

1. Preliminaries

I shall use the notation and terminology of Clifford and Preston (1961), with a few minor exceptions. All homomorphisms will be written as right operators and the set of all nonnegative integers, to which frequent reference is made in Sections 1–3, is denoted throughout by N.

It is convenient to recall some basic definitions. In an arbitrary semigroup S we define equivalences $\mathscr{L}$ and $\mathscr{R}$ by the rules:

$$(a, b) \in \mathscr{L} \Leftrightarrow Sa \cup a = Sb \cup b,$$
$$(a, b) \in \mathscr{R} \Leftrightarrow aS \cup a = bS \cup b.$$

It can be shown that, under the usual multiplication of relations, $\mathscr{L}$ and $\mathscr{R}$ commute; their product is $\mathscr{L} \vee \mathscr{R}$, the smallest equivalence containing them both, and this is denoted by $\mathscr{D}$. A semigroup is *bisimple* if and only if it consists of a single $\mathscr{D}$ class. By contrast, a semigroup S is *simple* if and only if it contains no two-sided ideal except S itself.

It is not difficult to see that every bisimple semigroup is simple; however, a simple semigroup need not be bisimple (see Example 2 below).

An *inverse semigroup* is a semigroup S satisfying the following two conditions:

(1) for all $a \in S$ there exists $x \in S$ such that $axa = a$;

(2) any two idempotents of S commute.

It should be noted that if $axa = a$, then ax and xa are idempotents; but, in general, these are distinct. An inverse semigroup can also be characterised as a semigroup S in which to each $a \in S$ there corresponds a unique element $a^{-1} \in S$ such that

$$aa^{-1}a = a, \qquad a^{-1}aa^{-1} = a^{-1}$$

[see Clifford and Preston (1961, Theorem 1.17)]. The element a^{-1} is called the *inverse* of a. It can readily be verified that, for all $a, b \in S$,

$$(a^{-1})^{-1} = a, \qquad (ab)^{-1} = b^{-1}a^{-1}, \qquad e^2 = e \Rightarrow e^{-1} = e.$$

Semigroups of this type were first discussed by Vagner (1952) and later, independently, by Preston (1954).

By an *inverse subsemigroup* of S we shall mean a subsemigroup T of S with the property that if $a \in T$, then $a^{-1} \in T$ also. Thus T is an inverse semigroup under the multiplication in S.

I shall be mainly concerned here with bisimple and simple inverse semigroups. In passing, it should be noted that there is a neat characterization of bisimplicity in terms of idempotents: an inverse semigroup S is bisimple if and only if to each pair of idempotents $e, f \in S$ there corresponds an element $a \in S$ such that $aa^{-1} = e$ and $a^{-1}a = f$. Further, it can be proved that any *finite* simple inverse semigroup is necessarily a group; thus the structures that we shall be dealing with are essentially infinite.

We end this introductory section with two examples, the first of which is very familiar.

EXAMPLE 1. *The bicyclic semigroup B.* Informally, we can describe B as the semigroup generated by two symbols x, y subject to the single defining relation $xy = 1$. For the present purpose it is more convenient to define it as follows. Let $B = N \times N$ (N denoting the set of non-negative integers) and define a multiplication in B by the rule that

$$(m, n)(p, q) = (m - n + t, q - p + t),$$

where $t = \max\{n, p\}$. Then B is a bisimple inverse semigroup. The set of idempotents is $\{(m, m) \in B: m \in N\}$ and B has an identity, namely $(0, 0)$.

This semigroup, known as the *bicyclic semigroup*, plays an important part in the general theory of simple semigroups. An idempotent e of a semigroup S is said to be *primitive* if and only if there is no idempotent f, distinct from e, such that $ef = fe = f$. Simple semigroups containing primitive idempotents (that is, *completely simple semigroups*) have been classified by Rees (1940). On the other hand, as was shown by Andersen [see Clifford and Preston (1961, Theorem 2.54)], every simple semigroup containing a nonprimitive idempotent must contain an isomorphic copy of B.

The second example is a subsemigroup of B.

EXAMPLE 2. *The semigroup* B_d. Let d be any positive integer and let

$$B_d = \{(m, n) \in B: m \equiv n \pmod{d}\}.$$

Then B_d is an inverse subsemigroup of B which is simple, but not bisimple if $d > 1$. In fact B_d has exactly d distinct $\mathscr{D}$ classes. It is an example of a simple regular ω semigroup (see Section 3).

2. Bisimple Inverse Semigroups

The systematic study of what we now call bisimple inverse semigroups was begun by Clifford. In a fundamental paper (Clifford, 1953) he shows how to construct the most general bisimple inverse semigroup with an identity, starting from a certain type of semigroup obeying the right cancellation law.

Let S be a bisimple inverse semigroup with an identity 1 and let $P = \{x \in S: xy = 1 \text{ for some } y \in S\}$. Then P is a subsemigroup of S (*the right unit subsemigroup*) satisfying the following two conditions:

(1) P is right cancellative and has an identity 1;

(2) to each pair of elements $a, b \in P$ there corresponds $c \in P$ such that

$$Pa \cap Pb = Pc.$$

Clearly P is just the $\mathscr{R}$ class of S containing 1.

Conversely, given a semigroup P satisfying conditions (1) and (2), we can construct a bisimple inverse semigroup S with an identity whose right unit subsemigroup is isomorphic to P.

Examples of semigroups satisfying (1) and (2) are plentiful. Some general results on semigroups with an identity and satisfying a one-sided cancellation law have been obtained by Rees (1948).

Recently Clifford's theory has been extended to cover the case of bisimple inverse semigroups without an identity (Reilly, 1968). The right cancellative semigroup P is replaced by a certain type of partial semigroup (called an *RP system*) which is an abstract version of an arbitrary $\mathscr{R}$ class of a bisimple inverse semigroup S; the structure of S is then expressed in terms of such an RP system.

More recently again, Reilly and Clifford (1968) have shown how a bisimple inverse semigroup can be represented as a set of ordered triples with a suitably defined multiplication, two components of each triple being drawn from an RP system and the third from a group. This representation was partly motivated by the corresponding result first obtained by Reilly (1966) for the special case of bisimple ω semigroups (see below). Unfortunately it is not possible to give a fuller description of this important line of development here.

I want to outline an alternative approach to the structure problem for bisimple inverse semigroups (see Section 4). The starting point is the notion of a "uniform semilattice."

A *semilattice* is a commutative semigroup E of idempotents. We can define a partial ordering $\leqslant$ on E by the rule that $e \leqslant f$ if and only if $ef = e$. Under this, any two elements of E have a greatest lower bound, namely, their product. Conversely, if we start with a partially ordered set E in which any two elements have a greatest lower bound, and if we define multiplication in E by taking the product of two elements to be their glb, then E becomes a commutative semigroup of idempotents. Note that $Ee = \{x \in E: x \leqslant e\}$ for all $e \in E$.

Let S be an inverse semigroup. The set of all idempotents of S will be denoted by E_S. It is a subsemigroup of S and is called *the semilattice of* S.

A semilattice E is said to be *uniform* if and only if $Ee \simeq Ef$ for any two elements $e, f \in E$. There is a close connection between uniform semilattices and bisimple inverse semigroups; this is expressed in the following theorem (Munn, 1966).

Theorem 1. *A semilattice is uniform if and only if it is the semilattice of a bisimple inverse semigroup.*

This result suggests that we might attempt to classify bisimple inverse semigroups by means of their semilattices.

It is easy to see that the only finite uniform semilattice is that consisting of a single element: moreover, a bisimple inverse semigroup with a one-element semilattice is necessarily a group. The natural next case to consider is that of a bisimple inverse semigroup S for which $E_S = \{e_i: i \in N\}$, where

$$e_0 > e_1 > e_2 > \cdots.$$

We call S a *bisimple ω semigroup*. The bicyclic semigroup B is a special case; here $E_S = \{(m, m): m \in N\}$ and

$$(0, 0) > (1, 1) > (2, 2) > \cdots.$$

The structure of such semigroups was determined by Reilly (1966). His construction will now be described. Let G be a group and let α be an endomorphism of G. Let $S = N \times G \times N$ and define a multiplication in S by the rule that

$$(m; g; n)(p; h; q) = (m - n + t; \quad g\alpha^{t-n}h\alpha^{t-p}; \quad q - p + t),$$

where $t = \max\{n, p\}$ and α^0 represents the identity automorphism of G. Denote the groupoid so formed by $S(G, \alpha)$.

Then we have the following theorem.

Theorem 2 (Reilly). *$S(G, \alpha)$ is a bisimple ω semigroup and every bisimple ω semigroup is, to within isomorphism, of this form.*

Note that the bicyclic semigroup B is obtained by taking G to be the one-element group. Theorem 2 constituted an important step in the development of the theory of simple semigroups, as it was the first explicit structure theorem beyond Rees' theorem for completely simple semigroups.

Similar results for other classes of bisimple inverse semigroups with specific (totally ordered) semilattices have since been obtained by Warne (1967, 1968).

3. Regular ω Semigroups

A natural question arising from Reilly's result on bisimple ω semigroups is the following. What can be said if we retain the same semilattice, but drop the restriction of bisimplicity?

An inverse semigroup S is called a *regular ω semigroup* if and only if $E_S = \{e_i : i \in N\}$, where

$$e_0 > e_1 > e_2 > \cdots.$$

It turns out that the structure of such semigroups can be completely described in terms of groups and homomorphisms (Munn, 1968).

One type of regular ω semigroup can be constructed as follows. Let $\{G_i: i \in N\}$ be a family of pairwise-disjoint groups and, for each $i \in N$, let γ_i be a homomorphism of G_i into G_{i+1}. For each pair $(i, j) \in N \times N$ such that $i < j$ let

$$\alpha_{i,j} = \gamma_i \gamma_{i+1} \cdots \gamma_{j-1}$$

and for each $i \in N$ let $\alpha_{i,i}$ denote the identity automorphism of G_i. Let

$$S = \bigcup_{i=0}^{\infty} G_i$$

and define a multiplication on S (extending that in each G_i) by the rule that

$$a_i b_j = (a_i \alpha_{i,t})(b_j \alpha_{j,t}),$$

where $a_i \in G_i$, $b_j \in G_j$, and $t = \max\{i, j\}$. Then it can be shown that S is a regular ω semigroup: we call it the *union of an ω chain of groups*. This construction, in a more general form, was first given by Clifford (1941). It is easy to see that each subset $T_n = \bigcup_{i=n}^{\infty} G_i$ is an ideal of S and that $\bigcap_{n=0}^{\infty} T_n = \emptyset$.

By the *kernel* of a semigroup S we mean a two-sided ideal of S contained in every ideal of S. Every finite semigroup has a kernel; however, an infinite semigroup need not, as the above example shows. The next theorem characterises regular ω semigroups without a kernel (Munn, 1968).

Theorem 3. *Let S be a regular ω semigroup. The following conditions on S are equivalent.*

(1) *S has no kernel.*

(2) *The idempotents of S are central ($e^2 = e \Rightarrow ex = xe$ for all $x \in S$).*

(3) *S is the union of an ω chain of groups.*

If S does have a kernel K, then K is a *simple regular ω semigroup.* The semigroup B_d in Section 1 is an example of a simple regular ω semigroup.

We now show how to construct any simple regular ω-semigroup from a finite collection of groups and homomorphisms. Let d be a positive integer and let $\{G_i: i = 0, \ldots, d-1\}$ be a family of pairwise-disjoint groups. Let $\{\gamma_i: i = 0, \ldots, d-1\}$ be any family of homomorphisms linking the groups in the manner shown:

$$G_0 \xrightarrow{\gamma_0} G_1 \xrightarrow{\gamma_1} G_2 \xrightarrow{\gamma_2} \cdots \longrightarrow G_{d-1} \xrightarrow{\gamma_{d-1}} G_0 .$$

For all $n \in N$ let $\gamma_n = \gamma_{n(\mathrm{mod}\, d)}$. For $(m, n) \in N \times N$ such that $m < n$, write

$$\alpha_{m,n} = \gamma_m \gamma_{m-1} \cdots \gamma_{n-1}$$

and for all $n \in N$ let $\alpha_{n,n}$ denote the identity automorphism of $G_{n(\mathrm{mod}\, d)}$. Let S be the set of all ordered triples $(m; a_i; n)$, where $m, n \in N$, $0 \leqslant i \leqslant d-1$ and $a_i \in G_i$. Define a multiplication in S by the rule that

$$(m; a_i; n)(p; b_j; q) = (m - n + t; (a_i\alpha_{u,w})(b_j\alpha_{v,w}); q - p + t),$$

where $t = \max\{n, p\}$, $u = nd + i$, $v = pd + j$, and $w = \max\{u, v\}$. Denote the groupoid so formed by $S(d; G_i; \gamma_i)$. Then we have the following theorem (Munn, 1968).

Theorem 4. *$S(d; G_i; \gamma_i)$ is a simple regular ω semigroup with exactly d distinct $\mathscr{D}$ classes and every simple regular ω semigroup is, to within isomorphism, of this form.*

The main feature of interest in this result is that the semigroups whose structure is described are simple, but not necessarily bisimple. Theorem 2 is obtained as a special case by taking $d = 1$.

An extension of the theorem gives the structure of a regular ω semigroup S with kernel $K \neq S$. Combining this with Theorem 3 we obtain a complete description of the structure of arbitrary regular ω-semigroups.

4. Fundamental Bisimple Inverse Semigroups and the Split Extention Theorem

Let us now return to the bisimple case. The objective in this section is to express the structure of certain bisimple inverse semigroups ultimately in terms of groups and uniform semilattices.

Recall that a *congruence* ρ on a semigroup S is an equivalence with the property that, for all $x \in S$,

$$(a, b) \in \rho \Rightarrow (xa, xb) \in \rho \qquad \text{and} \qquad (ax, bx) \in \rho.$$

Denote the ρ class containing $a \in S$ by $a\rho$. Then S/ρ, the set of all

ρ classes, becomes a semigroup under the multiplication ($\circ$) defined by $(a\rho) \circ (b\rho) = (ab)\rho$ and the natural mapping of S onto S/ρ is a homomorphism.

We say that ρ is *idempotent separating* if and only if each ρ class contains at most one idempotent of S. Howie (1964) has shown that an inverse semigroup S possesses a greatest idempotent-separating congruence μ; this can be described as follows:

$$(a, b) \in \mu \Leftrightarrow a^{-1}ea = b^{-1}eb \quad \text{for all idempotents} \quad e \in S.$$

It can readily be proved that $\mu \subseteq \mathscr{H}$, where $\mathscr{H}$ denotes the equivalence $\mathscr{R} \cap \mathscr{L}$. Since any congruence $\rho \subseteq \mathscr{H}$ is necessarily idempotent separating [see Clifford and Preston (1961, Lemma 2.15)] it follows that the idempotent-separating congruences on an inverse semigroup are just the congruences ρ such that $\rho \subseteq \mathscr{H}$. Examples can be given to show that $\mathscr{H}$ itself need not be a congruence; that is, it may happen that $\mu \neq \mathscr{H}$.

An inverse semigroup S will be termed *fundamental* if and only if it possesses no idempotent-separating congruence other than the identity congruence ι. Thus S is fundamental if and only if $\mu = \iota$.

Theorem 5. *Let S be a [bisimple] inverse semigroup. Then S/μ is a fundamental [bisimple] inverse semigroup with semilattice isomorphic to E_S.*

The importance of the concept of a fundamental bisimple inverse semigroup lies in the fact that such a semigroup can be given a simple characterisation in terms of mappings (Theorem 6). Let $\mathscr{I}_E$ denote the set of all partial one-to-one transformations of a set E. This becomes a semigroup under the usual multiplication of relations; we call it the *symmetric inverse semigroup on E*. Now let E be a semilattice and let T_E denote the subset of $\mathscr{I}_E$ consisting of all α such that the domain and codomain of α are principal ideals of E and α is an isomorphism. Then T_E is an inverse subsemigroup of $\mathscr{I}_E$ with semilattice isomorphic to E (Munn, 1966). Next suppose that E is uniform. An inverse subsemigroup S of T_E will be called *transitive* if and only if to each pair $(e, f) \in E \times E$ there corresponds $\alpha \in S$ such that Ee is the domain and Ef the codomain of α. Clearly T_E itself is transitive.

We then have the following result.

Theorem 6. *Let E be a uniform semilattice and let S be a transitive inverse subsemigroup of T_E; then S is a fundamental bisimple inverse semigroup and $E_S \cong E$. Conversely, any fundamental bisimple inverse semigroup with (uniform) semilattice E is isomorphic to a transitive inverse subsemigroup of T_E.*

Combining Theorems 5 and 6 we see that if S is a bisimple inverse semigroup with semilattice E, then S/μ is isomorphic to a transitive inverse subsemigroup of T_E. The following special case is of some interest. Let E be such that each principal ideal of E is inversely well ordered (that is, each nonempty subset of each principal ideal of E contains a greatest element); then $\mu = \mathscr{H}$ and $S/\mathscr{H} \cong T_E$ (Munn, 1966). This holds, in particular, if E itself is inversely well ordered, as is the case for a bisimple ω semigroup.

The remainder of the discussion concerns the problem of constructing nonfundamental bisimple inverse semigroups from fundamental ones and groups. I shall not attempt to describe the general situation here but shall instead confine myself to a particular case in which the solution is comparatively straightforward.

Let ρ be a congruence on a semigroup S^*. We say that S^* *splits over* ρ if and only if there exists a subsemigroup S of S^* which is also a cross section (that is, a set of representatives) of the ρ classes. Now let S^*, S be bisimple inverse semigroups and let G be a group. Then we shall call S^* *a split extension of* G *by* S if and only if there exists an idempotent-separating congruence ρ on S^* such that

(1) $S^*/\rho \cong S$,

(2) $e^*\rho \cong G$, for some idempotent $e^* \in S^*$, and

(3) S^* splits over ρ.

Suppose that S^* is a split extension of G by S. Then it can be shown that $E_{S^*} \cong E_S$. Let ρ be an idempotent-separating congruence on S^* satisfying (1), (2), and (3) and let μ denote the greatest idempotent-separating congruence on S^*. Then $\rho = \mu$ if and only if S is fundamental. The bisimple ω semigroup $S(G, \alpha)$ is a split extension of G by B; in this case $\rho = \mu = \mathscr{H}$.

The final theorem gives the structure of a split extension of G by S. We need some further notation. Let S be a bisimple inverse semigroup and let the $\mathscr{R}$ class [$\mathscr{L}$ class] of S containing $a \in S$ be denoted by R_a [L_a]. Let e be any idempotent of S and let $P_e = R_e \cap eSe$ (the right unit subsemigroup of the subsemigroup eSe of S). Let C be a cross section of the $\mathscr{H}$ classes of S in R_e and, for all $a \in S$, let a_1 denote the unique element of C that lies in $L_{aa^{-1}}$. Then we can prove that, for all $a, b \in S$, the elements

$$p = (ab)_1 a_1^{-1}, \qquad q = (ab)_1 ab_1^{-1}$$

both belong to P_e.

Now let G be an arbitrary group. Let *end* G denote the semigroup of all endomorphisms of G and let θ: $P_e \rightarrow$ *end* G be an antihomomorphism with the property that $e\theta$ is the identity automorphism of G. Write $p\theta = \theta_p$ for all $p \in P_e$. Define a multiplication in $G \times S$ by the rule that

$$(g, a)(h, b) = (g\theta_p h\theta_q, ab),$$

where $p = (ab)_1 a_1^{-1}$ and $q = (ab)_1 a b_1^{-1}$. By the remark above, $p, q \in P_e$ and so this multiplication is well defined. Denote the groupoid so formed by

$$S^*(S, G, e, C, \theta).$$

Theorem 7. *$S^*(S, G, e, C, \theta)$ is a bisimple inverse semigroup which is a split extension of G by S. Conversely, every split extension of G by S is, to within isomorphism, of this type.*

When S is a group the above construction gives the semidirect product of G by S in the usual group-theoretic sense.

From the results of this section we can obtain the structure of the most general bisimple inverse semigroup S^* that splits over μ (its greatest idempotent-separating congruence) in terms of a group and a uniform semilattice. Let E be a uniform semilattice. Let S be any transitive inverse subsemigroup of T_E; then S is a fundamental bisimple inverse semigroup with semilattice isomorphic to E. Now let G be a group. Construct any semigroup S^* of the form $S^*(S, G, e, C, \theta)$. Then S^* is a bisimple inverse semigroup which is a split extension of G by S. Since S is fundamental, S^* splits over μ. Conversely, let S^* be any bisimple inverse semigroup which splits over μ and let E be the semilattice of S^*. Then S^*/μ is isomorphic to a transitive inverse subsemigroup S of T_E. Let e^* be any idempotent of S^* and let $G = e^*\mu$, the μ class of S^* containing e^*. Then G is a subgroup of S^* and $S^* \simeq S^*(S, G, e, C, \theta)$ for a suitable choice of e, C, and θ.

To conclude, I should mention that the construction can be generalized in two ways. First, we can extend it to cover the case of 0-*bisimple* inverse semigroups. (By a 0-bisimple semigroup we mean a semigroup S with a zero element and such that the set of all nonzero elements is a $\mathscr{D}$ class of S.) Second, we can discard the "splitting" condition. This necessitates the introduction of factor sets analogous to those that occur in the Schreier theory of group extensions. It is hoped that an account of these developments will be given elsewhere.

Appendix

Proofs of Theorems 5 and 6 will be included in a forthcoming paper entitled "Fundamental inverse semigroups." We give here a proof of

Theorem 7. Various elementary properties of inverse semigroups will be assumed [see Clifford and Preston (1961, Section 1.9)].

Let S be a bisimple inverse semigroup, let e be an idempotent of S, and let C be a cross section of the $\mathscr{H}$ classes of S that are contained in R_e. For each $a \in S$ we denote by a_1 the unique element of C lying in $L_{aa^{-1}}$. (The existence of such an element is guaranteed by the bisimplicity of S.) Since $a_1 a_1^{-1} \in R_e$, $a_1^{-1} a_1 \in L_{aa^{-1}}$ and each of these sets contains exactly one idempotent, it follows that

$$a_1 a_1^{-1} = e, \qquad a_1^{-1} a_1 = aa^{-1}.$$

Hence

$$a_1 aa^{-1} = a_1, \qquad aa^{-1} a_1^{-1} = a_1^{-1}.$$

These properties of a_1 will be used without further comment. Let $P_e = R_e \cap eSe$. It is easy to see that $P_e = \{x \in R_e : xe = x\}$ and that it is a right cancellative subsemigroup with identity e.

The following lemma, of a technical nature, is required for the proof of the theorem.

Lemma. *Let $a, b \in S$ and let*

$$p = (ab)_1 a_1^{-1}, \qquad q = (ab)_1 ab_1^{-1}.$$

Then

(1) $pa_1 = (ab)_1$,

(2) $qb_1 = (ab)_1 a$,

(3) $p, q \in P_e$.

PROOF. We note first that

$$(ab)_1 = (ab)_1 (ab)(ab)^{-1} = (ab)_1\, abb^{-1}a^{-1}.$$

This is used in all three parts below.

(1) $pa_1 = (ab)_1 a_1^{-1} a_1 = (ab)_1 abb^{-1}a^{-1}.\, aa^{-1} = (ab)_1 abb^{-1}a^{-1} = (ab)_1$.

(2) $qb_1 = (ab)_1 ab_1^{-1} b_1 = (ab)_1 abb^{-1}a^{-1}.\ abb^{-1} = (ab)_1 abb^{-1}a^{-1}a = (ab)_1 a$.

(3) From (1), we have that $pp^{-1} = pa_1 (ab)_1^{-1} = (ab)_1 (ab)_1^{-1} = e$. Also $qq^{-1} = (ab)_1 ab_1^{-1} b_1 a^{-1} (ab)_1^{-1} = (ab)_1 abb^{-1}a^{-1}(ab)_1^{-1} = (ab)_1 (ab)_1^{-1} = e$. Hence $p, q \in R_e$. Furthermore, $e = a_1 a_1^{-1} = b_1 b_1^{-1}$ and so $pe = p$, $qe = q$. Thus $p, q \in P_e$.

Now let G be a group and let $\theta\colon p \mapsto \theta_p$ be an antihomomorphism of P_e into *end* G, the endomorphism semigroup of G, such that θ_e is the identity automorphism of G. In view of part (3) of the lemma we can define a multiplication in $G \times S$ by

$$(g, a)(h, b) = (g\theta_p h\theta_q, ab),$$

where

$$p = (ab)_1 a_1^{-1}, \qquad q = (ab)_1 ab_1^{-1};$$

this gives the groupoid $S^*(S, G, e, C, \theta)$.

PROOF OF THEOREM 7. (A) *$S^*(S, G, e, C, \theta)$ is a bisimple inverse semigroup which is a split extension of G by S.*

We first show that S^* is a semigroup. Let $g, h, k \in G$ and $a, b, c \in S$. Then

$$\begin{aligned}[(g, a)(h, b)](k, c) &= ((g\theta_p h\theta_q)\theta_r k\theta_s, abc) \\ &= (g\theta_{rp} h\theta_{rq} k\theta_s, abc), \end{aligned} \tag{1}$$

where

$$p = (ab)_1 a_1^{-1}, \qquad q = (ab)_1 ab_1^{-1}, \qquad r = (abc)_1 (ab)_1^{-1}, \qquad s = (abc)_1 abc_1^{-1}.$$

Also

$$\begin{aligned}(g, a)[(h, b)(k, c)] &= (g\theta_v (h\theta_t k\theta_u)\theta_w, abc) \\ &= (g\theta_v h\theta_{wt} k\theta_{wu}, abc),\end{aligned}$$

where

$$t = (bc)_1 b_1^{-1}, \qquad u = (bc)_1 bc_1^{-1}, \qquad v = (abc)_1 a_1^{-1}, \qquad w = (abc)_1 a(bc)_1^{-1}.$$

To establish associativity, it is enough to show that

$$rp = v, \qquad rq = wt, \qquad s = wu.$$

By part (1) of the lemma, with ab replacing a, c replacing b, and r replacing p, we have that $r(ab)_1 = (abc)_1$; hence

$$rp = r(ab)_1 a_1^{-1} = (abc)_1 a_1^{-1} = v.$$

Similarly,

$$rq = r(ab)_1 ab_1^{-1} = (abc)_1 ab_1^{-1}.$$

But by part (2) of the lemma, with bc replacing b and w replacing q, we have that $w(bc)_1 = (abc)_1 a$ and so

$$wt = w(bc)_1 b_1^{-1} = (abc)_1 ab_1^{-1}.$$

Hence $rq = wt$. Further,

$$wu = w(bc)_1 bc_1^{-1} = (abc)_1 abc_1^{-1} = s.$$

Thus S^* is a semigroup.

Next we show that S^* is an inverse semigroup. Let $(g, a) \in S^*$. Taking $b = a^{-1}$, $c = a$, and $k = g$ in Eq. (1) above we find that

$$(g, a)(h, a^{-1})(g, a) = (g\theta_e h\theta_x g\theta_e, a) = (g(h\theta_x) g, a), \tag{2}$$

where $x = a_1 a(a^{-1})_1^{-1}$. Now

$$\begin{aligned} x^{-1}x &= (a^{-1})_1 a^{-1} a_1^{-1} a_1 a(a^{-1})_1^{-1} = (a^{-1})_1 a^{-1} a a^{-1} a (a^{-1})_1^{-1} \\ &= (a^{-1})_1 (a^{-1})_1^{-1} = e. \end{aligned}$$

Hence $x^{-1} \in R_e$. Also $xx^{-1} = e$, since $x \in P_e$. Hence $x^{-1}e = x^{-1}$ and so $x^{-1} \in P_e$. Choose $h = g^{-1}\theta_{x^{-1}}$. Then

$$g(h\theta_x) g = g(g^{-1}\theta_{xx^{-1}}) g = g(g^{-1}\theta_e) g = gg^{-1}g = g.$$

Thus, from Eq. (2),

$$(g, a)(h, a^{-1})(g, a) = (g, a).$$

We now examine the idempotents of S^*. Let $(g, a) \in S^*$ and suppose that $(g, a)^2 = (g, a)$. Then $a^2 = a$ and $g\theta_p g\theta_q = g$, where

$$\begin{aligned} p &= (a^2)_1 a_1^{-1} = a_1 a_1^{-1} = e, \\ q &= (a^2)_1 a a_1^{-1} = a_1(aa^{-1})\, a_1^{-1} = a_1 a_1^{-1} = e. \end{aligned}$$

Hence $g^2 = g$ and so $g = 1$, the identity of G. Conversely, if $a^2 = a$, then $(1, a)^2 = (1, a)$. Thus the set of idempotents of S^* is

$$\{(1, a) \in S^*\colon a^2 = a\}.$$

Since the idempotents of S commute, it follows that so also do those of S^*. Thus S^* is an inverse semigroup.

To see that S^* is bisimple, consider any two idempotents $(1, a)$, $(1, b)$ $(a^2 = a,\ b^2 = b)$. Since S is bisimple, there exists $c \in S$ such that $cc^{-1} = a$, $c^{-1}c = b$. But $(1, c)(1, c)^{-1}$ is an idempotent in S^* and the S component of $(1, c)^{-1}$ is c^{-1}. Hence $(1, c)(1, c)^{-1} = (1, cc^{-1}) = (1, a)$. Similarly, $(1, c)^{-1}(1, c) = (1, b)$. It follows that S^* is bisimple.

Define an equivalence ρ on S^* by the rule that

$$((g, a), (h, b)) \in \rho \Leftrightarrow a = b.$$

It is immediate that ρ is a congruence on S^*. Further, from the form of the idempotents in S^* it is clear that ρ is idempotent separating. Let e^* be any idempotent in S^*; thus $e^* = (1, a)$, where $a^2 = a$. Then

$$e^*\rho = \{(g, a): g \in G\}$$

and it is easily verified that the mapping $g \mapsto (g, a)$ is an isomorphism from G to $e^*\rho$. Finally, let

$$X = \{(1, a): a \in S\}.$$

Then X is a cross section of the ρ classes of S^* and is a subsemigroup of S^* isomorphic to S. Thus S^* splits over ρ and $S^*/\rho \cong S$.

(B) *Let S be a bisimple inverse semigroup and let G be a group. Then every bisimple inverse semigroup S^* that is a split extension of G by S is isomorphic to a semigroup of the form $S^*(S, G, e, C, \theta)$.*

Let S^* be a bisimple inverse semigroup on which is defined an idempotent-separating congruence ρ such that

(1) $S^*/\rho \cong S$,

(2) $G \cong e^*\rho$ for some idempotent $e^* \in S$, and

(3) S^* splits over ρ.

We shall, without loss of generality, assume that S is a subsemigroup of S^* that is also a cross section of the ρ classes. Since $e^*\rho$ is an idempotent of S^*/ρ, the element e of S contained in $e^*\rho$ is an idempotent; hence, since ρ is idempotent separating, $e = e^*$. We shall also assume, without loss of generality, that $G = e\rho$.

Let $a \in S$ and let the $\mathscr{R}$, $\mathscr{L}$, $\mathscr{H}$ classes of S and S^* containing a be denoted by R_a, L_a, H_a and R_a^*, L_a^*, H_a^*, respectively. We shall show that $R_a = R_a^* \cap S$. Clearly $R_a \subseteq R_a^* \cap S$. Suppose now that $x \in R_a^* \cap S$. Since $x \in S$ and S is an inverse semigroup, it follows that $x \in R_{xx^{-1}}$. But $xx^{-1} = aa^{-1}$, since $xx^{-1}, aa^{-1} \in R_a^*$ and this set contains exactly one idempotent. Hence $x \in R_{aa^{-1}} = R_a$. Thus $R_a^* \cap S \subseteq R_a$ and so $R_a = R_a^* \cap S$. Similarly, $L_a = L_a^* \cap S$ and so $H_a = H_a^* \cap S$. Since S meets every $\mathscr{H}$ class of S^* (because $\rho \subseteq \mathscr{H}$), each $\mathscr{H}$ class of S^* contains exactly one $\mathscr{H}$ class of S.

Let $P_e = R_e \cap eSe$, $P_e^* = R_e^* \cap eS^*e$. Since $G = e\rho$, we have that G is a left normal divisor of P_e^*, that is, a normal subgroup of the group H_e^* such that $pG \subseteq Gp$ for all $p \in P_e^*$ [Reilly and Clifford (1968, Section 2)]. In particular, $pG \subseteq Gp$ for all $p \in P_e$, since $P_e \subseteq P_e^*$. Hence since P_e is right cancellative, we can define $\theta_p\colon G \to G$ for all $p \in P_e$ by the rule that

$$pg = (g\theta_p)\,p \qquad (g \in G). \tag{3}$$

Then θ_p is an endomorphism of G (Rees, 1948); further, for all $g \in G$ we have that $g = eg = (g\theta_e)\,e = g\theta_e$ and so θ_e is the identity automorphism of G. Define $\theta\colon G \to \mathit{end}\ G$ by setting $p\theta = \theta_p$ for all $p \in P_e$. Then, for all $g \in G$ and for all $p, q \in P_e$, we have that

$$(g\theta_{pq})\,pq = pqg = p(g\theta_q)\,q = (g\theta_q\theta_p)\,pq$$

and so, since P_e is right cancellative, $g\theta_{pq} = g\theta_q\theta_p$. Thus θ is an antihomomorphism.

Now choose a cross section C of the $\mathscr{H}$ classes of S contained in R_e. For all $a \in S$ let a_1 denote the unique element of C in $L_{aa^{-1}}$. We shall show that $S^* \cong S^*(S, G, e, C, \theta)$.

Consider the mapping $\phi\colon G \times S \to S^*$ defined by

$$(g, a)\,\phi = a_1^{-1}ga_1a.$$

We prove first that ϕ is bijective. Denote the natural homomorphism of S^* onto S by $\rho^\natural$; then

$$(a_1^{-1}ga_1a)\,\rho^\natural = a_1^{-1}ea_1a = a_1^{-1}a_1a = aa^{-1}a = a. \tag{4}$$

Now suppose that $(g, a)\,\phi = (h, b)\phi$ for $g, h \in G$ and $a, b \in S$. Then $(g, a)\,\phi\rho^\natural = (h, b)\,\phi\rho^\natural$ and so $a = b$, by Eq. (4). Hence

$$a_1(a_1^{-1}ga_1a)\,a^{-1}a_1^{-1} = b_1(b_1^{-1}hb_1b)\,b^{-1}b_1^{-1}$$

and therefore, since $a_1a_1^{-1} = b_1b_1^{-1} = e$, we have that $g = h$. Thus ϕ is injective. Now the cross section C of the $\mathscr{H}$ classes of S in R_e is also a cross section of the $\mathscr{H}$ classes of S^* in R_e^*; for each $\mathscr{H}$ class of S^* contains exactly one $\mathscr{H}$ class of S and $R_e = R_e^* \cap S$. Let $a^* \in S^*$. Then $a^* = t^{-1}xu$ for some $t, u \in C$ and $x \in H_e^*$ [see Clifford and Preston (1961, Theorem 3.4)]. But $H_e\,(= H_e^* \cap S)$ is also a cross section of the cosets of G in H_e^* and so $x = gr$ for some $g \in G$, $r \in H_e$. Thus

$$a^* = t^{-1}gru. \tag{5}$$

Write $a = t^{-1}ru$. Then $a \in S$ and

$$a_1^{-1}a_1 = aa^{-1} = t^{-1}ruu^{-1}r^{-1}t = t^{-1}rer^{-1}t = t^{-1}rr^{-1}t = t^{-1}et = t^{-1}t.$$

But a_1, $t \in C$ and so $t = a_1$. Furthermore,

$$ru = (er)u = (tt^{-1})ru = t(t^{-1}ru) = a_1 a.$$

Hence, from Eq. (5), $a^* = a_1^{-1} g a_1 a$. This shows that ϕ is surjective.

We complete the proof by showing that ϕ is an isomorphism from $S^*(S, G, e, C, \theta)$ to S^*. First, for any $a, b \in S$,

$$\begin{aligned} a_1 a b_1^{-1} &= a_1(aa^{-1}a)(bb^{-1}b_1^{-1}) \\ &= a_1 a(bb^{-1})(a^{-1}a)\, b_1^{-1} \\ &= a_1(ab)(ab)^{-1}ab_1^{-1} \\ &= a_1(ab)_1^{-1}(ab)_1 ab_1^{-1} \\ &= p^{-1}q, \end{aligned}$$

where $p = (ab)_1 a_1^{-1}$ and $q = (ab)_1 ab_1^{-1}$. By part (3) of the lemma, $p, q \in P_e$. Now, from Eq. (3), for $g, h \in G$,

$$gp^{-1} = (pg^{-1})^{-1} = [(g^{-1}\theta_p)\, p]^{-1} = p^{-1}(g^{-1}\theta_p)^{-1} = p^{-1}(g\theta_p)$$

and $qh = (h\theta_q)q$. Hence

$$\begin{aligned} (a_1^{-1} g a_1 a)(b_1^{-1} h b_1 b) &= a_1^{-1} g(p^{-1}q)\, hb_1 b \\ &= a_1^{-1}[p^{-1}(g\theta_p)][(h\theta_q)\, q]\, b_1 b \\ &= (pa_1)^{-1}(g\theta_p h\theta_q)(qb_1 b) \\ &= (ab)_1^{-1}(g\theta_p h\theta_q)(ab)_1 ab, \end{aligned}$$

by parts (1) and (2) of the lemma. Thus

$$(g, a)\phi(h, b)\phi = [(g, a)(h, b)]\phi$$

and so ϕ is an isomorphism.

This completes the proof of Theorem 7.

ACKNOWLEDGMENT

I wish to take this opportunity to thank the organizers of the Symposium for kindly inviting me to take part.

REFERENCES

Clifford, A. H. (1941). Semigroups admitting relative inverses. *Ann. Math.* [2]**42**, 1037–1049.

Clifford, A. H. (1953). A class of *d*-simple semigroups. *Amer. J. Math.* **75**, 547–556.

Clifford, A. H. and Preston, G. B. (1961). "The Algebraic Theory of Semigroups," Vol. 1 (Math. Surveys, No. 7). Amer. Math. Soc., Providence, Rhode Island.

Howie, J. M. (1964). The maximum idempotent-separating congruence on an inverse semigroup. *Proc. Edinburgh Math. Soc.* [2]**14**, 71–79.
Munn, W. D. (1966). Uniform semilattices and bisimple inverse semigroups. *Quart. J. Math. Oxford Ser.* [2]**17**, 151–159.
Munn, W. D. (1968). Regular ω-semigroups. *Glasgow Math. J.* **9**, 46–66.
Preston, G. B. (1954). Inverse semi-groups. *J. London Math. Soc.* **29**, 396–403.
Rees, D. (1940). On semi-groups. *Proc. Cambridge Philos. Soc.* **36**, 387–400.
Rees, D. (1948). On the ideal structure of a semi-group satisfying a cancellation law. *Quart. J. Math. Oxford Ser.* [2]**19**, 101–108.
Reilly, N. R. (1966). Bisimple ω-semigroups. *Proc. Glasgow Math. Assoc.* **7**, 160–167.
Reilly, N. R. (1968). Bisimple inverse semigroups. *Trans. Amer. Math. Soc.* **132**, 101–114.
Reilly, N. R. and Clifford, A. H. (1968). Bisimple inverse semigroups as semigroups of ordered triples. *Canad. J. Math.* **20**, 25–39.
Vagner, V. V. (1952). Generalized groups (in Russian). *Dokl. Akad. Nauk SSSR* **84**, 1119–1122.
Warne, R. J. (1967). Bisimple inverse semigroups mod groups. *Duke Math. J.* **34**, 787–811.
Warne, R. J. (1968). *I*-bisimple semigroups. *Trans. Amer. Math. Soc.* **130**, 367–386.

*Algebraic Theory of Finite Semigroups**

Structure Numbers and Structure Theorems for Finite Semigroups

JOHN RHODES[†]

Department of Mathematics
University of California
Berkeley, California

1. Introduction

All semigroups considered are of finite order.

Herein we wish to state some structure theorem and define some structure numbers for finite semigroups. We give few proofs—mostly references. We consider complexity, p length, and Jordan-Hölder theorems valid for finite semigroups. The kernel of the ideas presented here first was given by Krohn *et al.* [*12*] (see especially the introduction). Arbib, Krohn, Rhodes, and Tilson, in the recent book "Algebraic Theory of Machines, Languages, and Semigroups" [*14*, Chapters 1, 5–9] exposite the relevant basic semigroup theory, define complexity, and obtain definitive results for determining the complexity of a semigroup which is a union of groups. The reader is referred to the above volume for extensive background although this paper is reasonably self-contained (modulo proofs) (see also [*21–24*]).

In the following, *Theorem* means there exists a proof, perhaps unpublished. *Conjecture* means there will probably exist a proof soon, but there is none yet. *Fantasy* means fantasy.

This paper will have served its purpose if the uninitiated are given a road map of the existing theory or the experts are led to new questions,

* This research was sponsored in part by the United States Air Force, Office of Scientific Research, Grant Number AF-AFOSR-68-1477.

[†] Alfred P. Sloan Research Fellow.

and possibly some new answers. We offer here some new questions and some new ways to generate questions (see Section 3). In short the purpose is an attempt to create more understanding of the structure of finite semigroups.

In the last section some very brief indication is given of how these ideas and theorems for finite semigroups might possibly be extended to compact semigroups.

2. The Prime Decomposition Theorem for Finite Semigroups

S, S_1, T, T', etc. denote finite semigroups. We write $S \mid T$, read S divides T, if and only if S is a homomorphic image of a subsemigroup $T' \leqslant T$, i.e., $S \twoheadleftarrow \leqslant T$. Group theorists often say "section" instead of "divide."

Let Y: $S_1 \to \text{Endo}(S_2)$ be a homomorphism with $Y(s_1)(s_2)$ written as ${}^{s_1}(s_2)$. Thus ${}^{s_1 s_1'}(s_2) = {}^{s_1}({}^{s_1'}(s_2))$ and ${}^{s_1}(s_2 s_2') = {}^{s_1}(s_2){}^{s_1}(s_2')$. Then $S_2 \times_Y S_1$, read the *semidirect product* of S_2 by S_1 with respect to the connecting homomorphism Y, is the semigroup with elements $S_2 \times S_1$ and multiplication $(s_2, s_1) \cdot (s_2', s_1') = (s_2\, {}^{s_1}(s_2'), s_1 s_1')$.

In the following $S_n \times_Y S_{n-1} \times_Y \cdots \times_Y S_1$ denotes

$$(\cdots (S_n \times_{Y_{n-1}} S_{n-1}) \times_{Y_{n-2}} \cdots \times_{Y_1} S_1)$$

for some Y_{n-1}: $S_{n-1} \to \text{Endo}(S_n)$, Y_{n-2}: $S_{n-2} \to \text{Endo}(S_n \times_{Y_{n-1}} S_{n-1})$, etc.

Let X be a finite, nonempty set. Then X^r denotes the semigroup with elements X and multiplication $ab = b$ all $a, b \in X$. S^I denotes a semigroup S with an I adjoined as an identity. By definition $U_3 = \{a, b\}^{rI}$ so

U_3	I	a	b
I	I	a	b
a	a	a	b
b	b	a	b

From a machine theoretic point of view U_3 is a flip-flop.

By definition UNITS $= \{S$: S divides $U_3\}$. Thus, up to isomorphism there are four units, namely $U_0 = \{a\} \cong \{0\}$, $U_1 = \{a, b\}^r$, $U_2 = \{a\}^I \cong \{b\}^I \cong \{0\}^I$, and U_3.

By definition PRIMES $= \{G\colon G$ is a finite simple group and $G \neq \{1\}\}$ PRIMES$(S) = \{P \in$ PRIMES and $P \mid S\}$. If $\mathcal{S}$ is a collection of semigroups, then PRIMES$(\mathcal{S}) = U\{$PRIMES$(S)\colon S \in \mathcal{S}\}$.

By definition $S \in$ IRR, read S is irreducible, if and only if $S \mid S_2 \times_Y S_1$ implies $S \mid S_2$ or $S \mid S_1$.

The following theorem is the starting place for all that follows.

(2.1) **Theorem.** (a) Let S be given. Then

$$S \text{ divides } S_n \times_Y S_{n-1} \times_Y \cdots \times_Y S_1 \tag{2.1}$$

for some $S_n, \ldots, S_1$ and some Y's such that each $S_i = U_3$ or S_i is a Jordan-Hölder factor of a maximal subgroup of S. In particular $S_i \in$ UNITS $\cup$ PRIMES(S) for $i = 1, \ldots, n$.

(b) PRIMES $\cup$ UNITS $=$ IRR.

Theorem 2.1 was first stated and proved by Krohn and Rhodes in 1962 [*9*, *11*]. Zeiger gave another proof [*30*]. For a recent exposition see Chapters 4 and 5 [*14*].

Noteworthy special cases of Theorem 2.1 are the following. By definition say C is a *combinatorial* semigroup if and only if the maximal subgroups of C are singletons or equivalently PRIMES(C) is empty.

(2.2) **Corollary.** C is combinatorial if and only if

$$C \text{ divides } U_3 \times_Y \cdots \times_Y U_3 \tag{2.2}$$

for some Y's.

For some applications of Corollary 2 see Section 5.5 by Krohn *et al.* [*14*] or Section 1 by Rhodes [*19*] and Lemma 3.4 of Rhodes and Tilson [*24*].

Let $\mathcal{S}$ be a collection of semigroups. Let $K(\mathcal{S})$ denote the closure of $\mathcal{S}$ under division and semidirect product, i.e., $K(\mathcal{S}) = \bigcap\{\mathcal{S}'\colon \mathcal{S} \subseteq \mathcal{S}'$ and $S_1, S_2 \in \mathcal{S}'$ implies $S_2 \times_Y S_1 \in \mathcal{S}'$, and $S \in \mathcal{S}'$ and T divides S implies $T \in \mathcal{S}'\}$ (see Section 5.2 of Krohn *et al.* [*14*]).

Then we have the following.

(2.3) **Corollary.** (1) K(PRIMES) $=$ all finite groups.

(2) $K(U_3) =$ all combinatorial semigroups.

(3) $K(\text{PRIMES} \cup U_3) =$ all finite semigroups.

(4) $S \in K(\mathcal{S} \cup U_3)$ if and only if PRIMES$(S) \subseteq$ PRIMES$(\mathcal{S})$.

For details see Chapter 5 by Krohn *et al.* [*14*].

3. The Plot

Since, $K(\text{PRIMES} \cup U_3) =$ all finite semigroups by Corollary 2.3, we see that all finite semigroups are constructed (via semidirect product and division) by putting together two dissimilar basic types of semigroups, namely simple groups and U_3, respectively. But $K(\text{PRIMES}) =$ all finite groups and $K(U_3) =$ all finite combinatorial semigroups so we can lump together the consecutive simple groups and lump together the consecutive U_3's. Thus we can take the basic types to be groups and combinatorial semigroups, respectively. Otherwise stated, we have that semidirect products and divisors of groups are groups and that semidirect products and divisors of combinatorial semigroups are combinatorial. Thus Theorem 2.1 implies that for each S we can solve

$$S \text{ divides } C_{n+1} \times_Y G_n \times_Y C_{n-1} \times_Y \cdots \times_Y C_1 \times_Y G_1 \times_Y C_0$$

for some $C_{n+1}, \ldots, C_0, G_1, \ldots, G_n$ where $C_{n+1}, \ldots, C_0$ are combinatorial semigroups and $G_n, \ldots, G_1$ are groups.

In this situation algebraic esthetic sense dictates that one classify the objects (in this case semigroups) by the minimal number of alternations of the two basic types required to construct the given object. This algebraic plot is often used. For example, if the objects are logical formulas (well-formed formulas) and the basic elements are $\exists$ and $\forall$, then the number of alternations of $\exists$ and $\forall$ form the basis for logical hierarchies. If the objects are taken to be p-solvable groups (see Hall and Higman [6]; Section 5 and the Appendix) and the basic types p groups and p' groups, then the p length is the number of alternations required (where we count only the number of p groups) (see Section 5). This definition agrees with the standard group theoretic definition.

Sometimes the algebraic objects can be built from only one basic type of object and in this case we simply count the minimal number of basic terms required.

For example, if the objects are solvable groups and the basic type of object is nilpotent group, then this leads to the Fitting length defined as usual. Let $F(G)$ be the unique maximal nilpotent normal subgroup of G (it exists!). Let $F_0(G) = \{1\}$ and $F_{n+1}(G) = F(G/F_n(G))$ considered as a normal subgroup of G [i.e., $F_{n+1}(G) = \mathcal{N}^{-1}[F(G/F_n(G))]$ where $\mathcal{N}: G \twoheadrightarrow G/F(G)$]. Then the Fitting length of G is the smallest integer n so that $F_n(G) = \{1\}$. It is revealing that the Fitting length of $G \neq \{1\}$ can be defined as the smallest integer n so that

$$G \text{ divides } N_n \times_Y \cdots \times_Y N_1$$

where $N_1, \ldots, N_n$ are nilpotent groups.

An example from semigroup theory we will use is where the objects are combinatorial semigroups and the basic objects are bands (equals semigroups S such that $s^2 = s$ for all $s \in S$). Then the *band length* of the combinatorial semigroup C is the smallest positive integer n so that

$$C \text{ divides } B_n \times_Y \cdots \times_Y B_1$$

where $B_n, \ldots, B_1$ are bands.

In summary, the plot is to construct via semidirect products and division certain semigroups S from the basic class X or from the basic classes Y and Z. Then count the minimal number of X's required or the minimal number of alternations of Y and Z's required to obtain S and classify the objects S via this structure number. To be useful S, X, Y, and Z should possess the following properties. All four classes should be closed under division and direct products while S is closed under semidirect products and X, Y, and Z are not closed under semidirect products.

In this paper we will consider the combinations given in Table I.

TABLE I

Objects	Basic types	Structure number	Section
Semigroups	Groups, combinatorials	Group complexity, $\#_G(S)$	4
π-solvable semigroups	π groups, π' semigroups	π length, $l_\pi(S)$	5 and Appendix
Combinatorial semigroups	Bands	Band length, $\#_B(C)$	6
Semigroups	Union of groups Semigroups	Union of group length, $\#_e(S)$	6

Now the theorems take the form of axiomitizing the functions $\#_G$, l_π, etc., or relating $\#_G(S)$, etc. to other properties of S defined in terms of homomorphisms or subsemigroups of S. This is an old and good plot in group theory (see, for example, Hall and Higman [*6*]).

The assertion here is that these are good questions since they lead to interesting new theorems involving the structure of finite semigroups.

An obvious but very important extention of these ideas is to consider equations of the form (2.1) but with the semidirect product replaced by a wreath product (see Section 7) and then count the minimal number of simple groups occurring (with repetitions). We are thus led to Jordan-Hölder-type theorems for semigroups (see Section 7).

The plot has been laid. We now introduce the *dramatis personae.*

4. Complexity

Definition. Let S be given. Then $\#_G(S)$, read the (group) complexity of S, is the smallest nonnegative integer n such that

(4.1) S divides $C_{n+1} \times_Y G_n \times_Y C_{n-1} \times_Y \cdots \times_Y C_1 \times_Y G_1 \times_Y C_0$

where $C_{n+1}, \ldots, C_0$ are combinatorial semigroups (or equivalently by Corollary 2.2, C_k satisfies 2.2) and $G_n, \ldots, G_1$ are groups. For extensive background see Krohn *et al.* [*14*, Chapter 5].

REMARK. Complexity was first defined by Rhodes around 1963 and the first theorems were published by Krohn and Rhodes [*12*; *14*, Chapter 9]. Recent contributions to the theory of complexity have been given by Allen [*1*], Rhodes [*22–24*], Stiffler [*26*], Tilson [*24*, *27*], and Zalcstein [*28*]. In Chapter 9 by Krohn *et al.* [*14*] complexity for semigroups that are union of groups is exhaustivally studied.

Let $N = \{0, 1, 2, \ldots\}$ denote the nonnegative integers. Let $\mathscr{S}$ denote the collection of all finite semigroups. Then

$$\#_G: \mathscr{S} \to N.$$

The following elementary properties are obvious.

(4.2)a $\#_G(S) = 0$ if and only if S is combinatorial.

(4.2)b If $G \neq 1$ is a group, then $\#_G(S) = 1$.

(4.2)c $S \mid T$ implies $\#_G(S) \leqslant \#_G(T)$.

Examples. (4.3)a(1) $\#_G$(Abelian semigroup) $\leqslant 1$.

(2) $\#_G$(inverse semigroup) $\leqslant 1$ (Tilson) and more generally,

(3) If $\{a, b\}^r = U_1$ does not divide S, then $\#_G(S) \leqslant 1$ (see Rhodes and Tilson [*24*]).

(4.3)b $\#_G$(0-simple semigroup) $\leqslant 1$. (See Arbib *et al.* [*14*, Section 6.17]).

(4.3)c Let $G \neq 1$ be a group. Let $(2^G, \cdot)$ be the set of all subsets of G under the usual multiplication of subsets, $X \cdot Y = \{x \cdot y: x \in X$ and $y \in Y\}$. Then

$$\#_G(2^G) = 1.$$

This follows since it can be verified that the regular principal factors of 2^G are 0-simple inverse semigroups. Thus $\{a, b\}^r$ cannot divide 2^G and the result follows from (4.3)a(3).

(4.3)d Let $X_n = \{1, \ldots, n\}$ and let $F_R(X_n)$ denote the semigroup of all functions of X_n into itself under the composition $(f \cdot g)(n) = g(f(n))$, i.e., consider the functions as acting on the right of X_n. Then

$$\#_G(F_R(X_n)) = n - 1$$

(see Rhodes [*19*, Section 5]).

(4.3)e Let F be a finite field. Let $\mathscr{M}(n, F)$ denote the semigroup of all $n \times n$ matrices with coefficients in F under matrix multiplication. Then if $|F| > 2$,

$$\#_G(\mathscr{M}(n, F)) = n.$$

In fact, let $\mathscr{SRM}(n, F)$ be the subsemigroup of strictly row-monomial matrices (i.e., nonzero exactly once in each row). Then if $|F| > 2$, we have

$$\#_G(\mathscr{SRM}(n, F)) = n.$$

We will give a proof of (4.3)e later. (See above Corollary (4.26).)

(4.3)f Let $G \neq 1$ be a group, and let n be a positive integer. Then there exists a semigroup S such that (1) S is a union of groups, each isomorphic to G, and (2) $\#_G(S) = n$ (see Krohn and Rhodes [*12*, Remark 7.1]).

(4.3)g Let $\wr$ denote a wreath product (to be defined in Section 7) Then for nontrivial groups $G_1, \ldots, G_n$ we have

$$\#_G((U_3, U_3) \wr (G_n, G_n) \wr (U_3, U_3) \wr \cdots \wr (G_1, G_1) \wr (U_3, U_3)) = n$$

see Arbib *et al.* [*14*, Theorem 6.2.10].

Given a semigroup S, we wish to determine its complexity $\#_G$. More generally we ask what general properties does the function $\#_G\colon \mathscr{S} \to N$ possess? In particular could we axiomitize $\#_G$?

Let $p_j\colon S_1 \times \cdots \times S_n \twoheadrightarrow S_j$ be the jth projection epimorphism. We write $S \leqslant\leqslant S_1 \times \cdots \times S_n$, read S is a subdirect product of $S_1, \ldots, S_n$ if and only if S is isomorphic with a subsemigroup $S' \leqslant S_1 \times \cdots \times S_n$ such that $p_j(S') = S_j$ for $j = 1, \ldots, n$.

Let θ: $\mathscr{S} \to N$ then:

(4.4) **Axiom I.** Let $S \leqslant\leqslant S_1 \times \cdots \times S_n$. Then

$$\theta(S) = \max\{\theta(S_i): i = 1, \ldots, n\}.$$

Proposition. $\#_G$ satisfies Axiom I. The proof is easy; see Arbib *et al.* [*14*, Section 6.2.2(c)].

The importance of Axiom I is that it is sufficient to compute $\theta(S)$ only for those S which are subdirectly indecomposible (i.e., $S \leqslant\leqslant S_1 \times \cdots \times S_n$ implies $S \cong S_j$ for some j). We will see later that the subdirectly indecomposible semigroups have some rather special and useful properties (see Krohn *et al.* [*14*, Section 8.2.19]).

(4.5) **Axiom II.** (fundamental lemma of complexity). Let I be a combinatorial ideal of S. Then $\theta(S) = \theta(S/I)$; $\theta(\{0\}) = 0$.

Here S/I denotes the usual Rees quotient [*2*, *14*].

We wish to reformulate Axiom I and Axiom II in a more revealing, but equivalent, form. To do this we need to introduce some basic results on homomorphisms.

(4.6) **Notation and Examples.** (4.6)a θ: $S \twoheadrightarrow T$ denotes that θ as an epimorphism (equals, throughout this paper, onto homorphism) of S onto T.

(4.6)b θ: $S \underset{\gamma}{\twoheadrightarrow} T$ denotes θ: $S \twoheadrightarrow T$ and that θ is one-to-one when restricted to each subgroup of S.

Important sources of γ epimorphisms are the following.

(4.6)b(1) Example. Let C be a combinatorial semigroup. Then $S = C \times_Y T \underset{\gamma}{\twoheadrightarrow} T$ (see Krohn *et al.* [*14*, Section 8.3.24(b)]).

(4.6)b(2) Example. Clearly $S \underset{\gamma}{\twoheadrightarrow} S/I$ if and only if I is combinatorial.

In all that follows α denotes one of the Green relations $\alpha = \mathscr{L}$, $\mathscr{R}$, $\mathscr{H}$, or $\mathscr{J}$. Then

(4.6)c θ: $S \underset{\gamma(\alpha)}{\twoheadrightarrow} T$ denotes that θ is one to one when restricted to each α class of S.

(4.6)c(1) Example. Let C be a combinatorial semigroup. Then $S = C \times_Y T \underset{\gamma(\mathscr{H})}{\twoheadrightarrow} T$ (see Krohn *et al.* [*14*, 8.3.24(b)]).

(4.6)d θ: $S \underset{\alpha}{\twoheadrightarrow} T$ if and only if $\theta(s_1) = \theta(s_2)$ implies $s_1 \,\alpha\, s_2$.

(4.6)d(1) Example. Let S be a semigroup which is a union of groups. Let $(2^S, \bigcap)$ denote the semigroup of all subsets of S under intersection. Let φ: $S \to 2^S$ be defined by $\varphi(\alpha) = S^1 s S^1$. Then φ is a homomorphism and $\varphi: S \underset{\mathscr{J}}{\twoheadrightarrow} \varphi(S)$. This result is due to Clifford (see Rhodes and Tilson [*14*, 7.22.4], or Clifford and Preston [*2*]).

The most important source of $\mathscr{L}$ epimorphisms is shown by the following.

(4.6)d(2) EXAMPLES. Let G be a group, T a monoid, $Y: T \rightarrow \text{Endo}(G)$, with $Y(1)$ the identity mapping. Then

$$G \times_Y T \underset{\mathscr{L}}{\twoheadrightarrow} T$$

The restriction of an α epimorphism to a subsemigroup is not necessarily an α epimorphism again. To remedy this defect we introduce the following.

(4.6)e $\theta: S \underset{\alpha'}{\twoheadrightarrow} T$ if and only if s_1 and s_2 are regular elements of S (for definitions see Arbib [*14*] or Clifford and Preston [*2*]) and $\theta(s_1) = \theta(s_2)$ implies $s_1 \alpha s_2$. See Krohn *et al.* [*14*, Chapter 8].

We then have the following.

(4.7) **Proposition.** The restriction on an α' epimorphism to a subsemigroup is an α' epimorphism.

PROOF. See the proof in Tilson's appendix to this paper, Proposition 4.13, and Krohn *et al.* [*14*, 8.3.9].

Some basic results about homomorphisms are as follows.

(4.8) **Proposition.** Let $\theta: S \twoheadrightarrow T$. Then θ can be written as $\theta = \theta_n \cdots \theta_1$ where each θ_j is an epimorphism and $\theta_1, \theta_3, \theta_5, \ldots$ are $\gamma(\mathscr{H})$ epimorphisms and $\theta_2, \theta_4, \theta_6, \ldots$ are $\mathscr{H}$ epimorphisms.

An equivalent reformulation of Proposition 4.8 is the following.

By definition the epimorphism θ is a maximal proper epimorphism (MPE) if and only if $\theta = \theta_2\theta_1$ implies exactly one of θ_2, θ_1 is one-to-one.

(4.8)′ **Proposition.** θ a MPE implies θ is either a $\gamma(H)$ or an $\mathscr{H}$ epimorphism.

See Krohn *et al.* [*14*, 8.1.14] or Rhodes [*19*] for a proof of Proposition 4.8.

(4.9) **Proposition.** There exists a functorially minimal γ image of S, i.e., there exists $S \underset{\gamma}{\twoheadrightarrow} S^\gamma$ such that given $\theta: S \underset{\gamma}{\twoheadrightarrow} T$ there exists $\varphi: T \twoheadrightarrow S^\gamma$ so that $\varphi\theta$ equals $S \underset{\gamma}{\twoheadrightarrow} S^\gamma$. Automatically φ is a γ epimorphism.

PROOF. See Rhodes [*19*, Section 6] or Krohn *et al.* [*14*, 8.3.12]. Also see Tilson's Appendix to this paper.

In the following let β denote any of α or α' as α ranges over the four Green relations.

(4.10) **Proposition.** There exists a functorially minimal β image of S, i.e., there exists $S \underset{\beta}{\twoheadrightarrow} S^\beta$ such that given $\theta: S \underset{\beta}{\twoheadrightarrow} T$ there exists $\varphi: T \twoheadrightarrow S^\beta$ so that $\varphi\theta$ equals $S \underset{\beta}{\twoheadrightarrow} S^\beta$. Automatically φ is a β epimorphism.

Proof. If $\beta = \alpha$, let $\equiv$ be the congruence on S given by $s_1 \equiv s_2$ if and only if $(ss_1r)\,\alpha\,(ss_2r)$ for all $s, r \in S^1$. Then it is well known and obvious that $S \underset{\alpha}{\twoheadrightarrow} S^\alpha$ is given by $S \twoheadrightarrow S/\equiv$.

For the α' cases see Krohn *et al.* [*14*, Section 8.3.9] and Tilson's appendix to this paper, Proposition 4.14.

Remarks on Epimorphisms. For an analysis of $\mathscr{H}$ epimorphisms see Munn [*18*] and Rhodes [*21*, Section 5]. The collection of all $\mathscr{H}$ epimorphisms on S form a modular lattice (in fact, every two such congruences commute) with a one and a zero. Each $\mathscr{H}$ epimorphism θ satisfies a homomorphism theorem equally as well as for groups in the sense that a finite sequence, ker θ, of normal subgroups of the Schützenberger groups associated with S can be assigned to θ in such a way that ker θ determines θ in a natural manner. No such theorem is valid for $\gamma(\mathscr{H})$ epimorphisms. However, quoting from the introduction of Rhodes [*21*]:

> Clearly every epimorphism θ which is not one-to-one can be written as $\theta = \theta_n \cdots \theta_1$ with each θ_k an MPE. The above results imply that each MPE is a $\gamma(\mathscr{H})$-epimorphism or an $\mathscr{H}$-epimorphism. Further, $\cdots$ every MPE θ has a $\mathscr{J}$-class J in its domain such that θ is one-to-one on the complement of J. Thus an analysis of θ via the Green-Rees theorems applied to J is available. This allows us to prove $\cdots$ that each MPE lies in exactly one of four classes I, II, III, or IV. Class I is the class of the $\mathscr{H}$-epimorphisms, and classes II, III and IV subdivide the MPE's which are $\gamma(\mathscr{H})$-epimorphisms.
>
> The above classification of MPE's is ... useful in proving (and discovering) statements true for all finite semigroups by the popular method of considering the "minimal counter-example" (i.e., induction) and then applying the classification theorem. Of course the statement is valid by induction for each MPE image, so that it is necessary only to "pull the statement through the MPE" via the classification theorem for MPE (thus contradicting the existence of a counter-example). The recent results announced by the author in [22, 23] are proved by the aid of this technique.

Also see Rhodes [*21*, Section 5], Krohn *et al.* [*14*, Chapter 8], and Tilson's appendix to this paper for further results on epimorphisms.

Our promised reformulation of Axiom II is the following.

(4.11) **Axiom II′.** If $S \underset{\gamma}{\twoheadrightarrow} T$, then $\theta(S) = \theta(T)$.

We have the following.

(4.12) **Proposition.** Axiom I and Axiom II are equivalent with Axiom I and Axiom II′.

PROOF. See Krohn *et al.* [*14*, 9.3.4].

(4.13) **Theorem.**† $\#_G$ satisfies Axiom II. Thus $\#_G$ satisfies Axioms I, II, and II′.

PROOF. See Rhodes [*22*, *23*], and Note Added in Proof.

REMARKS. The axioms for complexity were first formulated by Rhodes and first appeared in Krohn and Rhodes [*12*] and Krohn *et al.* [*14*, Chapter 9]. For semigroups which are union of groups Axiom II was first verified by Krohn and Rhodes [*12*]. See also Krohn *et al.* [*14*, Chapter 9] for another exposition. Rhodes [*22*] gave the first proof for arbitrary finite semigroups.† See Rhodes [*23*] for a discussion of the long messy proof. Rhodes [*22*] has shown that it is sufficient to prove that $S \underset{\gamma(\mathscr{H})}{\twoheadrightarrow} T$ implies $\#_G(S) = \#_G(T)$.† To prove this, an algebraic form of Zeiger's proof of Theorem 2.1 given by Zeiger [*30*] or Zeiger [*14*, Chapter 4] is utilized together with the classification of MPE given by Rhodes [*21*] and the machine methods of Krohn *et al.* [*14*, Chapter 5]. Allen [*1*] also algebraitizes Zeiger's proof but in such a manner that simultaneously generalizes Rees construction and Zeiger's construction.

We now give some corollaries of Axiom II for $\#_G$.

(4.14) **Corollary.**† $S \underset{\mathscr{L}'}{\twoheadrightarrow} T$ implies $\#_G(T) \leqslant \#_G(S) \leqslant \#_G(T) + 1$.

PROOF. (For notation and terminology see Krohn *et al.* [*14*, Chapter 8] and the appendix of this paper.) Let $Q(RM) = \text{glb}\{Q' : Q'$ is a congruence on S and S/Q' a RM semigroup$\}$. Define $S^{RM} = S/Q(RM)$. Then it is easy to verify that

$$S^{RM} \cong (RM_{J_1} \times \cdots \times RM_{J_n})\, \Delta(S)$$

where $J_1, \ldots, J_n$ runs over the regular $\mathscr{J}$ classes of S (by mimicking the proof of Krohn *et al.* [*14*, 8.3.4]) and $S \underset{\gamma}{\twoheadrightarrow} S^{RM}$ since RM_{J_k} is one-to-one on the subgroups of J_k. Now by Krohn *et al.* [*14*, 8.2.17(b)] $T = RM_{J_k}(S) \leqslant (G_k{}^0, R(G_k{}^0)) \text{ w } (B_k{}^0, RLM_{J_k}(T))$, where G_k is a maximal subgroup of S contained in J_k. Thus:

$$\begin{aligned} S^{RM} &\leqslant\leqslant RM_{J_1}(S) \times \cdots \times RM_{J_n}(S) \\ &\leqslant (G_1{}^0, R(G_1{}^0)) \text{ w } (B_1{}^0, RLM_{J_1}(RM_{J_1}(S)) \times \cdots \\ &\qquad \times (G_n{}^0, R(G_n{}^0)) \text{ w } (B_n{}^0, RLM_{J_n}(RM_{J_n}(S)). \end{aligned}$$

† See Note Added in Proof, page 162.

But by Krohn *et al.* [*14*, 8.3.6(c), 8.3.9(c)]

$$S^{\mathscr{L}'} \leqslant\leqslant RLM_{J_1}(S) \times \cdots \times RLM_{J_n}(S)$$

and thus $\#_G(S^{\mathscr{L}'}) = \max_k \#_G(RLM_{J_k}(S))$ by Axiom I. Then $\#_G(S) = \#_G(S^{RM})$ by Axiom II and $\#_G(S^{RM}) = \max_k \#_G(RM_{J_k}(S))$ by Axiom I and $\max_k(\#_G(RM_{J_k}(S))) \leqslant \max_k(\#_G(RLM(S_{J_k})) + 1)$ by Eqs. (4.15), and this last expression equals $\#_G(S^{\mathscr{L}'}) + 1$. Thus $\#_G(S) \leqslant \#_G(S^{\mathscr{L}'}) + 1$. The corollary now follows immediately.

We are now able to state and prove the following beautiful corollary.

(4.16) **Corollary.**† (continuity of complexity with respect to homomorphisms). Let $\theta: S \twoheadrightarrow T$, with $\#_G(S) = n \geqslant k = \#_G(T)$. Then there exists $S = S_n \twoheadrightarrow S_{n-1} \twoheadrightarrow S_{n-2} \twoheadrightarrow \cdots \twoheadrightarrow S_k = T$ so that the composite epimorphism is θ and $\#_G(S_j) = j$ for $j = k, k+1, \ldots, n$.

PROOF. Let $\theta: S \twoheadrightarrow T$ be a MPE. It clearly suffices to show that $\#_G(S) \leqslant \#_G(T) + 1$. But by Proposition 4.8 θ is either a $\gamma(\mathscr{H})$ or an $\mathscr{L}$ epimorphism. Now use Axiom II′ and Corollary 4.14.

(4.17) **Corollary.**† $\#_G(S) = \max\{\#_G(\varphi(S)): \varphi$ is an irreducible complex matrix representation of $S\}$.

PROOF. The direct sum of the φ's give a γ epimorphism by Rhodes [*20*]. Now use Axiom II′.

Many functions $\theta: \mathscr{S} \to N$ satisfy Axioms I and II. For example, θ identically zero; $\theta(S) = 1$ if S is noncombinatorial and $\theta(S) = 0$ if S is combinatorial; $\#_G$. See Remark (4.50) for other examples. We wish to introduce a third axiom which will make θ unique (if it exists at all). See Krohn *et al.* [*14*, Chapter 9].

S is a group mapping (GM) semigroup if and only if S has a unique 0-minimal noncombinatorial ideal I so that S acts faithfully on I by right multiplication and also by left multiplication. $RLM(S)$, where S is a GM semigroup, is the action made faithful of S by right multiplication on the principal left ideals of I.

We have in general:

(4.18) **Proposition.** Let S be a GM semigroup. Then $RLM(S) = S^{\mathscr{L}'}$ and

(4.18)(1) $$\#_G(S) = \#_G(S^{\mathscr{L}'}) + 1$$

or

(4.18)(2) $$\#_G(S) = \#_G(S^{\mathscr{L}'}).$$

† See Note Added in Proof, page 162.

PROOF. $RLM(S) = S^{\mathscr{L}'}$ follows from Krohn *et al.* [*14*, 8.3.25(d)]. The remainder follows from Krohn *et al.* [*14*, 8.2.17(b)].

Let $\mathscr{P}$ be a property of semigroups, i.e., $\mathscr{P} \subseteq \mathscr{S}$ and $S \in \mathscr{P}$, $S \cong T$ implies $T \in \mathscr{P}$. We now state:

(4.19) **Axiom III.** (with respect to $\mathscr{P}$). Let $S \neq 1$ be a GM semigroup. Then

$$\theta(S) = \begin{cases} \theta(RLM(S)) + 1 & \text{if } S \in \mathscr{P} \\ \theta(RLM(S)) & \text{if } S \notin \mathscr{P}. \end{cases}$$

(4.20) **Proposition.** Let $\mathscr{T}$ be a collection of semigroups closed under homomorphic images. Let $\mathscr{P}$ be a property of semigroups. Then there exists at most one function $\theta\colon \mathscr{T} \to N$ such that θ satisfies Axioms I, II, and III with respect to $\mathscr{P}$. θ, when it exists, is called a G-complexity function for $\mathscr{T}$ with respect to $\mathscr{P}$.

PROOF. See Krohn *et al.* [*14*, 9.1.3].

(4.21) **Definition.** S is a pure group mapping (PGM) semigroup if and only if S is GM semigroup and (4.18)(1) holds for S.

We have:

(4.22) **Theorem.**† $\#_G$ is the unique G-complexity function for $\mathscr{S}$ with respect to pure.

We clearly obtain:

(4.23) **Corollary.**† $\#_G(S)$ equals the longest nonnegative integer n such that there exists a series

$$S \twoheadrightarrow PGM_1 \twoheadrightarrow RLM(PGM_1) \twoheadrightarrow \cdots \twoheadrightarrow PGM_n \twoheadrightarrow RLM(PGM_n) \tag{4.24}$$

where PGM_k denotes a PGM semigroup ($\neq 1$) for $k = 1, \ldots, n$.

PROOF. First $n \leqslant \#_G(S)$ follows from the definition of PGM. The reverse inequality $\#_G(S) \leqslant n$ follows from Krohn *et al.* [*14*, 8.2.19(b)], Axiom II, and the definition of PGM. See the proof of Theorem 9.2.5 of Krohn *et al.* [*14*].

From Corollary 4.23 we see that one approach to computing complexity is to give a criterion for PGM. In this direction we have:

(4.25) **Proposition.** Let $S \neq 1$ be a GM semigroup with respect to the 0-minimal ideal I.

(a) Suppose $S^{\mathscr{I}'}$ is combinatorial, e.g., S is a union of groups. Then S is a PGM semigroup.

† See Note Added in Proof, page 162.

(b) Suppose the idempotents from any two distinct nonzero $\mathscr{L}$ classes of I generate a noncombinatorial subsemigroup of I. Then S is a *PGM* semigroup.

PROOF. For (a) see Tilson's Appendix, Corollary 5.8.

We next outline a proof of (b). (For terminology, see Krohn *et al.* [*14*]). By Rees theorem $I \cong \mathscr{M}^0(G; A, B; C)$. We notice that the idempotents of two distinct $\mathscr{L}$ classes $b_1, b_2 \in B$ generate a noncombinatorial subsemigroup of I if and only if there exists no normalization of C such that $C(b_k, a) \in \{0, 1\}$ for all $a \in A$, $k = 1, 2$. Thus the hypothesis of (b) is equivalent with the assertion that no two distinct rows of C can be normalized to zeros and ones. When two rows b_1 and b_2 can be so normalized, we write $b_1 \equiv b_2$.

Now it is obvious that if $S \neq 1$ is a non-*PGM* semigroup, then $C(S) \neq (\mathbf{G}, n)$ for some n since $C(RLM(S)) = (\mathbf{C}, k)$ for some k by Krohn *et al.* [*14*, Lemma 9.2.8]. Further, $n \leqslant k + 1$ by Krohn *et al.* [*14*, 8.2.17].

Now suppose by way of contradiction that S satisfies the conditions of (b) but S is not a *PGM* semigroup. Then

$$S \text{ divides } C_m \wr G_{m-1} \wr C_{m-2} \wr G_{m-3} \wr \cdots = T$$

where $C_m, C_{m-2}, \ldots$ are combinatorial semigroups and $G_{m-1}, G_{m-3}, \ldots$ are nontrivial groups. Further, we can assume m is as small as possible subject to the above. We suppose $S \overset{\theta}{\twoheadleftarrow} T' \leqslant T$. Let $I^{\#} = I - \{0\}$ and let J be the unique minimal $\mathscr{J}$ class of T' contained in $\theta^{-1}(I^{\#})$. Then $\theta(J) = I^{\#}$. Let $p_{-1}: C_m \wr G_{m-1} \wr \cdots \twoheadrightarrow G_{m-1} \wr C_{m-2} \wr G_{m-3} \wr \cdots$ be the natural projection epimorphism. Let p also denote p_{-1} restricted to T'. Let J' be the unique $\mathscr{J}$ class of $p(T')$ containing $p(J)$. Since $I^{\#}$ is regular, $I^{\#}$, J, and J' are all regular $\mathscr{J}$ classes. By Rees theorem $I^0 \cong \mathscr{M}(G; A, B; C)$, $J^0 \cong \mathscr{M}^0(H, X, Y; D)$ and $(J')^0 \cong \mathscr{M}^0(K; R, Z; E)$ and the corresponding mappings θ and p can be transfered to the Rees matrix semigroups (see Rhodes and Tilson [*14*, Section 7.2]). $\theta: J^0 \twoheadrightarrow I$ is an epimorphism but $p_{-1}: J^0 \twoheadrightarrow (J')^0$ is only a partial homomorphism. Then we have

$$\theta((h)_{xy}) = \theta^*(h)_{\alpha(x)\beta(y)} \in I^{\#}$$

and

$$p_{-1}((h)_{xy}) = (\lambda(x)\, p^*(h)\, \delta(y))_{r(x)\, s(y)} \in J.$$

Now p_{-1} is γ by Krohn *et al.* [*14*, 8.3.24(b)] so by Rhodes and Tilson [*14*, Proposition 7.2.5] $s(y) = s(y')$ implies $y \equiv y'$. But $y \equiv y'$ clearly implies $\beta(y) \equiv \beta(y')$. But the hypothesis of (b) gives that $\beta(y) \equiv \beta(y')$

implies $\beta(y) = \beta(y')$. This proves the critical assertion that the mapping $\beta s^{-1}: Z \to B$ is well defined and onto. Next we observe that $p_{-2}: G_{m-1} \wr C_{m-2} \wr \cdots \twoheadrightarrow C_{m-2} \wr \cdots$ restricted to T' is an $\mathscr{L}'$ epimorphism (see Krohn *et al.* [*14*, 8.3.24(a) and 8.3.9]).

Now for each $b \in B$ choose $b' \in Y$ such that $\beta(b') = b$ and for each $s \in S$ choose $s' \in T'$ so that $\theta(s') = s$. Then we have that $b \in B$, $s_1, \ldots, s_n \in S$ and $bs_1 \cdots s_n \neq 0$ implies

$$(\beta s^{-1})(s(b')\, p_{-2}(s_1) \cdots p_{-2}(s_n)) = bs_1 \cdots s_n .$$

Now this equation and an obvious extension of Rhodes [*21*, Lemma 2.4] gives

$$C(RLM(S)) \leqslant (\mathbf{C}, 1) \oplus C(p_{-2}(T')).$$

But $p_{-2}(T') \leqslant C_{m-2} \wr G_{m-3} \wr \cdots$ so $C(p_{-2}(T')) \leqslant (\mathbf{C}, m-2)$ and thus $C(RLM(S)) \leqslant (\mathbf{C}, m-2)$. But $C(S) \leqslant (\mathbf{G}, 1) \oplus C(RLM(S))$ by Krohn *et al.* [*14*, 8.2.17] and thus $C(S) \leqslant (\mathbf{G}, m-1)$. But this violates the minimality of m. This completes the proof.

Let $G \neq 1$ be a group.

We can apply (4.25)b to show that $\#_G(\mathscr{SRM}(G, n)) = n$. (See (4.3)e.) First $RLM(\mathscr{SRM}(G, n)) = F_R(X_n)$ and second $\mathscr{SRM}(G, n)$ is a PGM semigroup since it satisfies the hypothesis of (4.25)b as the reader can verify. Thus since $\#_G(F_R(X_n)) = n - 1$ (by Rhodes [*19*, Section 5]), we have $\#_G(\mathscr{SRM}(G, n)) = n$.

One corollary of Corollary 4.23 and (4.25)a is:

(4.26) **Corollary.**[†] Let S be a semigroup which is a union of groups or more generally with $S^{\mathscr{I}'}$ a combinatorial semigroup. Then $\#_G(S)$ equals the largest nonnegative integer n such that there exists a series

$$S \twoheadrightarrow GM_1 \twoheadrightarrow RLM(GM_1) \twoheadrightarrow \cdots \twoheadrightarrow GM_n \twoheadrightarrow RLM(GM_n) \tag{4.27}$$

where GM_k denotes a GM semigroup ($\neq 1$) for $k = 1, \ldots, n$.

Corollary 4.26 was first proved by Krohn and Rhodes [*12*]. For another exposition see Krohn *et al.* [*14*, Chapter 9]. This corollary gives a satisfactory way to determine the complexity of a semigroup which is the union of groups.

However, in the more general situation where Proposition 4.25 does not apply, determining complexity by determining which GM homomorphic images are PGM, is probably the wrong approach, even though it is completely successful for semigroups which are unions of groups. See Krohn *et al.* [*14*, Chapter 9].

[†] See Note Added in Proof, page 162.

Considering series (4.27) for arbitrary semigroups will of course give upper bounds for complexity as is seen by examining the proof of (4.23). Consider the series

(4.28) $$S \twoheadrightarrow S^{\gamma} \twoheadrightarrow S^{\gamma\mathscr{L}'} \twoheadrightarrow S^{\gamma\mathscr{L}'\gamma} \twoheadrightarrow \cdots.$$

Define $\#_L(S)$ equal to the number of proper (i.e., non-one-to-one) $\mathscr{L}'$ homomorphisms in the series (4.28). Let $\#_1(S)$ be the largest nonnegative integer n such that there exists a series (4.27) where GM_k denotes a GM semigroup ($\neq 1$) for $k = 1, \ldots, n$.

Then we have:

(4.29) **Proposition.**† Let S be a semigroup. Then:

(a) $\#_G(S) \leqslant \#_L(S)$ and equality holds if S is a union of groups.

(b) $\#_G(S) \leqslant \#_1(S)$ and equality holds if S is a union of groups.

Proof. (a) $\#_G(S) \leqslant \#_L(S)$ follows from Axiom II and Corollary 4.14 and equality holds by Krohn *et al.* [*14*, Theorem 9.2.5] when S is a union of groups.

(b) $\#_G(S) \leqslant \#_1(S)$ follows from the proof given for Corollary 4.23 and equality holds by Krohn *et al.* [*14*, Theorem 2.5] when S is a union of groups.

The following is what we consider to be the best approach to complexity. Let $s \in S$. Then, following Green, (see Krohn *et al.* [*14*] or Clifford and Preston [*2*]) let $L[s] = \{r \in S: S^1 r = S^1 s\}$. $L[s]$ is by definition the $\mathscr{L}$ class of S containing s and by definition $s\mathscr{L}r$ if and only if $S^1 s = S^1 r$. We write $L[s] \leqslant L[r]$ if and only if $S^1 s \subseteq S^1 r$. Clearly $\leqslant$ is a well-defined partial ordering on the $\mathscr{L}$ classes of S.

(4.30) **Definition.** T is a *type-I* semigroup if and only if there exists elements of T, $t_1, \ldots, t_n$, such that $L[t_1] > L[t_2] > \cdots > L[t_n]$ and T is generated by $L[t_1] \cup \cdots \cup L[t_n]$.

We write this as $T = \langle L[t_1] > \cdots > L[t_n] \rangle$.

(4.31) **Example.** (a) Let $S = F_R(X_n)$ be as defined in (4.3)d. Then S is type I since $S = \langle L[1] > L[l_{n-1}] \rangle$ where 1 is the identity of S and l_{n-1} is any elements of S, such that $| X_n l_{n-1} | = n - 1$, i.e., l_{n-1} has exactly $n - 1$ elements in its range. In fact $S = \langle H_1, l_{n-1} \rangle$ where H_1 is the group of units of S, i.e., all permutations on X_n.

(b) A note of caution. Let $s_1, \ldots, s_n$ be elements of S. Then $T = \langle L[s_1] > \cdots > L[s_n] \rangle$ may not be a type-I semigroup since $L[s_Y]$ may not be $\mathscr{L}$ classes of T, even though $L[s_Y]$ is an $\mathscr{L}$ class of S.

† See Note Added in Proof, page 162.

By definition $IG(S)$ equals the subsemigroup of S generated by the idempotents of S, i.e., $IG(S) = \langle x: x^2 = x \in S \rangle$.

(4.32) **Definition.** Let $\#_I(S)$ be the length of the longest sequence of subsemigroups $T_1, T_2, \ldots, T_n$ of S satisfying

(1) T_1 is a noncombinatorial type-I semigroup.

(2) T_j is a noncombinatorial type-I subsemigroup of $IG(T_{j-1})$ for $j = 2, \ldots, n$;

(3) $IG(T_n)$ is combinatorial.

We now state the following important conjecture.

(4.33) **Conjecture.**† $\#_I(S) = \#_G(S)$ for all S.

At this moment we know:

(4.34) **Proposition.** $\#_I(S) \leqslant \#_G(S)$

and:

(4.35) **Proposition.** If S is a union of groups, then $\#_I(S) = \#_G(S)$.

(4.36) **Proposition.** If S has at most two nonzero $\mathscr{J}$ classes, then $\#_I(S) = \#_G(S)$.

PROOFS. $\#_I(S) \leqslant \#_G(S)$ is proved by Rhodes and Tilson [*24*]. If S is a union of groups, then Rhodes has proved that $\#_I(S) = \#_G(S)$. This follows from the proof of Theorem 9.2.5 of Krohn *et al.* [*14*] and in particular from Lemma 9.2.29 of Krohn *et al.* [*14*] by noting that $y_n, \ldots, y_1$ can be chosen as idempotents with $L[y_n] \geqslant \cdots \geqslant L[y_1]$, in fact with $y_j y_k = y_j$ for $k \geqslant j$, and then

$$T \equiv T_n = \langle L[y_n] > \cdots > L[y_1] \rangle.$$

Proposition 4.36 is due to Tilson and appears with his ingenious proof in his thesis [*27*].

(4.37) **Remark.**† (1) Proving Conjecture 4.33, if it is true, is quite important. It may be necessary to strengthen the definition of type I and take subsemigroups somewhat larger than $IG(T_K)$.

(2) The methods of Allen [*1*] (see remarks after Theorem 4.13) and the methods of Tilson [*27*] proving Proposition 4.36 and the techniques of Krohn and Rhodes [*12, 21–23*] should prove valuable in attacking Conjecture 4.33.

(3) Let $F_R(X_n)$ be the semigroup of all functions of X_n into itself considered acting on the right and let $F_L(X_n)$ denote the reverse semigroup. From (4.31) we have $F_R(X_n) = \langle H_1, l_{n-1} \rangle$ so that both

† See Note Added in Proof, page 162.

$F_L(X_n)$ and $F_R(X_n)$ are type-I semigroups. Further, $IG(F_R(X_n)) = (F_R(X_n) - H_1) \cup \{1\}$ and $IG(F_L(X_n)) = (F_L(X_n) - H_1) \cup \{1\}$. Thus $F_R(X_{n-1}) | F_R(X_n)$ and then it is easy to verify by induction that $\#_I(S) \geqslant n - 1$ for $S = F_R(X_n)$ or $F_L(X_n)$. Thus by (4.34) $\#_G(S) \geqslant n - 1$. But by Zeiger $\#_G(F_R(X_n)) \leqslant n - 1$ (see Rhodes [*19*, Section 5]) and by Allen [*1*], $\#_G(F_L(X_n)) \leqslant n - 1$. Thus $\#_G(S) = \#_I(S) = n - 1$ if S equals $F_R(X_n)$ on $F_L(X_n)$.

(4.38) Zalcstein [*28*] and later Allen [*1*] constructed semigroups S such that for given integers n and k:

(a) S is a union of groups,

(b) $\#_G(S) = n$.

(c) $\#_G(r(S)) = k$. Here $r(S)$ denotes the reverse semigroup of S, i.e., in $r(S)$, $s_1 \cdot s_2 = s_2 s_1$.

Denote a semigroup satisfying (a)–(c) by $S_{n,k}$. Then notice $S_{n,k} \times S_{m,l} = S_{a,b}$, $a = \max(n, m)$ and $b = \max(k, l)$, so it is sufficient to construct $S_{n,1}$ since $r(S_{m,n}) = S_{n,m}$.

We conjecture that the difference of $| \#_G(S) - \#_G(r(S))| = d(S)$ is related to the semigroup algebra $C(S)$ generated by S over the complex numbers, the Cartan invariants of $C(S)$ and its homomorphic images, the character theory of S (see Rhodes [*20*]), and possibly the Hochschild homology of $C(S)$. Along these lines we have the theorems of Rhodes [*20*] that $\theta = \theta_j$ of Krohn *et al.* [*14*, Theorem 9.2.5] from which we have the following corollary. (For terminology see Krohn *et al.* [*14*, Chapter 8]). We say S satisfies (**) if and only if S is a union of groups and if J is a $\mathscr{J}$ class of S (so T is a simple subsemigroup of S) and $J \cong \mathscr{M}(G; A, B, C)$ and A' is the equivalence classes of A under the relation "proportional on the right" and B' is the equivalence classes of B under the relation "proportional on the left," then the number of members of A' left fixed by s equals the number of members of B' left fixed by s.

(4.39) **Corollary.** Let S satisfy (**). Then $\#_G(S) = \#_G(r(S))$ or $d(S) = 0$.

PROOF. Use Rhodes [*20*] or $\theta = \theta j$ of Krohn *et al.* [*14*, Theorem 9.2.5].

We conjecture the following:

(4.40) **Proposition.** (a) $C(S)$ semisimple implies $\#_G(S) = \#_G(r(S))$ or $d(S) = 0$.

(b) For each integer n there exists S_n such that $C(S_n)$ is semisimple and $\#_G(S_n) = n$.

PROOF. Zalcstein has announced a proof of (b). The structure of those S with $C(S)$ semisimple is known. See Clifford and Preston [2, Chapter 5]. However, the truth of (a) is still open. A curious result is the following.

Suppose S is a finite semigroup which is the union of groups. Further, suppose for each pair of $\mathscr{J}$ classes $J_1 < J_2$ and G_2 maximal subgroup of S contained in J_2 we have G_2 transitive on its range in the mapping semigroup ($\mathscr{L}$ classes of J_1, G_2). See Krohn *et al.* [14, 8.3.30–8.3.32]. (That is, if L_1, L_2 two $\mathscr{L}$ classes of J_1 and $L_1 \cdot 1 = L_1$, $L_2 \cdot 1 = L_2$ for $1 = 1^2 \in G_2$, then there exists $g_2 \in G_2$ such that $L_1 \cdot g_2 = L_2$.) When this condition holds for all $J_1 < J_2$, we say S is *right transitive.*

Then we have:

(4.41) **Proposition.** Suppose S is a finite semigroup which is a union of Abelian groups. Further suppose S is right transitive. Then

$$\#_G(S) \geqslant \#_G(r(S))$$

where $r(S)$ denotes the reverse semigroup.

Thus S and $r(S)$ both right transitive implies $\#_G(S) = \#_G(r(S))$. (S is left transitive by definition if and only if $r(S)$ is right transitive. Thus a reformulation is: S right and left transitive implies $\#_G(S) = \#_G(r(S))$ or $d(S) = 0$.)

PROOF. (In outline see Krohn *et al.* [14, Chapter 8] for details.) Consider the subsemigroup $T = J_1 \cup G_2$. Then consider $eTe = eTe \cup G_2$, where $1 = e = e^2$ is the identity of G_2. Then $(\mathscr{L}(eJ_1e), G_2)$ is (by hypothesis) a *transitive* permutation group and $\ker GM_{J_1}|_{G_2} = N \,\Delta\, G_2$ is independent of being computed in S, T, or eTe etc. Now consider $(GM(eJ_1e), G_2)$ and let the kernel of the action by G_2 be $N_2 \,\Delta\, G_2$. So if $GM(eJ_1e) \cong \mathscr{M}(H_1; A_1, B_1; C_1)$, then $(H_1 \times B_1, G_2/N_2)$ is a faithful monomial representation of G_2/N_2 transitive when restricted to B_1. See Hall [5, Chapter 14] or Zassenhaus [29, Chapter V]. Now by using the well-known form of all transitive monomial representation (proved in the above references) together with the assumption that H_1 and G_2 are Abelian, we find that by conjugating the monomial representation by some strictly row monomial $B_1 \times B_1$ matrix with coefficients in H_1, π, the form becomes

$$g_2 \rightarrow \begin{pmatrix} \theta(g_2) & & \bigcirc \\ & \ddots & \\ \bigcirc & & \theta(g_2) \end{pmatrix} = M(g_2)$$

for each $g_2 \in G_2$ which is the identity on B_1 where θ: $(G_2)_b \twoheadrightarrow H_1$ is a homomorphism from the subgroup $(G_2)_b = \{g_2 \in G_2: bg_2 = b\}$ into H_1. We notice since G_2 is *Abelian* that $(G_2)_b = \{g_2 \in G_2: g_2$ is the identity on all $B\}$ i.e., $(G_2)_b = \{(G_2)_{b'}: b' \in B_1\}$. Thus ker $RLM\ GM\,|_{G_2} = (G_2)_b$.

Now for $g_2 \in (G_2)_b$, $M(g_2)$ lies in the center of $\mathscr{SRM}(B_1, H_1)$ (strictly row monomial matrices $\cdots$) since H_1 is Abelian and the form of $M(g_2)$. Thus in any normalization of $GM(eJ_1e)$, $M(g_2)$ does not change, since normalizations lead to conjugations of $M(g)$. But now using the linked equations (see Krohn *et al.* [*14*, 8.2.21–8.2.24 and especially 8.2.23]) we see that if $g_2 \in RLM\ GM\,|_{G_2}$, then $g_2 \cdot a_1 = a_1$ for all $a_1 \in A_1$. Thus $g_2 \in RLM\ GM\,|_{G_2}$ implies $g_2 \in LLM\ GM\,|_{G_2}$. Now by the results of Krohn *et al.* [*14*, Chapter 9] we have $\#_G(S) \geqslant \#_G(r(S))$.

Another conjecture is as follows:

(4.42) **Conjecture.** Let M be a maximal proper subsemigroup of S. Then $\#_G(M) \leqslant \#_G(S) \leqslant \#_G(M) + 1$.

An equivalent formulation is:

(4.42)′ **Conjecture.** (continuity of complexity with respect to subsemigroups). Let S be a semigroup with subsemigroup T. Suppose $\#_G(T) = k < n = \#_G(S)$. Then there exists subsemigroups $T = S_k \leqslant S_{k+1} \leqslant \cdots \leqslant S_n = S$ such that $\#_G(S_j) = j$.

In this direction we have:

(4.43) Let S be a semigroup which is a union of groups. Then Propositions 4.42 and (4.42)′ hold for S.

PROOF. See Krohn and Rhodes [*12*] or Krohn *et al.* [*14*, Corollary 9.3.2].

(4.44) **Remark.** (a) Information of the form proper maximal subsemigroup M of S can take is given in Graham *et al.* [*3*] or Rhodes and Tilson [*14*, 7.3.3].

(b) An approach to Conjecture 4.42 is to prove Conjecture 4.33 and then use this together with (a).

Of course Corollary 4.16 and Conjecture 4.42′ would prove the following.

(4.45) **Conjecture** (continuity of complexity with respect to division). Let $S \mid T$ and suppose $\#_G(S) = k < n = \#_G(T)$. Then there exists $S = S_k \mid S_{k+1} \mid \cdots \mid S_n = T$ such that $\#_G(S_j) = j$ for $j = k, \ldots, n$.

Of course Corollary 4.16 and (4.43) imply the following.

(4.46) Let T be a union of groups. Then Conjecture 4.45 holds for S.

A generalization of Axiom II [see (4.5) and (4.11)–(4.13)] is the following conjecture.

(4.47) **Conjecture.** Let I be an ideal of S. Then

$$\#_G(S) \leqslant \#_G(S/I) + \#_G(I).$$

Probably the proofs of Axiom II can be extended to Conjecture 4.42. Of course if I is taken to be combinatorial, Conjecture 4.42 becomes Axiom II.

We might take Conjecture 4.47 a step further and ask about equality.

(4.48) **Fantasy.** (splitting theorem). Let S be a semigroup with $\#_G(S) \geqslant 2$. Then there exists semigroup T with ideal I so that

$$T \underset{\gamma}{\twoheadrightarrow} S$$

with

$$\#_G(T/I), \qquad \#_G(I) \neq 0$$

and

$$\#_G(T) = \#_G(T/I) + \#_G(I).$$

(4.49) **Remark.** Suppose Fantasy 4.48 could be proved but with $\#_G$ replaced by $\#_I$. Also suppose (4.47) could be proved. Finally suppose $\#_I(S) \leqslant 1$ implies $\#_G(S) = \#_I(S)$, i.e., (4.33) holds when $\#_I(S) \leqslant 1$. Then (4.33) would follow since by induction on $n = \#_I(S)$ we have

$$\begin{aligned} \#_I(S) = \#_I(T) = \#_I(T/I) + \#_I(I) &= \#_G(T/I) + \#_G(I) \\ &\geqslant \#_G(T) = \#_G(S) \end{aligned}$$

since $T \underset{\gamma}{\twoheadrightarrow} S$. But then $\#_I(S) = \#_G(S)$ by Proposition 4.34.

(4.50) **Remark.** It is interesting to consider all functions $\theta\colon \mathscr{S} \to N$ where $\mathscr{S}$ is the collection of all semigroups, and θ satisfies Axioms I and II. The basic question is which functions arise from some "plot" in Section 3.

We notice there are many functions satisfying Axioms I and II. For example, let π be a right-sided infinite sequence of L's and R's. Then define $\theta = \#_\pi$ just as $\#_I$ in Definition 4.32 is defined but where we change conditions (1) and (2) to the condition that T_j or $r(T_j)$, respectively, is type I, depending on whether $\pi(j)$ is R or L, respectively. Then $\#_\pi$ satisfies Axioms I and II.

5. π Length for Finite Semigroups

Tilson's Appendix to this paper gives a detailed account of π complexity and π length for finite semigroups so we will restrict ourselves in this section to a general outline of the theory. All undefined notation and omitted details can be found in the Appendix.

(5.1) **Notation.** π denotes a set of prime integers and π' the complementary set of prime integers, e.g., $\{2, 3\}' = \{5, 7, 11, \ldots\}$. We let p, q denote prime integers. Any standard group theoretic terminology applied to semigroups means every maximal subgroup of S possesses the property, e.g., S is a π semigroup if and only if maximal subgroups of S are π groups. Of course, G is a π group if the prime p divides the order of G implies that $p \in \pi$.

(5.2) **Definition.** Let S be a semigroup. Then $l_\pi(S)$, read the *π-length of* S, is the smallest nonnegative integer n such that

$$S \text{ divides } S_n \times_Y P_n \times_Y S_{n-1} \times_Y \cdots \times_Y S_1 \times_Y P_1 \times_Y S_0 \tag{5.3}$$

where $P_n, \ldots, P_1$ are π groups and $S_n, \ldots, S_0$ are π' semigroups.

S is by definition π *solvable* if and only if some solution of (5.3) exists, i.e., if and only if $l_\pi(S)$ is well defined.

The importance of π length is shown by the following.

(5.4) **Remark.** (a) If primes denotes all primes, then $l_{\text{primes}} = \#_G$ and all semigroups are primes solvable.

(b) Let G be a group. Let p be a prime. We let $\pi = \{p\}$ and in this case write l_π as l_p. Then $l_p(G)$ as defined by (5.2) agrees with the definition of $l_p(G)$ as given by Hall and Higman [*6*]. For details see Tilson's Appendix.

(c) $l_\pi(S)$ is defined if and only if the maximal subgroups of S are π solvable in the sense of Hall and Higman [*6*]. See Section 1 of Tilson's Appendix.

Thus we see that π length extends the standard group theoretic concept of π length from groups to semigroups and simultaneously generalizes complexity.

(5.5) **Notation.** $\mathscr{S}_\pi$ denotes the collection of all π-solvable semigroups. $\mathscr{S}$ denotes the collection of all finite semigroups. $\mathscr{S} = \mathscr{S}_{\text{primes}}$. Then $l_\pi \colon \mathscr{S}_\pi \to N$. $\mathscr{S}_\pi$ is closed under division and direct, subdirect and semidirect products. See the Appendix.

Hall and Higman [*6*] (see also Higman [*7*]) prove the following:

(5.6) **Theorem.** (Hall-Higman). Let G be a p-solvable group, of p length $l_p(G)$, and let the exponent of its Sylow p subgroup be p^{e_p} (i.e., e_p is smallest positive integer such that $x \in G$ and $x^{p^y} = 1$ implies $y \geqslant e_p$). Then $l_p(G) \leqslant 3e_p$.

The motivation behind the following results and conjectures is on one hand to generalize the results and conjectures of Section 4 on $\#_G$ to l_π and on the other hand to extend the group theoretic results of Hall and Higman to semigroups.

As a beginning we have the following.

(5.7) **Axiom I** (see (4.4)) holds for l_π . Or more precisely if $S \in \mathscr{S}_\pi$ and $S \leqslant\leqslant S_1 \times \cdots \times S_n$, then $S_j \in \mathscr{S}_\pi$ and

$$l_\pi(S) = \max\{l_\pi(S_j) : j = 1, \ldots, n\}.$$

PROOF. The proof is easy. See Theorem 3.6 of Tilson's Appendix.

One of the major results is the following.

(5.8) **Theorem.**† Axioms II and II′ [see (4.5) and (4.11)–(4.13)] hold for l_π . More precisely if $S \in \mathscr{S}_\pi$ and $S \underset{\gamma}{\rightarrow} T$, then $T \in \mathscr{S}_\pi$ and $l_\pi(S) = l_\pi(T)$.

PROOF. Rhodes' proof [22] of Axiom II for $\#_G$ can be modified to yield the theorem.

Actually Theorem 5.8 can be extended in the following manner.

(5.9) **Definition.** $\theta: S \underset{\pi}{\twoheadrightarrow} T$ if and only if the kernel of θ restricted to each subgroup of S is a π' group.

Then:

(5.10) **Theorem.**† $S \in \mathscr{T}_\pi$ and $S \underset{\pi}{\twoheadrightarrow} T$ implies $T \in \mathscr{T}_\pi$ and $l_\pi(S) = l_\pi(T)$.

PROOF. Theorem 5.10 follows from Theorem 5.8 by standard techniques. See Theorem 3.6 of Tilson's Appendix.

We also have the analog of 4.14. (See Section 4 of Tilson's Appendix for terminology.)

(5.11) **Proposition.**† $S \in \mathscr{S}_\pi$ and $S \underset{\pi' + \mathscr{L}'}{\twoheadrightarrow} T$ implies $T \in \mathscr{S}_\pi$ and $l_\pi(T) \leqslant l_\pi(S) \leqslant l_\pi(T) + 1$.

PROOF. See Corollary 4.29 of Tilson's Appendix.

As a corollary of Theorem 5.8 and Proposition 5.11 we have the following.

(5.12) **Corollary** (continuity of π length with respect to homomorphisms). Let $S \in \mathscr{S}_\pi$ and let $\varphi: S \twoheadrightarrow T$ be an epimorphism and let $l_\pi(S) = n$ and $l_\pi(T) = k$. Then there exists epimorphisms

† See Note Added in Proof, page 162.

$S = S_n \twoheadrightarrow S_{n-1} \twoheadrightarrow \cdots \twoheadrightarrow S_k = T$ so that the composite epimorphism is φ and $l_\pi(S_j) = j$ for $j = k, \ldots, n$.

(5.13) **Notation.** By definition $HH_\pi(S) = \max\{l_\pi(G): G$ is a (maximal) subgroup of $S\}$. If G is a group, then $p^{e_p(G)}$ is the exponent of a Sylow p subgroup of G. By definition $e_p(S) = \max\{e_p(G): G$ is a maximal subgroup of $S\}$.

By examining the proofs of Proposition 5.11 and Corollary 4.14 it is not difficult to show the following.

(5.14) **Proposition.**[†] Let $S \in \mathscr{S}_\pi$ and $S \xrightarrow[\mathscr{L}']{} \!\!\!\!\!\! \twoheadrightarrow T$. Then $T \in \mathscr{S}_\pi$ and $l_\pi(T) \leqslant l_\pi(S) \leqslant HH_\pi(S) + l_\pi(T)$.

We recall that $\#_L(S)$ was defined just after (4.28). Now by combining upper bounds for complexity (see Proposition 4.29) and the group theoretic upper bound for p length of p-solvable group yields the following.

(5.15) **Theorem.**[†] Let S be a p-solvable semigroup. Then

$$l_p(S) \leqslant \#_L(S) \cdot HH_{p'}(S) \leqslant \#_L(S) \cdot 3e_p(S)$$

PROOF. Theorem 5.6 implies $HH_p(S) \leqslant 3e_p(S)$, so it suffices to show $l_p(S) \leqslant \#_L(S) \cdot HH_p(S)$. By way of contradiction suppose this inequality is false and let S be a counterexample of smallest possible order. By Theorem 5.10, $l_p(S) = l_p(S^\gamma)$ and trivially $\#_L(S) = \#_L(S^\gamma)$ and $HH_p(S) = HH_p(S^\gamma)$. Thus it follows from the minimal nature of S that $S = S^\gamma \neq 1$ and so $|S^{\mathscr{L}'}| < |S|$ and induction applies to $S^{\mathscr{L}'}$. Trivially we have

$$1 + \#_L(S^{\mathscr{L}'}) = \#_L(S) \tag{5.16}$$

since $S = S^\gamma$ and

$$HH_p(S^{\mathscr{L}'}) \leqslant HH_p(S) \tag{5.17}$$

since $S \twoheadrightarrow S^{\mathscr{L}'}$. Also Proposition 5.14 yields

$$l_p(S) \leqslant l_p(S^{\mathscr{L}'}) + HH_p(S). \tag{5.18}$$

Then

$$\begin{aligned} l_p(S) &\leqslant l_p(S^{\mathscr{L}'}) + HH_p(S) \leqslant \#_L(S^{\mathscr{L}'}) \cdot HH_p(S^{\mathscr{L}'}) + HH_p(S) \\ &= (\#_L(S) - 1)\, HH_p(S^{\mathscr{L}'}) + HH_p(S) \leqslant (\#_L(S) - 1)\, HH_p(S) + HH_p(S) \\ &= \#_L(S)\, HH_p(S) \end{aligned}$$

where we use (5.16–5.18) and induction applied to $S^{\mathscr{L}'}$.

[†] See Note Added in Proof, page 162.

(5.19) REMARK. (a) We *conjecture* that Theorem 5.15 remains true if $\#_L(S)$ is replaced by $\#_G(S)$.

(b) Theorem 5.15 is still very crude. Refinements can come about as follows. Consider the Schützenberger representations by row monomial matrices with group coefficients (see Rhodes and Tilson [*14*, Chapter 7] or Clifford and Preston [*2*]) which arise in the study of complexity (see Krohn *et al.* [*14*, Chapter 8 and 9, especially 9.24(g)–(h)], and Tilson's Appendix). Then replace each group entry of the monomial matrices by the Hall-Higman representations of characteristic p (given by conjugation on the Frattini subgroup of the second term of the upper p series (see Hall and Higman [*5*, 18.4; *6*; *7*]). This gives representations of characteristic p. Now apply Theorem B of Hall and Higman [*6*]. These methods should sharpen Theorem 5.15.

Analogous to Conjecture 4.42 we can do the following.

(5.20) **Conjecture.** Let $S \in \mathscr{S}_\pi$. Let M be a maximal proper subsemigroup of S. Then

$$l_\pi(M) \leqslant l_\pi(S) \leqslant l_\pi(M) + 1$$

The π length form of Conjecture 4.42′ is equivalent with Conjecture 5.20.

We are able to verify Conjecture 5.20 for p-solvable semigroups which are unions of groups.

In the following $O_\pi(G)$ denotes the unique maximal normal π subgroup of G. The following proof is due to Nick Burgoyne.

(5.21) **Proposition.** Let G be p-solvable and $M \subset G$ a proper maximal subgroup of G; then

$$l_p(M) \geqslant l_p(G) - 1.$$

PROOF (N. Burgoyne). (i) Use induction on $l_p(G)$. The result is true if $l_p(G) = 1$. Suppose that $O_{p'}(G) \neq 1$ and that $O_{p'}(G) \not\subseteq M$, then $G = MO_{p'}(G)$ and so $l_p(M) = l_p(G)$. So assume $O_{p'}(G) \subseteq M$. Now the removal of a p' normal subgroup does not change p length so we can assume that $O_{p'}(G) = 1$. Hence $O_p(G) \neq 1$.

(ii) If $O_p(G) \not\subseteq M$, then $G = MO_p(G)$ and therefore

$$G/O_p(G) \cong M/M \cap O_p(G).$$

Hence $O_p(M) = M \cap O_p(G)$. Therefore

$$l_p(M) \geqslant l_p(M/O_p(M)) = l_p(G/O_p(G)) = l_p(G) - 1.$$

(iii) So suppose $O_p(G) \subseteq M$. If $O_{pp'}(G) \nsubseteq M$, then $G = MO_{pp'}(G)$ and so $l_p(M/O_p(G)) = l_p(G/O_p(G))$. As in (ii) we conclude that $l_p(M) \geqslant l_p(G) - 1$. We may finally assume that $O_{pp'}(G) \subseteq M$.

(iv) Note that $O_{p'}(M)$ centralizes $O_p(G)$ and so by Lemma 1.2.3 of Hall and Higman [*6*] we must have $O_{p'}(M) \subseteq O_{p'}(G) = 1$. Similarly $O_p(M)/O_p(G)$ centralizes $O_{pp'}(G)/O_p(G)$ and again by Lemma 1.2.3 we must have $O_p(M) = O_p(G)$.

(v) From $O_{p'}(M) = 1$ and $O_p(M) = O_p(G)$ we have

$$l_p(M/O_p(G)) = l_p(M) - 1.$$

Now by induction we have $l_p(M/O_p(G)) \geqslant l_p(G/O_p(G)) - 1 = l_p(G) - 2$. Hence $l_p(M) - 1 \geqslant l_p(G) - 2$.

The above proof still holds if p is replaced by π.

(5.22) Conjecture 5.20 holds if S is a union of groups.

PROOF (outline). Examine the proof of Corollary 9.3.2 of Krohn *et al.* [*14*] which proves Conjecture 5.20 for $\pi =$ primes, i.e., for $\#_G$. Then use the generalization of Chapter 9 [*14*], from $\#_G$ to l_π, contained in Tilson's Appendix together with Proposition 5.21 to complete the proof.

We also *conjecture* the analog for l_π of Conjecture 4.45. In fact, appropriately reformulated, all the results and conjectures of Section 4 should extend to l_π. For example, let us consider Conjecture 4.33.

(5.23) **Notation.** We say that $x \in S$ is a π element if and only if x lies in a maximal subgroup G of S and x is a π element of G. $O^\pi(S)$ equals the subsemigroup of S generated by all the π' elements of S. Thus if S is a group, $S/O^\pi(S)$ is the unique maximal factor group of S which is a π group.

(5.24) **Definition** (see Definition 4.32). Let $\#_{I-\pi}(S)$ be the length of the longest sequence of subsemigroups $T_1, T_2, \ldots, T_n$ of S satisfying the following conditions.

(1) T_1 is a non-π' type-I semigroup and $O^\pi(T_1) = T_1$,

(2) T_j is a non-π' type-I subsemigroup of $O^{\pi'}(T_{j-1})$ for $j = 2, \ldots, n$;

(3) $O^{\pi'}(T_n)$ is a π' semigroup.

(5.25) **Conjecture.** Let $S \in \mathscr{S}_\pi$. Then $l_\pi(S) = \#_{I-\pi}(S)$.

(5.26) **Remark.** (a) Conjecture 5.25 holds for π-solvable groups.

(b) Conjecture 5.25 holds for $S \in \mathscr{S}_\pi$ which are unions of groups.

PROOF (outline). Examine the proof of Proposition 4.35 for $\#_G$.

Use Tilson's Appendix which extends Chapter 9 [*14*] to l_π and extend the old proof for $\#_G$ to l_π.

(5.27) **Remark.** (a) For groups, Hall and Higman bound l_p by measures of complexity of the Sylow p groups. Is there any analog of Sylow p groups for semigroups? Consider $S = (X_n, S_n) \le \cdots \le (X_1, S_1)$ (see Section 7) where each S_j is either a group or a combinatorial semigroup. Then does a Sylow theorem hold for S in the sense that every maximal p subsemigroup is conjugate by an inner automorphism?

(b) Let $S \in \mathscr{S}_\pi$. Then how large is $\max\{\#_G(T)\colon T \mid S$ and T is a π semigroup$\}$? In this direction from (5.26)b we have: Let $S \in \mathscr{S}_\pi$, S a union of groups and S p-closed i.e., products of p elements are p elements. Then $(S)_p = \{x \in S\colon x \text{ is a } p \text{ element}\}$ is the unique maximal p subsemigroup of S and $l_p(S_p) = \#_G(S_p) = l_p(S)$.

6. Combinatorial Semigroups and Burnside-Type Problems

Most of the results of this section appear in Stiffler [*26*].

By definition C is a combinatorial semigroup if and only if the subgroups of C are singletons. By Corollary 2.2 we know that C is combinatorial if and only if C divides $U_3 \times_Y \cdots \times_Y U_3$ for some Y's. Also $x^2 = x$ for all $x \in U_3$. Thus we can introduce the following definition for all finite combinatorial semigroups.

(6.1) **Definition.** B is a *band* if and only if $x = x^2$ for all $x \in B$. Thus B is a band if and only if B is the union of trivial groups.

By definition the *band length* of the combinatorial semigroup C is the smallest positive integer $n = \#_B(C)$ so that

$$C \text{ divides } B_n \times_Y \cdots \times_Y B_1$$

where $B_n, \ldots, B_1$ are bands.

Little is known about band length. However, we list a few results below. If C is a combinatorial semigroup, let $\#_l(C)$ by definition equal the smallest integer n such that $c^{n+1} = c^n$ for all $c \in C$. We say that $\#_l(C)$ is the *local class* of C.

(6.2) **Proposition.** (a) $\#_B$ satisfies Axiom I. Precisely, C combinatorial and

$$C \leqslant\leqslant C_1 \times \cdots \times C_k$$

implies C_j combinatorial and $\#_B(C) = \max\{\#_B(C_j): j = 1, \ldots, k\}$. Further, C_1 divides C_2 implies $\#_B(C_1) \leqslant \#_B(C_2)$.

(b) Let C be a combinatorial semigroup. Then $\#_l(C) \leqslant \#_B(C)$.

(c) For each positive integer n there exists a combitorial semigroup C_n so that $\#_B(C_n) = n$. In fact let $C_n = \langle x \rangle$ with $x^{n+1} = x^n$.

PROOF. The proof of (a) is similar to the corresponding proof for $\#_G$.

To prove (b) it suffices to show that if $B_1, B_2, \ldots$ are bands, then $\#_l(D_n = B_n \times_Y \cdots \times_Y B_1) \leqslant n$. But assuming the result for n and considering $(f, a) \in D_{n+1}$ (so $a^{n+1} = a^n$ by induction) we have

$$(f, a)^{n+1} = (f \cdot {}^a f \cdot \cdots \cdot {}^{a^n} f, a^{n+1})$$

and

$$(f, a)^{n+2} = (f \cdot {}^a f \cdot \cdots \cdot {}^{a^n} f \cdot {}^{a^{n+1}} f, a^{n+2}).$$

But $a^n = a^{n+1} = a^{n+2}$ and ${}^{a^n} f = {}^{a^{n+1}} f$ so ${}^{a^n} f \, {}^{a^{n+1}} f = ({}^{a^n} f)^2 = {}^{a^n} f$ since B_{n+1} is a band. Thus $(f, a)^{n+1} = (f, a)^{n+2}$ and this establishes the result.

To show (c) let C_n be the cyclic semigroup with generator x and relations $x^n = x^{n+1}$. Then $\#_l(C_n) = n$ so $\#_B(C_n) \geqslant n$ by (b). On the other hand, C_n divides $U_3 \mathrm{w} \cdots \mathrm{w} U_3$ (n times) (see Section 7) by Krohn *et al.* [*14*, 5.39]. Thus $\#_B(C_n) \leqslant n$ so $\#_B(C_n) = n$.

For further results see Stiffler [*26*].

(6.3) **Remark.** By "Burnside-type" problems we mean statements of the form S finite generated plus S satisfies the relations R implies S has finite order. Classically R is taken to be $s^n = 1$ for all $s \in S$ with n fixed. Then S is a finitely generated group with finite exponent n. That this implies S is finite is the Burnside conjecture. See Hall [*5*, Chapter 18].

When R is taken to be $s^2 = s$ for all $s \in S$, we are asking if free finitely generated bands are finite. We have the following.

(6.4) **Proposition.** (Green and Rees [*4*]). (a) S finitely generated and $s^2 = s$ for all $s \in S$ implies S is finite.

(b) S finitely generated and $s^n = s$ for all $s \in S$ and fixed $n \geqslant 2$ and the truth of the Burnside conjecture for the maximal subgroups of S (which are automatically finitely generated as can be deduced from the assumptions) implies S is finite.

Now using Proposition 6.4 we can show the following.

(6.5) **Proposition.** Let positive integers g and b be given. Then there exists only finitely many distinct semigroups C such that C is a finite combinatorial semigroup and C is generated by $\leqslant g$ elements and $\#_B(C) \leqslant b$.

PROOF (outline: for details see Stiffler [26]). Let $F(g)$ be the order of the unique largest band with g generators. $F(g)$ exists by (6.4)(a). Let

$$C \text{ divides } B_b \times_Y \cdots \times_Y B_1 = B.$$

Clearly we can choose $C' \leqslant B$ so that C' is generated by $\leqslant g$ elements and $C' \twoheadrightarrow C$. Further, we can assume C' projects fully onto B_1 for, if not, replace B_1 by the image of the projection. Thus the order of B_1 is $\leqslant F(g)$. Let $(f_1, b_1), \ldots, (f_k, b_1)$ be generators of C' with $k \leqslant F(g)$ and $f_j \in B_b \times_Y \cdots \times_Y B_2$. Let C_1' be the subsemigroup of $B_b \times_Y \cdots \times_Y B_2$ generated by $f_1, \ldots, f_k$. We can assume C_1' projects fully onto B_2. Thus $| B_2 | \leqslant F(k) \leqslant F(F(g))$. Continuing in this way we find that C' lies in a $B_b \times_Y \cdots \times_Y B_1$ of order $\leqslant F^b(g)$. ($F(g) = g$, $F^{n+1}(g) = F(F^n(g))$.) Thus the order of any semigroup satisfying the assumptions is $\leqslant F^b(g) \cdot \cdots \cdot F^1(g)$.

(6.6) **Remark.** (a) In his thesis Stiffler shows that there exists a semigroup $C_{g,b}$ which satisfies the hypothesis of Proposition 6.5 and every other semigroup satisfying the hypothesis of Proposition 6.5 is a homomorphic image of $C_{g,b}$.

(b) We can generalize band length as follows. Let e be a positive integer. Then define $\#_e(S)$, to be the smallest n such that

$$S \text{ divides } S_n \times_Y \cdots \times_Y S_1$$

and $s_j^{e+1} = s_j$ for all $s_j \in S_j$. Notice that this condition implies that S_j is a union of groups. Clearly $\#_1 = \#_B$. Then by the same proof as was given for Proposition 6.4 we can prove the following.

(6.7) **Proposition.** Let the Burnside conjecture be true for exponent e (e.g., $e = 6$; see Hall [5, Chapter 18]). Let positive integers g and b be given. Then there exists only finitely many distinct semigroups S such that S is finite and is generated by $\leqslant g$ elements and $\#_e(S)$ is defined and $\#_e(S) \leqslant b$.

It is known that S finitely generated and $s^2 = s^3$ for all $s \in S$ (i.e., $\#_l(S) \leqslant 2$) does not imply S is finite. In fact we have the following. Let $A_3 = \{a_1, a_2, a_3\}$ be an alphabet of 3 distinct letters. A sequence α on A_3 is said to be *square free* if and only if α is not of the form $\alpha' A A \alpha''$ where α', α'', and A are sequences on A_3 with α', α'' possibly null.

(6.8) **Proposition.** (Morse and Hedlund [17]). There exists an infinite sequence $\alpha = x_1 x_2 x_3 \cdots$ on A_3 which is square free.

(6.9) **Proposition** (Morse and Hedlund). There exists an infinite number of finite semigroups S with zero which are all generated by 3 elements and satisfy $s^2 = 0$ for all $s \in S$.

(6.10) **Proposition.** Let $C_1, C_2, \ldots, C_n, \ldots$ be an infinite number of distinct semigroups provided by Proposition 6.9. So $\#_I(C_j) \leqslant 2$ all j. Then $\lim_{j\to\omega} \#_B(C_j) = +\omega$.

PROOFS. Proposition 6.8 is proved by Morse and Hedlund [*17*].

To prove Proposition 6.9 let $\sum A_3$ denote the free semigroup on A_3 so $\sum A_3 = \{x_1 \cdots x_y : x_j \in A_3\}$ with multiplication concatenation. Let I be the ideal of $\sum A_3$ consisting of all non-square-free finite sequences. Let $S = \sum A_3/I$. Then $s^2 = 0$ for all $s \in S$ and S is generated by 3 elements. But if $\alpha = x_1x_2 \cdots x_n \cdots$ is a square-free infinite sequence given by Proposition 6.8 and $\alpha_j = x_1 \cdots x_j$ then $\alpha_1, \alpha_2, \ldots, \alpha_n, \ldots$ are all distinct considered in S. Let $I_n = \{x_1 \cdots x_y : x_j \in A_3 \text{ and } y \geqslant n\}$. I_n is an ideal, so $I_n \cup I$ is also an ideal. Then setting $C_n = \sum A_3/I \cup I_n$ proves Proposition 6.9 since $\alpha_1, \alpha_2, \alpha_3, \ldots, \alpha_n$ are n distinct elements of C_n.

The proof of Proposition 6.10 follows from Proposition 6.5.

(6.11) **Remark.** From Morse and Hedlund [*17*] a square-free sequence can be explicitly constructed. Thus $C_n = \sum A_3/I \cup I_n$ can be explicitly constructed and $\cdots \twoheadrightarrow C_3 \twoheadrightarrow C_2 \twoheadrightarrow C_1$ so $\#_B(C_1) \leqslant \#_B(C_2) \leqslant \cdots$ with $\lim_{n\to\omega} \#_B(C_n)\uparrow\omega$. However, the precise values $\#_B(C_n)$ have not been determined.

7. Jordan-Hölder Theorem for Finite Semigroups

The purpose of this section is to outline the form of a Jordan-Hölder theorem for finite semigroups. In the main we will restrict ourselves in this section to semigroups which are the union of solvable groups. The restriction to solvable groups is not essential but simplifies the notation. The restriction to union of groups semigroup is more critical and the proper generalization to arbitrary finite semigroups is discussed in Remark 7.13.

(7.1) **Notation.** In this section let $\mathscr{S}$ denote the collection of all finite semigroups which are the union of solvable groups. Let $\mathscr{P} = \{2, 3, 5, 7, \ldots\}$ denote the collection of prime integers. Let $N = \{0, 1, 2, \ldots\}$ denote the nonnegative integers. (S^I, S) denotes the right-regular representation of S acting on the semigroup S^I (= S with identity I adjoined). Precisely $(S^I, S) = (S^I, S, R)$, $R: S^I \times S \to S^I$ and $R(s, r) = sr$. Z_p denotes the cyclic group of order p.

We now quote from the introduction of Krohn and Rhodes [*12*].

(X, S) denotes the finite semigroup S acting faithfully on the right of the finite set X. One of the main problems in the study of finite semigroups is to determine all ways in which coordinates can be entered into X so that the action of S on X is in *triangular form*. (Precise definitions given below.)

An important class of semigroups, namely wreath products, are by definition already in triangular form.

Let (X_j, S_j) be given for $j = 1, \ldots, n$. Let $X = X_n \times \cdots \times X_1$. Let S be the semigroup of all functions $\psi: X \to X$ satisfying the following conditions:

[(7.2)] (Triangular Action). If $p_k: X \to X_k$ denotes the k-th projection map, then for each $k = 1, \ldots, n$ there exists

$$f: X_k \times \cdots \times X_1 \to X_k$$

such that

$$p_k\psi(t_n, \ldots, t_{k+1}, t_k, \ldots, t_1) = f_k(t_k, \ldots, t_1)$$

for all $t_i \in X_i$, $i = 1, \ldots, n$. That is, the new k-th coordinate resulting from the action of ψ depends only on the values of the old first k coordinates and ψ. We write $\psi = \mathrm{w}(f_n, \ldots, f_1)$.

[(7.3)] (k-th component action lies in S_k). We require $f_1 \in S_1$, and for all $k = 2, \ldots, n$ and all

$$\alpha = (t_{k-1}, \ldots, t_1) \in X_{k-1} \times \cdots \times X_1,$$

the function $g_\alpha: X_k \to X_k$ given by $g_\alpha(y_k) = f_k(y_k, t_{k-1}, \ldots, t_1)$ is an element of S_k.

Then $(X_n, S_n) \wr \cdots \wr (X_1, S_1) = (X, S)$ is the *wreath product* of $(X_n, S_n), \ldots, (X_1, S_1)$, and $(X_n, S_n) \mathrm{w} \cdots \mathrm{w} (X_1, S_1) = S$ is the abstract semigroup determined by (X, S).

Now if a triangulation of (X, S) is taken to mean a solution of

$$(X, S) \leqslant (X_n, S_n) \wr \cdots \wr (X_1, S_1)$$

with $S \leqslant S_n \mathrm{w} \cdots \mathrm{w} S_1$ (where $\leqslant$ denotes subsemigroup) and $X \subseteq X_n \times \cdots \times X_1$ then many transformation semigroups will have no non-trivial triangulations. For example, if $(X, S) = (D_n, F_R(D_n))$

where $F_R(D_n)$ is the semigroup of all functions on $D_n = \{1, \ldots, n\}$, acting on the right of D_n, then it can be shown that

$$(D_n, F_R(D_n)) \leqslant (X_n, S_n) \wr \cdots \wr (X_1, S_1)$$

implies $(D_n, F_R(D_n)) \leqslant (X_i, S_i)$ for some i with $1 \leqslant i \leqslant n$. Thus this definition of triangulation is not useful.

The proper definition of triangulation requires that we allow the space X to be expanded to Y and let T be chosen so that

$$(Y, T) \twoheadrightarrow (X, S) \quad \text{and} \quad (Y, T) \leqslant (X_n, S_n) \wr \cdots \wr (X_1, S_1).$$

Precisely, we say (X, S) divides (Y, T), or $(X, S) | (Y, T)$, if and only if there exists $Y' \subseteq Y$ and $T' \leqslant T$ so that $Y'T' \subseteq Y'$ and there exists $\theta: Y' \twoheadrightarrow X$ and an epimorphism $\varphi: T' \twoheadrightarrow S$ so that

$$\theta(y't') = \theta(y')\,\varphi(t')$$

for $y' \in Y'$, $t' \in T'$. For S_1, S_2 semigroups, we write $S_1 \mid S_2$ if and only if S_1 is a homomorphic image of a subsemigroup of S_2.

Now by definition, a *triangulation of* (X, S) *with component action* $(X_n, S_n), \ldots, (X_1, S_1)$ is a solution of

$$(X, S) | (X_n, S_n) \wr \cdots \wr (X_1, S_1). \tag{7.4}$$

Let (A, A^*) denote the transformation semigroup where A^* consists of the identity map and all constant maps on A. Notice $a \in A^*$ implies $a^2 = a$.

[From Section 2] we know that (X, S) satisfies an equation of the form [(7.4)] where each (X_i, S_i) can be chosen so that either $(X_j, S_j) = (X_j, X_j^*)$ or (X_j, S_j) is a finite *simple* group acting transitively.

Further, the simple groups can be chosen from among the Jordan-Hölder factors of the maximal subgroups of S. Also, if G is such a simple group, then in any solution of [(7.4)] G divides S_i for some i with $1 \leqslant j \leqslant n$.

S is a *combinatorial* semigroup (by definition) if and only if the *subgroups* of S have order one. Thus as a corollary [of the above theorem] S is combinatorial if and only if S satisfies

$$(X, S) | (X_n, X_n^*) \wr \cdots \wr (X_1, X_1^*) \tag{7.5}$$

for some sets $X_1, \ldots, X_n$.

The importance of determining the triangulations of (X, S) is evident. It is the canonical mathematical problem of entering coordinates so that the action is as transparent as possible. Further, an analysis of this problem has led to structure theorems for finite semigroups. Using these structure theorems, it is possible, for example, to extend the definitions and theorems of p-length of finite groups, introduced by Hall and Higman [[*6*]], to finite semigroups. Also a form of the Jordan-Hölder theorem can be extended to finite semigroups. [(See below.)] Triangulations are important in analyzing physical experiments which admit a model having a finite phase space, as for example in bacterial intermediary metabolism. Here simple groups play the role analogous to "eigenvectors". See [[*13*]]. Also triangulations are important in the mathematical theory of automata, finite state machines and switching circuits. [See [*14*].]

(7.6) **Notation.** Let $S \in \mathscr{S}$. Then an *admissible triangulation* of S is a solution $(*)$ of

$$(S^I, S) \text{ divides } (S_n{}^I, S_n) \wr \cdots \wr (S_n{}^I, S_1) \tag{7.7}$$

where each S_j is a combinatorial semigroup or $S_j = Z_p$ for some prime p. The *Jordan-Hölder function* for the admissible triangulation $(*)$ of S is the function $JH_S(*)\colon \mathscr{P} \to N$ where $JH_S(*)(p)$ is the number of times Z_p occurs among $S_1, S_2, \ldots, S_n$.

If $f, g\colon \mathscr{P} \to N$, then by definition $f \leqslant g$ if and only if $f(p) \leqslant g(p)$ for all $p \in \mathscr{P}$.

(7.8) **Conjecture** (Jordan-Hölder theorem for $\mathscr{S}$). Let $S \in \mathscr{S}$, i.e., let S be a union of solvable groups. Then there exists a unique function $JH(S)\colon \mathscr{P} \to N$ called the Jordan-Hölder function of S, which satisfies the following two properties.

(7.9) Let $(*)$ be an admissible triangulation of S. Then

$$JH(S) \leqslant JH_S(*).$$

(7.10) There exists an admissible triangulation of S such that

$$JH(S) = JH_S(*).$$

The reader can make the obvious modifications necessary for the analogous statement in the nonsolvable case. For example, replace $\mathscr{P}$ by simple groups, etc.

Unfortunately Conjecture 7.8 is false as it stands for arbitrary finite semigroups, e.g., for inverse semigroups see Rhodes and Tilson [*24*]. See however Remark 7.13.

To justify the name we have the following.

(7.11) **Proposition.** Let G be a finite group. Let $JH(G)$: PRIMES $\to N$ be defined as usual by $JH(G)(P)$ equals the number of times the simple group P occurs as a composition (or Jordan-Hölder) factor of G. Then $JH(G)$ satisfies (7.9) and (7.10).

In short, Conjecture 7.8 is true for groups.

PROOF. See Maurer and Rhodes [*16*] and Maurer [*15*].

(7.12) **Remark.** (a) Let $S \in \mathscr{S}$ and further suppose that if G_1 and G_2 are two maximal subgroups in distinct $\mathscr{J}$ classes of S (i.e., $S^1G_1S^1 \neq S^1G_2S^1$), then the orders of G_1 and G_2 are relatively prime. Then set $JH(S) = \sum \{JH(G)$: G ranges over a complete set of non-$\mathscr{J}$-equivalent maximal subgroups of $S\}$ and $\sum$ denotes pointwise addition of functions. Then it is not difficult, using the proof of Proposition 7.11, to show that this $JH(S)$ satisfies (7.9) and (7.10).

(b) Let S be the union of the two groups H and G with G the kernel of S. Let e be the identity of G. Then φ: $H \to G$ $\varphi(h) = h \cdot e = e \cdot h = e \cdot h \cdot e$ is a homomorphism of H into G. Now define $JH(S) = JH(G) + JH(\ker \varphi)$. Then this $JH(S)$ satisfies (7.9) and (7.10).

(c) A formula for $JH(S)$, when $S \in \mathscr{S}$, can be given. For details see Rhodes [*25*].

(d) Let $S = F_R(X_n)$. See (4.3)d. Then

$$\begin{aligned} JH(S) &= JH(S_n) + \cdots + JH(S_2) \\ &= nZ_2 + A_5 + \cdots + A_n + 2Z_3 \end{aligned}$$

where S_j is the symmetric group on j letters and A_j is the alternating group on j letters.

(7.13) **Remark.** (a) The statement of the Jordan-Hölder theorem for arbitrary finite semigroups is the same as Conjecture 7.8, except that the definition of admissible triangulation is changed. We must also demand in (7.7) that the epimorphism φ of the division of mapping semigroups be at least γ or possibly $\gamma + \mathscr{J}'$. We can not go into details here. In this case a deep question is the following: When is (7.10) satisfied by $(*)$ and $(*)$ has length the complexity?

8. Possible Extension of the Theory to Compact Semigroups

For references on compact semigroups see Hofmann and Mostert [*8*] and Day [*14*, Chapter 10].

Let α denote one of the Green relations $\mathscr{L}$, $\mathscr{R}$, or $\mathscr{H}$. Then from the proof of Krohn *et al.* [*14*, Proposition 8.3.19] we have the following.

(8.1) **Proposition.** Let S be a compact semigroup. Assume the following.

(8.2) There exists a finite number of compact semigroups

$$S = S_n, S_{n-1}, \ldots, S_0 = \{1\}$$

and epimorphisms (equals continuous onto homomorphism) so that

$$S \underset{\gamma}{\twoheadrightarrow} S_{n-1} \underset{\alpha'}{\twoheadrightarrow} S_{n-2} \underset{\gamma}{\twoheadrightarrow} S_{n-3} \twoheadrightarrow \cdots \twoheadrightarrow \{1\}$$

and such that each epimorphism is either a γ or an α' epimorphism.

Then if $\theta: S \twoheadrightarrow T$ is an arbitrary epimorphism, $\theta = \theta_m \cdots \theta_1$, where $\theta_1, \theta_3, \ldots$ are γ epimorphisms and $\theta_2, \theta_4, \ldots$ are α' epimorphisms.

PROOF (See Rhodes [*19*, Proposition 6.8] or Krohn *et al.* [*14*, Proposition 8.3.19]). *Is Proposition* 8.1 *valid if "α'" is replaced by "α" throughout?*

The first problem is to determine which compact semigroups satisfy the condition (8.2). *All*? At any rate let $\mathscr{C}$ denote the collection of compact semigroups satisfying (8.2).

Now the idea for classifying the members of $\mathscr{C}$ is the following. Let $\mathscr{I}$ denote a collection of compact semigroups about which detailed information is available and for $S \in \mathscr{C}$ let $\#_{\alpha-\mathscr{I}}(S)$ be the smallest integer n such that there exists a series

$$(8.3) \quad S \underset{\gamma}{\twoheadrightarrow} S_{11} \underset{\alpha'}{\twoheadrightarrow} S_{12} \underset{\gamma}{\twoheadrightarrow} S_{21} \underset{\alpha'}{\twoheadrightarrow} S_{22} \twoheadrightarrow \cdots \underset{\gamma}{\twoheadrightarrow} S_{n1} \underset{\alpha'}{\twoheadrightarrow} S_{n2}$$

with $S_{n2} \in \mathscr{I}$.

Then we can classify members of $\mathscr{C}$ via the values of the functions $\#_{\alpha-\mathscr{I}}$. When $\mathscr{I} = \{1\}$, we write $\#_\alpha$ in place of $\#_{\alpha-\mathscr{I}}$. *Compute* $\#_{\mathscr{H}}$ *for the examples of Chapter* D *of Hofmann and Mostert* [*8*] *and the many examples of Hunter and Anderson.* This type of classification is a standard theme in the work on compact semigroups. For example, taking $\mathscr{I}$

to be the collection of I semigroups, Mostert and Hofmann determine the structure of all compact semigroups H which satisfy

$$H \underset{\mathscr{H}}{\twoheadrightarrow} I \in \mathscr{I}.$$

They show only hormos satisfy the condition.

Clearly if $S \underset{\gamma}{\twoheadrightarrow} T$, then $\#_{\alpha-I}(S) = \#_{\alpha-I}(T)$. Thus because of this and Proposition 8.1 it is very important *to determine properties of compact semigroups preserved under epimorphisms which are one-to-one on each subgroup*. Here topological invariants from algebraic topology will be useful. For example, for compact connected semigroups the Alexander-Spanier or Cěch homology for S and T, with $S \underset{\gamma}{\twoheadrightarrow} T$, are isomorphic by the "first fundamental theorem of compact semigroups." See Hofmann and Mostert [*8*, Chapter A]. Also an analysis of α epimorphism is available. See Rhodes [*21*] and Munn [*18*]. For example, an *interesting problem* is to determine those compact semigroups with $\#_{\mathscr{H}-\mathscr{I}}$ equal to 1, i.e., those S such that

$$S \underset{\gamma}{\twoheadrightarrow} H \underset{\mathscr{H}}{\twoheadrightarrow} I, \qquad I \text{ an } I \text{ semigroup.}$$

By the results quoted above this is equivalent to determining those S such that

$$S \underset{\gamma}{\twoheadrightarrow} \text{hormos.}$$

However, the most important question is to obtain general properties of the functions $\#_{\alpha-\mathscr{I}}: \mathscr{C} \rightarrow N$ for various interesting classes $\mathscr{I}$. One can also mimic the definitions of $\#_I$ of Conjecture 4.33 for the compact case. Then one can ask is $\#_I \leqslant \#_L$, etc. by analogy with the previous sections on finite semigroups.

ACKNOWLEDGMENT

Bret Tilson has generously consented to allow his exposition of p length for semigroups to be published here as an appendix. We thank him for this and many other kindnesses.

REFERENCES

1. D. Allen, "Relations between the local and global structure of finite semigroups," Ph.D. thesis, Univ. of California, Berkeley, 1968.
   Present address: Bell Telephone Laboratories, Holmdel, New Jersey.
2. A. H. Clifford and G. B. Preston, "The Algebraic Theory of Semigroups," Vol. 1 (Math. Surveys No. 7). Amer. Math. Soc., Providence, Rhode Island, 1962.
3. N. Graham, R. Graham, and J. Rhodes, Maximal subsemigroups of finite semigroups, *J. Combinatorial Theory* **4**, 203–209 (1968).

4. J. A. Green and D. Rees, On semigroups in which $x^r = x$, *Proc. Cambridge Philos. Soc.* **48**, 35–40 (1952).
5. M. Hall, "The Theory of Groups." MacMillan, New York, 1959.
6. P. Hall and G. Higman, The p-length of a p-solvable group, and reduction theorems for Burnside's problem, *Proc. London Math. Soc.* **7**, 1–42 (1956).
7. G. Higman, p-length Theorems, *Amer. Math. Soc. Symp. Pure Math.* pp. 1–16 (1963).
8. K. H. Hofmann and P. S. Mostert, "Elements of Compact Semigroups." Merrill, Columbus, Ohio, 1966.
9. K. Krohn, and J. Rhodes, Algebraic theory of machines, *Proc. Symp. Math. Theory Automata*, (J. Fox, ed.), pp. 341–384, Polytech. Inst. Brooklyn (1962).
10. K. Krohn and J. Rhodes, Results on finite semigroups derived from the algebraic theory of machines, *Proc. Nat. Acad. Sci. U.S.A.* **53**, 499–501 (1965).
11. K. Krohn and J. Rhodes, Algebraic theory of machines. I. Prime decomposition theorem for finite semigroups and machines, *Trans. Amer. Math. Soc.* **116**, 450–464 (1965).
12. K. Krohn and J. Rhodes, Complexity of Finite Semigroups, *Ann. of Math.* **88**, 128–160 (1968).
13. K. Krohn, R. Langer, and J. Rhodes, Algebraic principles for the analysis of a biochemical system, *J. Comput. System Sci.* **1**, 119–136 (1967).
14. K. Krohn, J. Rhodes, and B. Tilson, Lectures on the Algebraic Theory of Finite Semigroups and Finite State Machines, *in* "Algebraic Theory of Machines, Languages, and Semigroups" (M. A. Arbib, ed.), Chapters 1, 5–9 (Chapter 6 with M. A. Arbib). Academic Press, New York, 1968.
15. W. D. Maurer, On minimal decompositions of group machines, Ph.D. thesis, Univ. of California, Berkeley, 1965.
16. W. D. Maurer and J. Rhodes, Decompositions of Group Machines (to be published).
17. M. Morse and G. Hedlund, Unending chess, symbolic dynamics and a problem in semigroups, *Duke Math. J.* **11**, 1–15 (1944).
18. W. D. Munn, A certain sublattice of the lattice of congruences on a regular semigroup, *Proc. Cambridge Philos. Soc.* **60**, 385–394 (1964).
19. J. Rhodes, Some results on finite semigroups, *J. Algebra* **4**, 471–504 (1966).
20. J. Rhodes, Complexity and Characters of Finite Semigroups, *J. Combinatorial Theory* (to be published).
21. J. Rhodes, A Homomorphism Theorem for Finite Semigroups, *J. Math. Systems Theory* **1**, 289–304 (1967).
22. J. Rhodes, Proof of the fundamental lemma of complexity (weak version) for arbitrary finite semigroups, *J. Combinatorial Theory* (to be published).
23. J. Rhodes, The fundamental lemma of complexity for arbitrary finite semigroups, *Bull. Amer. Math. Soc.* **74**, 1104–1109 (1968).
24. J. Rhodes and B. Tilson, Lower bounds for complexity of finite semigroups, *Math. Systems Theory* (to be published).
25. J. Rhodes, Jordan-Hölder theorem for finite semigroups (to be published).
26. P. Stiffler, Ph.D. thesis, Univ. of California, Berkeley (to appear).
27. B. Tilson, Ph.D. thesis, Univ. of California, Berkeley (to appear).
28. Y. Zalcstein, Ph.D. thesis, Univ. of California, Berkeley (to appear).
29. H. Zassenhaus, "The Theory of Groups." Chelsea, New York, 1949.
30. P. H. Zeiger, Cascade synthesis of finite-state machines, *Information and Control* **10**, 419–433 (1967), plus erratum.

NOTE ADDED IN PROOF. A gap has been found in the proof of Rhodes [*22*]. Let Axiom II″ be Axiom II′ with γ replaced by $\gamma(\mathscr{H})$. Then the existing correct part of Rhodes [*22*] proves Axiom II″ but not Axiom II′. The proof of the equivalence of Axiom II″ and Axiom II′ contained an error. Of course, Axiom II″ and Axiom II′ are trivially equivalent in the regular case. Probably Axiom II is true.

The proof of Corollary (4.14) is valid in the regular case using Axiom II″ or in general if $\mathscr{L}'$ is replaced by $\mathscr{L}$ and machine methods are used.

The statement and the proof of Corollary (4.16) are valid.

Corollary (4.17), Theorem (4.22), Corollary (4.23), and Corollary (4.26) are valid if S is restricted to be a regular semigroup.

Proposition (4.29) is valid if S is a regular semigroup and furthermore Proposition (4.29)(a) is valid for all semigroups if γ is replaced by $\gamma(\mathscr{H})$ and $\mathscr{L}'$ is replaced by $\mathscr{L}$ in (4.28).

In very recent unpublished work of Rhodes and Tilson, Conjecture (4.33) is shown to be false. However, by following Remark (4.37)(1), if $IG(T_K)$ is replaced by something larger (type-II semigroups), then substantial progress has been made on verifying this modified Conjecture (4.33). See forthcoming papers by Rhodes and Tilson.

Theorem (5.8) is valid for regular semigroups and for general finite semigroups if γ is replaced by $\gamma(\mathscr{H})$.

Theorem (5.10) and Proposition (5.11) and their proofs are valid for regular semigroups.

Corollary (5.12) and its proof are correct.

Proposition (5.14) and its proof are valid for regular semigroups and for general finite semigroups if $\mathscr{L}'$ is replaced by $\mathscr{L}$ and machine methods are used. Theorem (5.15) and its proof are valid for regular semigroups.

Appendix to "Algebraic Theory of Finite Semigroups"

On the p Length of p-Solvable Semigroups: Preliminary Results*

BRET R. TILSON

Department of Mathematics
University of California
Berkeley, California

Introduction

This paper extends the concept of p length for finite groups to finite semigroups and develops methods for computing the p length of a p-solvable semigroup in terms of certain homomorphism series of the semigroup. The p length of this paper, when restricted to groups, is the well-known p length for groups (see Hall and Higman [*3*]). The idea of p length for semigroups is due, naturally, to John Rhodes.

In this paper we assume the reader is acquainted with the terminology and results of Krohn *et al.* [*1*, Chapters 1, 5–9]. All semigroups considered herein are finite unless otherwise stated.

Let p be a prime integer. We say a semigroup is p solvable if and only if its maximal subgroups are p solvable. Also a semigroup is a p semigroup (p' semigroup) if and only if its maximal subgroups are p groups (p' groups). We say a semigroup S *divides* a semigroup T (written $S \mid T$) if and only if S is a homomorphic image of a subsemigroup of T. $S \text{ w } T$ denotes the wreath product of S and T. The prime decomposition theorem for finite semigroups of Krohn and Rhodes (Theorem 5.3.3 of Krohn *et al.* [*1*]) says that for any finite semigroup S, there exists semigroups $S_1, \ldots, S_n$ such that

$$S | S_n \text{ w } \cdots \text{ w } S_1 \qquad (*)$$

* This research was sponsored in part by the United States Air Force, Office of Scientific Research, Grant No. AFOSR 68-1477.

where the S_i are either simple groups that divide S or are combinatorial semigroups. When S is p solvable, these simple groups (called the PRIMES of S) are either p groups or p' groups. Now, the wreath product of p groups is a p group, and the wreath product of p' groups and combinatorial semigroups is a p' semigroup. So we conclude from $(*)$ that there exist semigroups $T_1, \ldots, T_m$ such that

$$S | T_m \text{ w } \cdots \text{ w } T_1 \qquad (**)$$

where the T_i are alternately p groups and p' semigroups. Then the p length of S, $l_p(S)$, is defined by considering all expressions of the form $(**)$ and counting the number of p groups used in each one. Then $l_p(S)$ is the smallest such number. (Compare this with the definition of group complexity, $\#_G(S)$, given in Chapter 6 of Krohn *et al.* [*1*].) If S is a group, then $l_p(S)$ as defined above equals the p length as defined by Hall and Higman [*3*]; this is proved in Proposition 1.20.

This paper is a generalization of the group complexity results of Rhodes found in Chapters 6, 8, and 9 of Krohn *et al.* [*1*]. Instead of using a single prime p, we express our results in a more general context by letting π be a set of prime integers and letting π' be the complementary set of primes. Then we have the π length, $l_\pi(S)$. By plugging $\pi = \{\text{all primes}\}$ and $\pi' = \emptyset$ into this paper, one gets back Chapters 6, 8 and most of 9 of Krohn *et al.* [*1*], i.e., $l_\pi = \#_G$.

The results of Krohn *et al.* [*1*, Chapter 9], relating subsemigroup structure to complexity are not generalized to p length here but will appear in a later paper. Also the paper by Rhodes and Tilson [*2*] will be extended to p length. Beyond that we hope to prove certain Sylow and Jordan-Hölder type theorems for semigroups, and we will try to use the results of Hall and Higman [*3*] to obtain a better understanding of complexity and the global structure of finite semigroups.

1. Definitions of π Complexity and π Length: Elementary Results

1.1 Definition. Let π be a set of prime integers and let π' be the complementary set of primes. Then:

(a) A π *group* is a finite group whose order is divisible only by the primes of π. A finite group is π *solvable* if and only if each of its composition factors is either a π group or a π' group (see Hall and Higman [*3*]).

(b) A π *semigroup* is a finite semigroup all of whose maximal subgroups are π groups. A finite semigroup is π *solvable* if and only if each of its maximal subgroups is π solvable.

(c) Let S be a semigroup. An element $s \in S$ is a π *element* if and only if s belongs to a subgroup of S and the order of s is divisible only by primes of π.

1.2 Definition. (a) Let $\mathscr{S}_\pi$ be the collection of all finite π semigroups. Similarly, define $\mathscr{S}_{\pi'}$. Let $\mathscr{S}$ be the collection of all finite π-solvable semigroups.

(b) Let Π be the set of all finite simple groups (PRIMES) whose orders are divisible only by primes of π. Similarly, define Π'.

1.3 Fact. (a) Both Π and Π' are closed under division by PRIMES. That is, if $P \in$ PRIMES and $Q \in \Pi$ (or Π'), then $P|Q$ implies $P \in \Pi$ (or Π'). Furthermore, Π and Π' are disjoint.

(b) $\mathscr{S}$, $\mathscr{S}_\pi$, and $\mathscr{S}_{\pi'}$ are closed under division and semidirect products, hence direct products and wreath products.

PROOF. (a) If P is a simple group and $P|Q \in \Pi$, then if p is a prime divisor of P, we have $p|O(P)|O(Q)$, so $p \in \pi$.

(b) Recall that PRIMES$(S) = \{P\colon P \in$ PRIMES and $P|S\}$ and PRIMES$(\mathscr{S}) = \{P\colon P \in$ PRIMES(S) for $S \in \mathscr{S}\}$. Then it is clear that PRIMES$(\mathscr{S}_\pi) = \Pi$, PRIMES$(\mathscr{S}_{\pi'}) = \Pi'$, and PRIMES$(\mathscr{S}) = \Pi \cup \Pi'$. Then by (a) it is easy to prove that $\mathscr{S}$, $\mathscr{S}_\pi$, and $\mathscr{S}_{\pi'}$ are closed under division. Suppose $S_1, S_2 \in \mathscr{S}$ (or $\mathscr{S}_\pi, \mathscr{S}_{\pi'}$) and let $P \in$ PRIMES$(S_2 \times_Y S_1)$. Then $P|S_2 \times_Y S_1$ and by the fact that simple groups (PRIMES) are irreducible with respect to semidirect products (see Krohn *et al.* [*1*, Lemma 5.3.6]), either $P|S_1$ or $P|S_2$. Thus $P \in \Pi \cup \Pi'$ (or Π, Π') so $S_2 \times_Y S_1 \in \mathscr{S}$ (or $\mathscr{S}_\pi, \mathscr{S}_{\pi'}$). ∎

1.4 Examples. (a) Let $\pi = \{$all prime integers$\}$, and $\pi' = \{$empty set$\}$.

Then $\mathscr{S} =$ all finite semigroups.

(b) Let p be a prime integer. Let $\pi = \{p\}$. Then $\mathscr{S} =$ all semigroups whose maximal subgroups are p solvable (we call such a semigroup a *p-solvable semigroup*), and $\mathscr{S}_\pi =$ all semigroups whose maximal subgroups are p groups (such a semigroup is called a *p semigroup*).

1.5 Remark. By the prime decomposition theorem for finite semigroups (Krohn *et al.* [*1*, Theorem 5.3.3]), any transformation semigroup (X, S) divides the wreath product of right regular representations of PRIMES(S) and combinatorial transformation semigroups. If S is π solvable, then any such wreath product can be rearranged by combining certain adjacent terms. Namely, combine all adjacent π groups, since the wreath product of π-transformation groups* is a π-transformation group, and combine all combinatorial semigroups and π' groups: the result is a member of $\mathscr{S}_{\pi'}$. We are now ready to define π complexity and π length. *From this point forth, all semigroups considered will be π solvable.*

1.6 Definition. Let (X, S) be a π-solvable transformation semigroup. Then define $\#_\pi(X, S)$, the *π-complexity number* of (X, S), to be the smallest integer n such that

$$(X, S) | (X_n, S_n) \wr \cdots \wr (X_1, S_1) \tag{1.1}$$

where either:

(a) $(X_1, S_1), (X_3, S_3), \ldots$ are π-transformation groups and $S_2, S_4, \ldots$ are π' semigroups; or

(b) $S_1, S_3, \ldots$ are π' semigroups and $(X_2, S_2), (X_4, S_4), \ldots$ are π-transformation groups.

The π *complexity* of (X, S), written $C_\pi(X, S)$, equals $(n, \mathbf{\Pi})$ if and only if (a) holds with $n = \#_\pi(X, S)$, but (b) never holds with $n = \#_\pi(X, S)$. $C_\pi(X, S) = (n, \mathbf{\Pi}')$ if and only if (b) holds with $n = \#_\pi(X, S)$, but (a) never holds with $n = \#_\pi(X, S)$. $C_\pi(X, S) = (n, \mathbf{\Pi} \vee \mathbf{\Pi}')$ if and only if both (a) and (b) can hold with $n = \#_\pi(X, S)$.

1.7 Proposition. (a) The set of all π complexities is a lattice under the ordering $\leqslant$, where $(n, \alpha) \leqslant (m, \beta)$ if and only if either $(n, \alpha) = (m, \beta)$, or $n < m$, or $n = m$ and $\alpha = \mathbf{\Pi} \vee \mathbf{\Pi}'$. The minimal element of the lattice is $(1, \mathbf{\Pi} \vee \mathbf{\Pi}')$.

(b) If $(X, S) | (Y, T)$, then $C_\pi(X, S) \leqslant C_\pi(Y, T)$.

(c) $C_\pi[(X_1, S_1) \times \cdots \times (X_n, S_n)] = \mathrm{LUB}\{C_\pi(X_i, S_i): i = 1, \ldots, n\}$.

Proof. The proofs of (a) and (b) are easy and omitted. For (c), refer to the proof of Fact 6.2.2(c) of Krohn *et al.* [1], which with a minor change will prove (c). ∎

1.8 Proposition. Let (X, S) be a transformation semigroup and let (S^1, S) be the right regular representation of S. Then $C_\pi(X, S) = C_\pi(S^1, S)$, except in the case where S is a π group and the identity of S does not act as the identity map on X. In this case we have

$$C_\pi(S^1, S) = \begin{cases} (1, \mathbf{\Pi} \vee \mathbf{\Pi}') & \text{if } S = \{1\} \\ (1, \mathbf{\Pi}) & \text{if } S \text{ is a nontrivial } \pi \text{ group} \end{cases}$$

* By transformation group, we mean a faithful transformation semigroup (X, S) where S is a group and the identity of S acts as the identity map on X.

while

$$C_\pi(X, S) = \begin{cases} (1, \mathbf{\Pi}') & \text{if } S = \{1\} \\ (2, \mathbf{\Pi} \vee \mathbf{\Pi}') & \text{if } S \text{ is a nontrivial } \pi \text{ group} \end{cases}$$

PROOF. Refer to Krohn *et al.* [*1*], Theorem 6.1.5, for the full details of this proof. An outline follows.

First, by Krohn *et al.* [*1*, Fact 5.2.14(c)], for any (X, S) we have

$$(S^1, S) | (X, S) \times \cdots \times (X, S) \qquad (|X| \text{ times})$$

so by 1.7(c),

$$C_\pi(S^1, S) \leqslant C_\pi(X, S).$$

For the reverse inequality, we first consider $(X, \{0\})$ where $\{0\}$ acts like the identity on X. With the method shown by Krohn *et al.* [*1*, Theorem 6.1.5], $C_\pi(X, \{0\}) \leqslant C_\pi(S, S)$ for any monoid S. Choosing for S a π group and then a π' group, we have $C_\pi(X, \{0\}) \leqslant (1, \mathbf{\Pi})$ and $C_\pi(X, \{0\}) \leqslant (1, \mathbf{\Pi}')$. Hence

$$C_\pi(X, \{0\}) = (1, \mathbf{\Pi} \vee \mathbf{\Pi}') \equiv C_\pi(\{0\}, \{0\}).$$

If (X, S) is a nontrivial π-transformation group, i.e., if S is a nontrivial π group and (X, S) is a transformation group, then by definition, $C_\pi(X, S) = (1, \mathbf{\Pi}) = C_\pi(S^1, S)$.

Now let (X, S) be any transformation semigroup, and consider the equation

$$(X, S) | (S^I \times I_n, S^I \times \{0\}) = (S^I, S^I) \times (I_n, \{0\})$$

derived by Krohn *et al.* [*1*, Theorem 6.1.5]. Here $\{0\}$ acts like the identity on I_n, so $C_\pi(X, S) \leqslant C_\pi(S^I, S^I)$. But S^I is isomorphic to the subsemigroup of $S^1 \times \{0\}^I$ consisting of $(S \times \{0\}) \cup \{(1, I)\}$, so $(S^I, S^I) \subseteq (S^1, S^1) \times (\{0\}^I, \{0\}^I)$ and

$$C_\pi(X, S) \leqslant \text{LUB}\{C_\pi(S^1, S^1), (1, \mathbf{\Pi}')\}. \tag{1.2}$$

Now $C_\pi(S^1, S^1) = C_\pi(S^1, S)$, for if G is a group, then $G^1 = G$ and if T is a π' semigroup, so is T^1. Furthermore, if $(S^1, S) | (X_2, S_2) \wr (X_1, S_1)$, then $(S^1, S^1) | (X_2, S_2^1) \wr (X_1, S_1^1)$. Thus from the definition of π complexity, $C_\pi(S^1, S^1) = C_\pi(S^1, S)$.

Now from (1.2) we have

$$\begin{aligned} C_\pi(X, S) &\leqslant \text{LUB}\{C_\pi(S^1, S), (1, \mathbf{\Pi}')\} \\ &= C_\pi(S^1, S) \quad \text{unless } S \text{ is } \{0\} \text{ or a nontrivial } \pi \text{ group.} \end{aligned} \tag{1.3}$$

Therefore $C_\pi(X, S) = C_\pi(S^1, S)$ unless S is $\{0\}$ or a nontrivial π group and the identity of S does not act like the identity map on X. In these two special cases, we have

$$(1, \mathbf{\Pi} \vee \mathbf{\Pi}') \leqslant C_\pi(X, \{0\}) \leqslant (1, \mathbf{\Pi}')$$

and

$$(1, \mathbf{\Pi}) \leqslant C_\pi(X, S) \leqslant (2, \mathbf{\Pi} \vee \mathbf{\Pi}'),$$

respectively. But in both cases, the π complexity cannot take on the lower bound, since neither $(X, \{0\})$ or (X, S) are, by assumption, transformation groups. Thus the respective π complexities must equal the upper bounds. ▮

1.9 Definition. Define the π *complexity of* S, written $C_\pi(S)$, by $C_\pi(S) \equiv C_\pi(S^1, S)$.

Of course, by Proposition 1.8, $C_\pi(S^1, S) = C_\pi(X, S)$ in all but the special cases mentioned above. However these special cases never, by definition, arise in the π-group, π'-semigroup decompositions that define π complexity, so they will not trouble us. Thus $C_\pi(S) = (1, \mathbf{\Pi} \vee \mathbf{\Pi}')$ if and only if $S = \{0\}$, $C(S) = (1, \mathbf{\Pi})$ if and only if S is a nontrivial π group, and $C(S) = (1, \mathbf{\Pi}')$ if and only if S is a nontrivial π' semigroup.

For all semigroups S, $C_\pi(S) = C_\pi(S^1)$, and if S is not a group, then $C_\pi(S^I) = C_\pi(S)$. If S is a group,

$$C_\pi(S^I) = \begin{cases} (2, \mathbf{\Pi} \vee \mathbf{\Pi}') & \text{if } S \neq \{0\} \\ (1, \mathbf{\Pi}') & \text{if } S = \{0\}. \end{cases}$$

These statements were proved in the proof of Proposition 1.8. The same statement can be made about S^0, i.e., $C_\pi(S^0) = C_\pi(S^I)$, for it is easy to show that $S|S^0|S \times \{0\}^I$.

1.10 Definition. We define addition $\oplus$ for π complexities in the obvious way:

$\oplus$	$(m, \mathbf{\Pi})$	$(m, \mathbf{\Pi}')$	$(m, \mathbf{\Pi} \vee \mathbf{\Pi}')$
		m even	
$(n, \mathbf{\Pi})$	$(n + m, \mathbf{\Pi})$	$(n + m - 1, \mathbf{\Pi}')$	$(n + m - 1, \mathbf{\Pi}')$
$(n, \mathbf{\Pi}')$	$(n + m - 1, \mathbf{\Pi})$	$(n + m, \mathbf{\Pi}')$	$(n + m - 1, \mathbf{\Pi})$
$(n, \mathbf{\Pi}' \vee \mathbf{\Pi})$	$(n + m - 1, \mathbf{\Pi})$	$(n + m - 1, \mathbf{\Pi}')$	$(n + m - 1, \mathbf{\Pi}' \vee \mathbf{\Pi})$
		m odd	
$(n, \mathbf{\Pi})$	$(n + m - 1, \mathbf{\Pi})$	$(n + m, \mathbf{\Pi}')$	$(n + m - 1, \mathbf{\Pi})$
$(n, \mathbf{\Pi}')$	$(n + m, \mathbf{\Pi})$	$(n + m - 1, \mathbf{\Pi}')$	$(n + m - 1, \mathbf{\Pi}')$
$(n, \mathbf{\Pi}' \vee \mathbf{\Pi})$	$(n + m - 1, \mathbf{\Pi})$	$(n + m - 1, \mathbf{\Pi}')$	$(n + m - 1, \mathbf{\Pi}' \vee \mathbf{\Pi})$

Notice that $\oplus$ is associative but not commutative. The addition $\oplus$ was defined so that next fact would be true.

1.11 Fact. If $S|(X_2, S_2) \text{ w } (X_1, S_1)$, then

$$C_\pi(S) \leqslant C_\pi(S_2) \oplus C_\pi(S_1). \quad \blacksquare$$

We now define the π length of a π-solvable semigroup which is a nonnegative integer directly related to C_π.

1.12 Definition. Let (X, S) be a transformation semigroup. Then the π *length of* (X, S), written $l_\pi(X, S)$, is the smallest nonnegative integer n such that

$$(X, S)|(Y_n, P'_n) \text{ w } (X_n, P_n) \text{ w } (Y_{n-1}, P'_{n-1}) \text{ w } \cdots \text{ w } (X_1, P_1) \text{ w } (Y_0, P'_0),$$

where the (X_i, P_i), $i = 1, \ldots, n$, are nontrivial π-transformation groups and the P'_i, $i = 0, \ldots, n$, are π' semigroups (all nontrivial except possibly P'_0 and P'_n).

1.13 Remark. Of course, l_π and C_π are directly related. If $C_\pi(X, S) = (n, \mathbf{\Pi})$, then

$$l_\pi(X, S) = \begin{cases} n/2 & \text{if } n \text{ even} \\ (n+1)/2 & \text{if } n \text{ odd.} \end{cases}$$

If $C_\pi(X, S) = (n, \mathbf{\Pi}')$, then

$$l_\pi(X, S) = \begin{cases} n/2 & \text{if } n \text{ even} \\ (n-1)/2 & \text{if } n \text{ odd.} \end{cases}$$

If $C_\pi(X, S) = (n, \mathbf{\Pi} \vee \mathbf{\Pi}')$, then

$$l_\pi(X, S) = \begin{cases} n/2 & \text{if } n \text{ even} \\ (n-1)/2 & \text{if } n \text{ odd.} \end{cases}$$

Then by Proposition 1.8, it is easy to verify that

$$l_\pi(X, S) = l_\pi(S^1, S) \quad \text{for any } (X, S),$$

even in the exceptional cases of (1.8).

1.14 Definition. Let S be a semigroup. Define the π *length of* S, written $l_\pi(S)$, by $l_\pi(S) = l_\pi(S^1, S)$. This is well defined by the preceding remark.

1.15 Proposition. (a) If $S|T$, then $l_\pi(S) \leqslant l_\pi(T)$

(b) $l_\pi[S_1 \times \cdots \times S_n] = \max\{l_\pi(S_i): i = 1, \ldots, n\}$
(c) If $S|(X_2, S_2) \le w (X_1, S_1)$, then $l_\pi(S) \leqslant l_\pi(S_2) + l_\pi(S_1)$.

PROOF. (a) and (c) are obvious, and (b) follows from Proposition 1.7(c). ∎

The purpose of this paper is to develop methods of computing the π length of π-solvable semigroups. Certain results are obtained for a restricted class of semigroup which include union of group semigroups. If π is chosen to be all prime integers, then the π length, l_π, becomes the group complexity, $\#_G$. This paper is a generalization of Krohn *et al.* [*1*, Chapters 6, 8, and 9] with occasional new results. These generalizations were motivated by the concept of p length of p-solvable groups, introduced by Hall and Higman [*3*]. In fact, if π consists of a single prime p, then the associated l_π when restricted to groups is just the p length, l_p [*3*]. This fact will be verified below. So, with this choice of π, l_π is the extension of group p length to semigroups.

1.16 Remark. We review two basic facts about groups and wreath products.

(a) Let G be a group with a normal subgroup N. Then G can be represented (faithfully) as a subgroup of the wreath product $(N, N) \mathrm{w} (G/N, G/N)$. This is known as the monomial representation. Thus, if $G = G_0 \rhd G_1 \rhd \cdots \rhd G_{n-1} \rhd G_n = \{1\}$ is a subnormal series of G, then

$$G \subseteq (G_0/G_1, G_0/G_1) \mathrm{w} (G_1/G_2, G_1/G_2) \mathrm{w} \cdots \mathrm{w} (G_{n-1}, G_{n-1}).$$

See the proof of Lemma 5.3.8 in Krohn *et al.* [*1*] for details.

(b) If G is a subgroup of a semidirect product of two semigroups, say $S_2 \times_Y S_1$, then G is an extension of a subgroup of S_2 by a subgroup of S_1. To wit, let $p_1: S_2 \times_Y S_1 \twoheadrightarrow S_1$ be the projection homomorphism. Then $p_1(G)$ is a subgroup of S_1, and $\ker(p_1|G)$ is isomorphic to a subgroup of S_2. See the proof of Lemma 5.3.6 in Krohn *et al.* [*1*] for details.

1.17 Fact. Let G be a group and N a normal subgroup of G. Then N and G/N are π groups if and only if G is a π group.

PROOF. π Semigroups are closed under division and wreath products. Thus, if G is a π group, then N and G/N are π groups. Conversely, let N and G/N be π groups. By the monomial representation of groups $G \subseteq (N, N) \mathrm{w} (G/N, G/N)$, a π group. Thus G is a π group. ∎

1.18 Corollary. Let G be a π-solvable group. Then there exists a unique maximal normal π subgroup of G.

PROOF. It is sufficient to prove that if N_1 and N_2 are normal π subgroups of G, then N_1N_2 is a normal π subgroup of G. Certainly N_1N_2 is normal. $N_1N_2/N_1 \cong N_2/(N_1 \cap N_2)$ and $N_2/(N_1 \cap N_2)$ is a homomorphic image of N_2, so N_1N_2/N_1 is a π group. By the above fact, then, N_1N_2 is a π group. ▮

1.19 Definition (refer to Hall and Higman [3]). Let G be a π-solvable group, and define the upper π series for G,

$$1 = P_0 \leqslant N_0 < P_1 < \cdots < P_l \leqslant N_l = G. \tag{1.4}$$

by defining P_i/N_{i-1} to be the largest normal π subgroup of G/N_{i-1}, $i = i, \ldots, l$, and defining N_i/P_i to be the largest normal π' subgroup of G/P_i, $i = 0, \ldots, l$. This series is well defined by (1.18). Then define the (*group*) π *length*, denoted temporarily by $\hat{l}_\pi$, by $\hat{l}_\pi(G) = l$.

Any series for G of the form (1.4) is called a π series for G, and the upper π series is a π series for G of minimal length. Also note that if $G|H$, then $\hat{l}_\pi(G) \leqslant \hat{l}_\pi(H)$. (See Hall and Higman [3] for details.)

We now will show that the π length for groups defined above agrees with the π length defined for semigroups.

1.20 Proposition. If G is a π-solvable group, then

$$l_\pi(G) = \hat{l}_\pi(G).$$

PROOF. Let

$$1 = P_0 \leqslant N_0 < P_1 < \cdots < P_l \leqslant N_l = G$$

be the upper π series for G, i.e., $\hat{l}_\pi(G) = l$. Then, as in Remark 1.16(a), we have

$$G|N_0 \text{ w } P_1/N_0 \text{ w } N_1/P_1 \text{ w } \cdots \text{ w } P_l/N_{l-1} \text{ w } N_l/P_l,$$

and the terms are alternatively π groups and π' (semi)groups. Hence $l_\pi(G) \leqslant \hat{l}_\pi(G)$.

Conversely, suppose $l_\pi(G) = n$ and

$$G \twoheadleftarrow G' \subseteq (Y_n, P_n') \text{ w } (X_n, P_n) \text{ w } \cdots \text{ w } (X_1, P_1) \text{ w } (Y_0, P_0')$$

where the (X_i, P_i) are π-transformation groups and the P_i' are π' semigroups. Furthermore, G' is a group; for if it is not a group, it contains a subgroup that maps onto G and G' can then be replaced by the subgroup. See Fact 1.1.9(c) of Krohn *et al.* [1].

Refer to Remark 1.16(b). Let

$$p_n': (Y_n, P_n') \text{ w } \cdots \text{ w } (Y_0, P_0') \twoheadrightarrow (X_n, P_n) \text{ w } \cdots \text{ w } (Y_0, P_0')$$

be the projection map, and let $\ker(p_n'|G') = V_0$ so $p_n'(G') \cong G'/V_0$. $V_0 \subseteq F(X, P_n')$ for some set X, so V_0 is a π' group. Now

$$G'/V_0 \subseteq (X_n, P_n) \text{ w } \cdots \text{ w } (Y_0, P_0').$$

Define $p_n: (X_n, P_n) \text{ w } \cdots \text{ w } (Y_0, P_0') \twoheadrightarrow (Y_{n-1}, P_{n-1}') \text{ w } \cdots \text{ w } (Y_0, P_0')$ to be the projection map, and let $\ker(p_n|G'/V_0) = U_1/V_0$. Then U_1/V_0 is either a normal π subgroup of G'/V_0 or $U_1/V_0 = \{1\}$. In any case continuing on in this manner yields a π series of length n at most. But $\hat{l}_\pi(G')$ is the minimum of the lengths of all π series of G'. Therefore $\hat{l}_\pi(G') \leqslant n = l_\pi(G)$, and $\hat{l}_\pi(G) \leqslant \hat{l}_\pi(G')$, so the reverse inequality, $\hat{l}_\pi(G) \leqslant l_\pi(G)$, is obtained. ∎

2. Reduction Homomorphisms and Semilocal Theory

In this section we generalize much of Krohn *et al.* [*1*, Chapter 8, Section 2]. The goal is to develop tools that will enable us to establish three axioms which uniquely characterize π length. Axiom I has already been stated in Propositions 1.15(a) and (b). Axiom II will say that if $\varphi: S \twoheadrightarrow T$ is a π homomorphism (all the group kernels of φ are π' groups), then $l_\pi(S) = l_\pi(T)$. Axiom III is more technical and must wait until later for its description.

Recall from Krohn *et al.* [*1*, Chapter 8], the definitions of the homomorphisms RM_J, LM_J, GGM_J, GM_J, RLM_J, and LLM_J, where J is a regular $\mathcal{J}$ class.

2.1 Definition. Let S be a semigroup with a regular $\mathcal{J}$ class J. Let G be a maximal subgroup of J and let N be normal in G. (We then say N is a *normal subgroup of* S). In Krohn *et al.* [*1*, Definition 8.3.27], the homomorphism $S \twoheadrightarrow S/(J, G, N)$ was defined. Descriptively, $S/(J, G, N)$ is obtained by throwing $F(J)$ away and reducing the group in J to G/N. *From this point forth* $S/(J, G, N)$ *will be denoted as* S/N, since given a normal subgroup N, its maximal subgroup, G, and $\mathcal{J}$ class, J, are implicitly known. It was shown that the semigroup S/N is independent (up to isomorphism) of the coordinate system chosen for J. Notice that S/N has a unique 0-minimal ideal (the image of $J \cup F(J)$) that is regular, so expressions such as $RM(S/N)$ makes sense.

2.2 Definition. Let N be a normal subgroup of S.

(a) Define the homomorphism RM_N on S by

$$S \twoheadrightarrow S/N \twoheadrightarrow RM(S/N).$$

That is, $RM_N(S) = RM(S/N)$. Thus $RM_N(S)$ is obtained from S by throwing away $F(J)$, reducing the group in J to G/N, and acting faithfully on the right of the image of J. If N is trivial, then $RM_N = RM_J$; if N is a maximal subgroup of S, then $RM_N = RLM_J$. $RM_N(S)$ is an RM (right-mapping) semigroup.

(b) Define LM_N dually. That is $LM_N(S) = LM(S/N)$. If N is trivial, then $LM_N = LM_J$, and if N is a maximal subgroup of S, then $LM_N = LLM_J$. $LM_N(S)$ is an LM (left-mapping) semigroup.

(c) Define GGM_N and GM_N by $GGM_N(S) = GGM(S/N)$ and $GM_N(S) = GM(S/N)$, respectively. If G/N is nontrivial, then $GGM_N = GM_N$, and if N is trivial, i.e., $N = \{1\}$, then $GGM_N = GGM_J$ and $GM_N = GM_J$. If G/N is trivial, then $GM_N(S) = \{0\}$ and $GGM_N = RM(LLM_J) = LM(RLM_J)$. $GGM_N(S)$ is a GGM (generalized group mapping) semigroup, and $GM_N(S)$ is a GM (group mapping) semigroup.

2.3 Lemma. Let N be a normal subgroup of S, let G be the maximal subgroup of S containing N, and let J be the $\mathscr{J}$ class containing N.

(a) Let $\equiv_N$ be the congruence on S associated with $S \twoheadrightarrow S/N$. Give J a Rees representation $\mathscr{M}^0(G; A, B; C) - \{0\}$. Then $\equiv_N$ identifies all elements in $F(J)$ and is the identity congruence on $S - [J \cup F(J)]$. Let $(g_i, a_i, b_i) \in J$, $i = 1, 2$. Then $(g_1, a_1, b_1) \equiv_N (g_2, a_2, b_2)$ if and only if $a_1 = a_2$, $b_1 = b_2$, and $g_1 g_2^{-1} \in N$.

(b) Let $s_1, s_2 \in S$. View elements of S as right translations on $J^0 \cong \mathscr{M}^0(G; A, B; C)$. (See Krohn *et al.* [*1*, Fact 7.2.14]). Let $s_i = (\delta_i, \psi_R{}^i)$, $i = 1, 2$, where $\psi_R{}^i \in F_R(B^0)$ and $\delta_i \in F(B^0, G^0)$ and

$$(g, a, b) \cdot s_i = (g, a, b)(\delta_i, \psi_R{}^i) = (g\delta_i(b), a, \psi_R{}^i(b)).$$

Then $RM_N(s_1) = RM_N(s_2)$ if and only if $\psi_R{}^1 = \psi_R{}^2$ and $\delta_1(b)\, \delta_2(b)^{-1} \in N$ or $\delta_1(b) = \delta_2(b) = 0$ for all $b \in B^0$. The dual statement is true for LM_N.

(c) Let $s_1, s_2 \in S$. Then $GGM_N(s_1) = GGM_N(s_2)$ if and only if

$$x_1 s_1 x_2 \equiv_N x_1 s_2 x_2 \qquad \text{for all} \quad x_1, x_2 \in J.$$

PROOF. (a) This follows directly from the definition.

(b) Let $s_i \to s_i'$ and $J \to J'$ under $S \twoheadrightarrow S/N$. Since $RM_N(S) = RM(S/N)$, we have $RM_N(s_1) = RM_N(s_2)$ if and only if $j's_1' = j's_2'$ in S/N for all $j' \in J'$. But this is equivalent to the condition that $js_1 \equiv_N js_2$ for all $j \in J$. Let $j = (g, a, b)$, so

$$js_1 = (g\delta_1(b), a, \psi_R{}^1(b)) \equiv_N (g\delta_2(b), a, \psi_R{}^2(b)) = js_2 .$$

If js_1 (and hence js_2) belong to $F(J)$, then $\psi_R{}^1(b) = \psi_R{}^2(b) = 0$ and $\delta_1(b) = \delta_2(b) = 0$. If $js_1, js_2 \in J$, then by (a), $\psi_R{}^1(b) = \psi_R{}^2(b)$ and $g\delta_1(b)[g\delta_2(b)]^{-1} \in N$ which implies $\delta_1(b)\,\delta_2(b)^{-1} \in N$. Use the dual proof for LM_N.

(c) By an argument similar to (b), $GGM_N(s_1) = GGM_N(s_2)$ if and only if $x_1's_1'x_2' = x_1's_2'x_2'$ in S/N for all $x_1', x_2' \in J'$ if and only if $x_1s_1x_2 \equiv_N x_1s_2x_2$ for all $x_1, x_2 \in J$ (see Krohn *et al.* [*1*, Definition 8.2.11]). ▮

2.4 Definition. Let S be a π-solvable semigroup, and let N be the largest normal π' subgroup of a maximal subgroup G in a $\mathscr{J}$ class J. Then define the homomorphisms πRM_J, πLM_J, πGGM_J, and πGM_J by

$$\pi RM_J = RM_N, \quad \pi LM_J = LM_N, \quad \pi GGM_J = GM_N, \quad \text{and} \quad \pi GM_J = GM_N .$$

The subscript J will be omitted when no confusion is possible. In the dual way, define $\pi' RM_J$, $\pi' LM_J$, $\pi' GGM_J$, and $\pi' GM_J$.

2.5 Definition. (a) Define a *πRM semigroup* (*$\pi' RM$ semigroup*) to be an RM semigroup whose distinguished $\mathscr{J}$ class contains no nontrivial normal π' subgroups (π subgroups).

(b) Define a *πLM semigroup* (*$\pi' LM$ semigroup*) dually.

(c) Define a *πGGM semigroup* (*$\pi' GGM$ semigroup*) to be a GGM semigroup whose distinguished $\mathscr{J}$ class contains no nontrivial π' subgroups (π subgroups).

(d) Define a *πGM semigroup* (*$\pi' GM$ semigroup*) to be either the trivial semigroup or to be a πGGM semigroup ($\pi' GGM$ semigroup) whose distinguished $\mathscr{J}$ class is noncombinatorial.

2.6 Fact. (a) $\pi RM_J(S)$, $\pi LM_J(S)$, $\pi GGM_J(S)$, and $\pi GM_J(S)$ are, respectively, πRM, πLM, πGGM, and πGM semigroups.

(b) πRM semigroups are πRM stable, i.e., if S is a πRM semigroup, then $\pi RM(S) = S$. Similarly πLM, πGGM, and πGM semigroups are, respectively, πLM, πGGM, and πGM stable.

PROOF. Clear. ▮

2.7 Definition. A $\mathscr{J}$ class is π *regular* if and only if it is noncombinatorial and its maximal subgroups are not π' groups.

2.8 Fact. If J is not a π-regular $\mathscr{J}$ class of S, then $\pi GM_J(S) = \{0\}$.

PROOF. Clear. ∎

2.9 Theorem. (a) Let J be a regular $\mathscr{J}$ class of S. Then the homomorphism $(LLM_J \times \pi GM_J \times \pi' RM_J)\Delta$ is 1 : 1 nonzero on J and sends $F(J)$ to zero. (Δ: $S \to S \times S \times S$, where $\Delta(s) = (s, s, s)$).

(b) Let $J_1, \ldots, J_k$ and $J_{k+1}, \ldots, J_n$ be the regular and null $\mathscr{J}$ classes of S, respectively. Then by virtue of Krohn *et al.* [*1*, Fact 8.2.3],

$$\begin{aligned} S \leqslant\leqslant \Pi\{LLM_{J_i}(S)\colon\ & i = 1, \ldots, k\} \\ \times\, \Pi\{\pi GM_{J_i}(S)\colon\ & i = 1, \ldots, k\} \\ \times\, \Pi\{\pi' RM_{J_i}(S)\colon\ & i = 1, \ldots, k\} \\ \times\, \Pi\{S/F(J_i)\colon\ & i = k+1, \ldots, n\}. \end{aligned}$$

Thus every semigroup can be written as a subdirect product of πGM, $\pi' RM$, LLM semigroups, and semigroups with nontrivial null ideals ($S/F(J_i)$).

PROOF. (a) Let G be a maximal subgroup of J, and let P and N be the largest normal π subgroup and π' subgroup of G, respectively. Then $\pi GM_J = GM_N$ and $\pi' RM_J = RM_P$. Give J a Rees representation $\mathscr{M}^0(G; A, B; C)$ and let $j_i = (g_i, a_i, b_i)$, $i = 1, 2$ belong to J. Suppose that

(1) $LLM_J(j_1) = LLM_J(j_2)$,
(2) $RM_P(j_1) = RM_P(j_2)$, and
(3) $GM_N(j_1) = GM_N(j_2)$.

By (1) $a_1 = a_2$, and $RM_P(j_1) = RM_P(j_2)$ implies $RLM_J(j_1) = RLM_J(j_2)$, so (2) implies $b_1 = b_2$. In the notation of Lemma 2.3, let $j_i = (\delta_i, \psi_R{}^i)$. Then $\delta_i(b) = C(b, a_i)\, g_i$. Since J is regular, there exists $b \in B$ such that $C(b, a_1) = C(b, a_2) \neq 0$. Thus by Lemma 2.3(b),

$$C(b, a_1)\, g_1[C(b, a_2)\, g_2]^{-1} \in P$$

which implies $g_1 g_2^{-1} \in P$. Again choose $b \in B$ such that $C(b, a_1) \neq 0$ and choose $c \in A$ such that $C(b_1, c) \neq 0$. Then choose elements (g, a, b) and (h, c, d) in J. Then (3) implies by Lemma 2.3(c) that

$$gC(b, a_1)\, g_1 C(b_1, c)\, h[gC(b, a_1)\, g_2 C(b_1, c)\, h]^{-1} \in N$$

which implies $g_1 g_2^{-1} \in N$. But $P \cap N = \{1\}$, so $g_1 = g_2$. Thus the homomorphism is 1 : 1 on J. The remainder of the assertion is obvious.

(b) This follows from Fact 8.2.3 of Krohn *et al.* [*1*]. ▮

2.10 Lemma. Let S be a subsemigroup of $(X_2, T_2) \le (X_1, T_1)$ and let $p_1: (X_2, T_2) \le (X_1, T_1) \twoheadrightarrow T_1$ be the projection homomorphism. Then S is a subsemigroup of $(X_2, T_2) \le (X_1, p_1(S))$.

PROOF. Clear. ▮

2.11 Lemma. Let (X_2, T_2) and (X_1, T_1) be mapping semigroups and let S be a subsemigroup of T_2. Then

$$(X_2, S) \mathrm{w} (X_1, T_1) \subseteq (X_2, T_2) \mathrm{w} (X_1, T_1)$$

PROOF. See Fact 5.2.14(d) of Krohn *et al.* [*1*]. ▮

2.12 Lemma. (a) $G \subseteq H$ implies $G^0 \subseteq H^0$.

(b) $[(G_2, G_2) \mathrm{w} (G_1, G_1)]^0 \subseteq (G_2{}^0, G_2{}^0) \mathrm{w} (G_1{}^0, G_1{}^0)$, where the G_i are groups.

PROOF. (a) Trivial.

$$\text{(b)}\quad [(G_2, G_2) \mathrm{w} (G_1, G_1)]^0 \cong (F' \times_Y G_1) \cup \{(c_0, 0)\} \subseteq (G_2{}^0, G_2{}^0) \mathrm{w} (G_1{}^0, G_1{}^0),$$

where c_0 is the constant map to zero and $F' = \{f \in F(G_1{}^0, G_2{}^0): f(x) = 0$ if and only if $x = 0\}$, since $F' = F(G_1, G_2)$. ▮

2.13 Proposition. Let S be an RM semigroup with distinguished ideal $J^0 \cong \mathscr{M}^0(G; A, B; C)$. If $N \lhd G$, then

$$S \subseteq (N^0, N^0) \mathrm{w} ((G/N)^0 \times B^0, RM_N(S)). \tag{2.1}$$

PROOF. By Proposition 8.2.17(b) of Krohn *et al.* [*1*]

$$S \subseteq (G^0, G^0) \mathrm{w} (B^0, RLM_J(S)).$$

By the monomial representation, $(G, G) \subseteq (N, N) \wr (G/N, G/N)$, so by Lemma 2.12, $(G^0, G^0) \subseteq (N^0, N^0) \wr ((G/N)^0, (G/N)^0)$. Then by Lemma 2.11,

$$S \subseteq (N^0, N^0) \mathrm{w} ((G/N)^0, (G/N)^0) \mathrm{w} (B^0, RLM_J(S)).$$

Now consider the projection homomorphism

$$p_1: (N^0, N^0) \mathrm{w} ((G/N)^0, (G/N)^0) \mathrm{w} (B^0, RLM_J(S)) \twoheadrightarrow ((G/N)^0, (G/N)^0) \mathrm{w} (B^0, RLM_J(S)).$$

The image of p_1 restricted to S is clearly $RM_N(S)$, so by Lemma 2.10,

$$S \subseteq (N^0, N^0) \text{ w } ((G/N)^0 \times B^0, RM_N(S)). \quad \blacksquare$$

2.14. Corollary. If S is an RM semigroup with normal subgroup N in the distinguished $\mathscr{J}$ class, then

$$l_\pi(RM_N(S)) \leqslant l_\pi(S) \leqslant l_\pi(N^0) + l_\pi(RM_N(S)). \tag{2.2}$$

PROOF. By Eq. (2.1) and Proposition 1.15, the upper bound is obtained. The lower bound results from the fact that $RM_N(S)$ is a homomorphic image of S. ▮

2.15. Proposition. (a) Let φ be a homomorphism of a semigroup S onto a GGM semigroup, and let (J, G, N) be a kernel of φ (see Definition 8.3.27(c) of Krohn *et al.* [*1*]). Let $\mathscr{P}$ be the property of homomorphisms of S defined by

$$\mathscr{P} = \{(\psi, T): \psi(J) \cap \psi[F(J)] = \emptyset \text{ and the group kernel of } \psi \text{ restricted to } G \text{ is contained in } N\}.$$

Then $(\varphi, \varphi(S))$ is the minimal homomorphic image of S with respect to $\mathscr{P}$.

(b) Let φ be a homomorphism of a semigroup S onto an RM semigroup, and let (J, G, N) be a kernel of φ. Also, suppose φ separates the $\mathscr{L}$ classes of J. Let $\mathscr{P}$ be the property of homomorphisms of S defined by

$$\mathscr{P} = \{(\psi, T): \psi(J) \cap \psi[F(J)] = \emptyset, \psi \text{ separates the } \mathscr{L} \text{ classes of } J, \text{ and the group kernel of } \psi \text{ restricted to } G \text{ is contained in } N\}.$$

Then $(\varphi, \varphi(S))$ is the minimal homomorphic image of S with respect to $\mathscr{P}$.

There is a dual statement for LM semigroups.

PROOF. (a) This is a restatement of Proposition 8.3.28 of Krohn *et al.* [*1*]. The proof is given there.

(b) Clearly $(\varphi, \varphi(S))$ belongs to $\mathscr{P}$. We must show that, if $\varphi(s_1) \neq \varphi(s_2)$ for some $s_1, s_2 \in S$, then $\psi(s_1) \neq \psi(s_2)$ for all $\psi \in \mathscr{P}$. Since $\varphi(S)$ is an RM semigroup with distinguished ideal $\varphi[J \cup F(J)]$, $\varphi(s_1) \neq \varphi(s_2)$ implies that there exists $j \in J$ such that $\varphi(js_1) \neq \varphi(js_2)$. Now js_1 and js_2 belong to $J \cup F(J)$. Suppose js_1 and js_2 are not $\mathscr{L}$ equivalent. Then by the definition of $\mathscr{P}$, $\psi(js_1) \neq \psi(js_2)$, so $\psi(s_1) \neq \psi(s_2)$. Therefore, assume $js_1 \mathscr{L} js_2$. Then $js_1, js_2 \in J$, for otherwise $\varphi(js_1) = \varphi(js_2) = 0$. This implies $js_1 \mathscr{R} js_2$, so in fact $js_1 \mathscr{H} js_2$. Now by the proof of (a) (Krohn *et al.* [1]), we can conclude that $\psi(js_1) \neq \psi(js_2)$, so $\psi(s_1) \neq \psi(s_2)$. ∎

2.16. Corollary. (a) If (J, G, N) is a kernel of $\varphi: S \twoheadrightarrow T$, where T is a GGM semigroup, then $GGM_N(S) \cong T$.

(b) If (J, G, N) is a kernel of $\varphi: S \twoheadrightarrow T$, where T is an RM semigroup and φ separates $\mathscr{L}$ classes of J, then $RM_N(S) \cong T$.

(c) If (J, G, N) is a kernel of $\varphi: S \twoheadrightarrow T$, where T is an LM semigroup and φ separates $\mathscr{R}$ classes of J, then $LM_N(S) \cong T$.

Proof. These follow immediately from the proposition. ∎

3. Axioms for π Length

3.1 Lemma. Let S be an RM semigroup. Then either

$$l_\pi(S) = 1 + l_\pi(\pi' RM(S))$$

or

$$l_\pi(S) = l_\pi(\pi' RM(S)).$$

Proof. From Eq. (2.2),

$$l_\pi(\pi' RM(S)) \leqslant l_\pi(S) \leqslant l_\pi(P^0) + l_\pi(\pi' RM(S))$$

where P is a π group. Since $P \subseteq P^0 \twoheadleftarrow P \times \{0\}^I$, we have

$$l_\pi(P^0) = l_\pi(P) \leqslant 1,$$

so the assertion follows. ∎

3.2 Definition. Let S be a πGM semigroup. If

$$l_\pi(S) = 1 + l_\pi(\pi' RM(S)),$$

then call S a *π-pure group mapping* (πPGM) *semigroup*. If

$$l_\pi(S) = l_\pi(\pi' RM(S)),$$

then call S a *non-πPGM semigroup*.

3.3 Definition. A homomorphism $\varphi: S \twoheadrightarrow T$ is a π *homomorphism* if and only if for each maximal subgroup G of S, $\ker(\varphi|G)$ is a π' subgroup (the trivial subgroup is allowed). We often denote a π homomorphism by $\varphi: S \underset{\pi}{\twoheadrightarrow} T$.

3.4 Definition. Let θ be a function from the collection of all π-solvable semigroups $\mathscr{S}$ into the nonnegative integers, N, satisfying the following three axioms:

Axiom I. If S is a subdirect product of semigroups $S_1, \ldots, S_n$ (written $S \leqslant\leqslant S_1 \times \cdots \times S_n$), then $\theta(S) = \max\{\theta(S_i): i = 1, \ldots, n\}$.

Axiom II. (a) $\theta(\{0\}) = 0$.

(b) If $\varphi: S \twoheadrightarrow T$ is a π epimorphism, then $\theta(S) = \theta(T)$.

Axiom III. Let S be a πGM semigroup. Then

$$\theta(S) = \begin{cases} \theta[\pi' RM(S)] + 1 & \text{if } S \text{ is } \pi PGM \\ \theta[\pi' RM(S)] & \text{if } S \text{ is non } \pi PGM. \end{cases}$$

Any function $\theta: \mathscr{S} \rightarrow N$ satisfying Axioms I–III, we call a *π-length function for $\mathscr{S}$.*

3.5 Proposition. There exists at most one π length function for $\mathscr{S}$.

Proof. Suppose θ_1 and θ_2 are two different π-length functions for $\mathscr{S}$. Let S be a semigroup of minimal order subject to the condition that $\theta_1(S) \neq \theta_2(S)$. Then by Axiom II(a), $S \neq \{0\}$. Furthermore, S is subdirectly indecomposible, or $S \leqslant\leqslant S_1 \times \cdots \times S_n$, where $|S_i| < |S|$, $i = 1, \ldots, n$. The latter is impossible, since by Axiom I $\theta_k(S) = \max\{\theta_k(S_i): i = 1, \ldots, n\}$ for $k = 1, 2$ and by the choice of S, $\theta_1(S_i) = \theta_2(S_i)$ by induction, $i = 1, \ldots, n$. Thus by Theorem 2.9 S is either an LLM semigroup, a semigroup with a nontrivial null ideal, a $\pi' RM$ semigroup, or a πGM semigroup.

If S is either of the first two, S has a nontrivial combinatorial ideal I, so $S \underset{\pi}{\twoheadrightarrow} S/I$ and $|S/I| < |S|$. By Axiom II(b) $\theta_k(S) = \theta_k(S/I)$, $k = 1, 2$, a contradiction. Thus S is not a LLM semigroup or a semigroup with a nontrivial null ideal.

If S is a $\pi' RM$ semigroup, let N be the largest normal π' subgroup of the distinguished $\mathscr{J}$ class of S. If $N = \{1\}$, then the distinguished $\mathscr{J}$ class of S is combinatorial, and this case can be handled like LLM above. Thus $N \neq \{1\}$, so $S \twoheadrightarrow S/N$ is a π homomorphism and $|S/N| < |S|$. Again by Axiom II(b) this is impossible. Hence S is a πGM semigroup.

Since S is a πGM semigroup and $S \neq \{0\}$, we have $|\pi' RM(S)| < |S|$. Thus $\theta_1(\pi' RM(S)) = \theta_2(\pi' RM(S))$, so by Axiom III $\theta_1(S) = \theta_2(S)$, a contradiction. Hence $\theta_1 \equiv \theta_2$. ∎

3.6 Theorem. l_π is a π-length function for $\mathscr{S}$.†

PROOF. By definition, l_π satisfies Axiom III (Definition 3.2). For Axiom I, if $S \leqslant\leqslant S_1 \times \cdots \times S_n$, then $S \subseteq S_1 \times \cdots \times S_n$ so

$$l_\pi(S) \leqslant l_\pi(S_1 \times \cdots \times S_n) = \max\{l_\pi(S_i): i = 1, \ldots, n\},$$

and $S \twoheadrightarrow S_i$, $i = 1, \ldots, n$, so $l_\pi(S) \geqslant l_\pi(S_i)$. Thus

$$\max\{l_\pi(S_i): i = 1, \ldots, n\} \leqslant l_\pi(S),$$

so l_π satisfies Axiom I. We must show that l_π satisfies Axiom II. Clearly $l_\pi(\{0\}) = 0$. Rhodes [4], proves that if $\varphi: S \twoheadrightarrow T$ is a γ homomorphism (1 : 1 on subgroups), then $\#_G(S) = \#_G(T)$. This is known as the fundamental lemma of complexity and is quite critical to the theory of complexity. The proof is long and difficult, despite the fact that the statement is short and simple. By a slight variation of the arguments used by Rhodes [4], one can deduce that if $\varphi: S \twoheadrightarrow T$ is a γ homomorphism, then $l_\pi(S) = l_\pi(T)$. Consequently, if I is a combinatorial ideal of S, then $l_\pi(S) = l_\pi(S/I)$. We use this as a starting point to show that if $\theta: S \twoheadrightarrow T$ is a π homomorphism, then $l_\pi(S) = l_\pi(T)$.

We can assume that θ is a maximal proper epimorphism (MPE), so θ is either a $\gamma(\mathscr{H})$ or an $\mathscr{H}$ homomorphism by Chapter 8.1 of Krohn *et al.* [1]. We also know that there exists a $\mathscr{J}$ class J of S such that θ is 1 : 1 on S–J. Further, there exists an ideal $I_1 \subseteq F(J)$ such that J is minimal in the $\mathscr{J}$ class ordering in S–I_1 and if we set $I_2 = J \cup I_1$, then θ is 1 : 1 on S–I_2 and θ separates I_2 and S–I_2, i.e., $\theta(I_2) \cap \theta(S\text{–}I_2) = \emptyset$. Notice that I_2 is an ideal of S. Then it is easy to see that $S/I_2 \cong \theta(S)/\theta(I_2)$. We claim we can choose $I_1 = F(J)$ and $I_2 = J \cup F(J)$. (See Lemma 8.1.18 of Krohn *et al.* [1].) We now proceed by cases.

CASE 1. J is a null $\mathscr{J}$ class. Let $\psi: S \to S/I_1$. Since ψ is 1 : 1 on J, $(\theta \times \psi)\Delta$ is 1 : 1 on S, so

$$S \leqslant\leqslant \theta(S) \times \psi(S) \qquad \text{and} \qquad l_\pi(S) = \max\{l_\pi(T), l_\pi[\psi(S)]\}.$$

Now $\psi(S)$ has a nontrivial combinatorial ideal, namely $\psi(I_2) = \psi(J \cup I_1)$, and $\psi(S)/\psi(I_2) \cong S/I_2$. Thus by assumption, $l_\pi[\psi(S)] = l_\pi(S/I_2)$. But S/I_2 is isomorphic to a homomorphic image of $\theta(S) = T$, so $l_\pi(T) \geqslant l_\pi(S/I_2) = l_\pi(\psi(S))$, so $l_\pi(S) = l_\pi(T)$.

CASE 2. J is a regular $\mathscr{J}$ class and θ is a $\gamma(\mathscr{H})$ homomorphism. Let G be a maximal subgroup of J and define $\psi: S \twoheadrightarrow S/G$. Then $\psi(S)$ has a combinatorial ideal, namely $\psi(I_2)$. Notice that ψ is an $\mathscr{H}$ homomorphism on J, and since θ is $\gamma(\mathscr{H})$, $(\psi \times \theta)\Delta$ is 1 : 1 on S. Now we proceed exactly as in Case 1 to get $l_\pi(S) = l_\pi(T)$.

† See Note Added in Proof, page 208.

CASE 3. J is a regular $\mathscr{J}$ class and θ is an $\mathscr{H}$ homomorphism. Thus J is separated from $F(J)$ under θ. Let G be a maximal subgroup of J and let $N = \ker \theta|G$. Since θ is a π homomorphism, N is a normal π' subgroup of G. Since θ is an $\mathscr{H}$ homomorphism, it preserves the $\mathscr{H}$ classes of J, so the congruence induced by θ, $\equiv_\theta$, can be described as follows:

$$s_1 \equiv_\theta s_2 \quad \text{if and only if} \quad \begin{cases} s_1, s_2 \in S - J & \text{and} \quad s_1 = s_2 \\ s_1, s_2 \in J & \text{and} \quad s_1 \equiv_N s_2 . \end{cases}$$

Then it is clear that by dividing out the ideal $\theta(F(J))$ from $\theta(S)$ we get S/N, i.e., $\theta(S)/\theta(F(J)) \cong S/N$.

Now consider $RM_J\colon S \twoheadrightarrow RM_J(S)$. RM_J is a $\gamma(\mathscr{H})$ homomorphism on J, so $(RM_J \times \theta)\Delta$ is $1:1$ on S, and again $l_\pi(S) = \max\{l_\pi(T), l_\pi(RM_J(S))\}$. Now by Proposition 2.13

$$RM_J(S) \subseteq (N^0, N^0) \text{ w } ((G/N)^0 \times B^0, RM_N[RM_J(S)])$$

But $l_\pi(N^0) = 0$, so $l_\pi(RM_J(S)) = l_\pi(RM_N[RM_J(S)])$. Now by Corollary 2.16(b), $RM_N(RM_J(S)) = RM_N(S)$, so $l_\pi[RM_J(S)] = l_\pi[RM_N(S)]$. But

$$T = \theta(S) \twoheadrightarrow S/N \twoheadrightarrow RM_N(S),$$

so $l_\pi(T) \geqslant l_\pi(RM_N(S)) = l_\pi(RM_J(S))$. Thus $l_\pi(S) = l_\pi(T)$. ∎

4. π Length and Homomorphisms

In this section and the next, several theorems relating π length to homomorphisms are proved. Most of these theorems hold only for a restricted class of semigroups which include union of groups semigroups But there is one theorem (Theorem 4.28) which holds for an arbitrary, finite, π-solvable semigroup S[†]: Find the longest homomorphism chain for S, starting with S and followed by a πPGM semigroup, followed by a $\pi' RM$ semigroup, and alternating πPGM–$\pi' RM$ until zero is reached. Count the number of nonzero πPGM semigroups in the chain. This number equals the π length of S.

But before these theorems can be proved, a number of tools must be developed.

4.1 Proposition. Let $\varphi\colon S \twoheadrightarrow T$ and suppose that T is a πRM, πLM, πGGM, or πGM semigroup with distinguished ideal I. Let J be the minimal $\mathscr{J}$ class of S such that $\varphi(J) = I^\#$. Let N be the unique

[†] See Note Added in Proof, page 208.

maximal normal π' subgroup of a maximal subgroup G in J. Then $RM_N(S) \twoheadrightarrow T$, $LM_N(S) \twoheadrightarrow T$, $GGM_N(S) \twoheadrightarrow T$, or $GM_N(S) \twoheadrightarrow T$, respectively.

PROOF. If $T = \{0\}$, the assertion is satisfied, so assume $T \neq \{0\}$. Give J^0 and I Rees matrix representations with respect to G and $\varphi(G)$ so that φ on J is in normalized form, i.e.,

$$\varphi(g, a, b) = (\omega(g), \psi_L(a), \psi_R(b)) \quad \text{where} \quad \omega = \varphi|G.$$

Let T be a πRM semigroup. Let $s_1, s_2 \in S$ and suppose

$$RM_N(s_1) = RM_N(s_2).$$

We must show that $\varphi(s_1) = \varphi(s_2)$.

For each $x \in J$, either $xs_1 \equiv_N xs_2$ in J or both xs_1 and $xs_2 \in B(J)$. In the latter case, by the minimality of J we have $\varphi(xs_1) = 0 = \varphi(xs_2)$. If $xs_1 \equiv_N xs_2$, then let $xs_1 = (g_1, a, b)$ and $xs_2 = (g_2, a, b)$. Then $g_1g_2^{-1} \in N$ and $\varphi(g_1g_2^{-1}) = \omega(g_1g_2^{-1}) \in \varphi(N)$. But $\varphi(N)$ is a normal π' subgroup of $\varphi(G)$, a maximal subgroup of I, and since T is πRM, the maximal subgroups of I have no nontrivial normal π' subgroups. Thus $\varphi(N) = 1$ and $\omega(g_1) = \omega(g_2)$. Thus $\varphi(xs_1) = \varphi(xs_2)$ for all $x \in J$, or equivalently, for all $i \in I$, $i\varphi(s_1) = i\varphi(s_2)$. Hence $\varphi(s_1) = \varphi(s_2)$, since T is an RM semigroup with respect to I. The dual argument proves the assertion if T is a πLM semigroup.

Let T be a πGGM semigroup. Let $s_1, s_2 \in S$ such that

$$GGM_N(s_1) = GGM_N(s_2).$$

For all $x_1, x_2 \in J$ either $x_1s_1x_2 \equiv_N x_1s_2x_2$ in J or $x_1s_1x_2$ and $x_1s_2x_2 \in B(J)$. By the same argument as above $\varphi(x_1s_1x_2) = \varphi(x_1s_2x_2)$ for all $x_1, x_2 \in J$, or for all $i_1, i_2 \in I$, $i_1\varphi(s_1)\, i_2 = i_1\varphi(s_2)\, i_2$. Since T is GGM, this implies $i_1\varphi(s_1) = i_1\varphi(s_2)$ for all $i_1 \in I$, which in turn implies $\varphi(s_1) = \varphi(s_2)$.

Let T be a πGM semigroup. Since $T \neq \{0\}$, $I^\#$ is π regular, which implies that J is π regular. Now the proof is identical to the πGGM case. ∎

4.2 Definition. Let S be a semigroup.

(a) Let $Q(\pi GM) = \text{glb}\{Q' \colon Q'$ is a congruence on S and S/Q' a πGM semigroup$\}$. Define $S^{\pi GM} = S/Q(\pi GM)$. Note that $S^{\pi GM}$ is not necessarily a πGM semigroup.

(b) Let $Q(\pi GGM) = \text{glb}\{Q' \colon Q'$ a congruence and S/Q' a πGGM semigroup$\}$. Define $S^{\pi GGM} = S/Q(\pi GGM)$. Note that $S^{\pi GGM}$ is not necessarily a πGGM semigroup.

(c) Let $Q(\pi RM) = \text{glb}\{Q' : Q' \text{ a congruence and } S/Q' \text{ a } \pi RM \text{ semigroup}\}$. Define $S^{\pi RM} = S/Q(\pi RM)$. $S^{\pi RM}$ is not a πRM semigroup in general.

(d) Define $S^{\pi LM} = S/Q(\pi LM)$ dually.

4.3 Fact. Let $J_1, \ldots, J_n$ be the regular $\mathscr{J}$ classes of S.

(a) $S^{\pi GM} \cong (\pi GM_{J_1} \times \cdots \times \pi GM_{J_n})\Delta(S)$.

(b) $S^{\pi GGM} \cong (\pi GGM_{J_1} \times \cdots \times \pi GGM_{J_n})\Delta(S)$.

(c) $S^{\pi RM} \cong (\pi RM_{J_1} \times \cdots \times \pi RM_{J_n})\Delta(S)$.

(d) $S^{\pi LM} \cong (\pi LM_{J_1} \times \cdots \times \pi LM_{J_n})\Delta(S)$.

PROOF. (a) Let Q_i be the congruence on S induced by πGM_{J_i}, $i = 1, \ldots, n$. Then Proposition 4.1 says that for each congruence Q, where S/Q is πGM, there exists an i such that $Q_i \subseteq Q$. Thus it is easy to see that $Q(\pi GM) = Q_1 \cap \cdots \cap Q_n$, so

$$S^{\pi GM} \cong (\pi GM_{J_1} \times \cdots \times \pi GM_{J_n})\, \Delta(S).$$

The proofs of (b), (c), and (d) are nearly identical. ▮

4.4 Definition. Let S be a semigroup and let $J_1, \ldots, J_n$ be the regular $\mathscr{J}$ classes of S. Define the *basic πRM semigroups of S* to be the set $\{\pi RM_{J_i}(S) : i = 1, \ldots, n\}$. Define the *basic* πLM, πGGM, and πGM semigroups similarly.

4.5 Corollary. (a) $S^{\pi GM}$ is a subdirect product of the basic πGM semigroups of S.

(b) $S^{\pi GGM}$ is a subdirect product of the basic πGGM semigroups of S.

(c) $S^{\pi RM}$ is a subdirect product of the basic πRM semigroups of S.

(d) $S^{\pi LM}$ is a subdirect product of the basic πLM semigroups of S.

PROOF. Clear from Fact 4.3. ▮

4.6 Lemma. Let T be a subsemigroup of S. Let $t_1, t_2 \in T$ with t_1 regular in T. Then $t_1 \mathscr{H} t_2$ in S if and only if $t_1 \mathscr{H} t_2$ in T.

PROOF. $t_1 \mathscr{H} t_2$ in T implies $t_1 \mathscr{H} t_2$ in S, clearly. Assume $t_1 \mathscr{H} t_2$ in S. Since t_1 is regular in T, there exists idempotents e_1 and e_2 such that $e_1 \mathscr{R} t_1$ and $e_2 \mathscr{L} t_1$ in T. Consider e_1 first. $e_1 t_1 = t_1$ and there exist $x \in T$ such that $t_1 x = e_1$. By Green, since $t_1 \mathscr{H} t_2$ in S, we have $t_2 x \mathscr{H} t_1 x = e_1$ in S. But the $\mathscr{H}$ class of S containing e_1 is a group, G, and $G \cap T$ is a group in T. Therefore $t_2 x \mathscr{H} e_1$ in T and there exists $y \in T$ such that $t_2 x y = e_1$. Also $e_1 t_2 = t_2$ since $e_1 \mathscr{R} t_2$ in S. Thus $e_1 \mathscr{R} t_2$ in T, so $t_1 \mathscr{R} t_2$ in T. Similarly, using e_2, we show that $t_1 \mathscr{L} t_2$ in T, so $t_1 \mathscr{H} t_2$ in T. ▮

4.7 Proposition. Let α be any of πGM, πGGM, πRM, πLM.

(a) $\psi\colon S \twoheadrightarrow T$ implies $S^\alpha \twoheadrightarrow T^\alpha$.

(b) If $T \subseteq S$, then $T^\alpha | S^\alpha$.

(c) $T|S$ implies $T^\alpha | S^\alpha$.

PROOF. (a) The proof is identical to that of Fact 8.3.7(a) of Krohn *et al.* [1] (does not depend on properties π, etc.).

(b) Let T be a subsemigroup of S. Let $\psi\colon S \twoheadrightarrow S^{\pi GM}$. We must show that $\psi(T) \twoheadrightarrow T^{\pi GM}$. Let Q_S and Q_T be the congruences associated with $S \twoheadrightarrow S^{\pi GM}$ and $T \twoheadrightarrow T^{\pi GM}$, respectively. Then it is sufficient to show that for $t_1, t_2 \in T$, if $t_1 \not\equiv t_2 \pmod{Q_T}$, then $t_1 \not\equiv t_2 \pmod{Q_S}$. Suppose $t_1 \not\equiv t_2 \pmod{Q_T}$. Then there exists a $\mathscr{J}$ class J' of T with maximal subgroup G' and maximal normal π' subgroup $N' \lhd G'$ and $x_1, x_2 \in J'$ such that $x_1 t_1 x_2 \not\equiv_{N'} x_1 t_2 x_2$. Let J be the $\mathscr{J}$ class of S containing J', G be the maximal subgroup of J containing G', and let N be the maximal normal π' subgroup of G. Notice that $N \cap G' \subseteq N'$. At least one of $x_1 t_1 x_2$ and $x_1 t_2 x_2$ must belong to J', so let $x_1 t_1 x_2 \in J'$. If $x_1 t_2 x_2 \notin J$, then $x_1 t_1 x_2 \not\equiv_N x_1 t_2 x_2$ in S. If $x_1 t_2 x_2 \in J$, then $x_1 t_1 x_2 \mathscr{H} x_1 t_2 x_2$ in S. But $x_1 t_1 x_2$ is regular in T so by Lemma 4.6, $x_1 t_1 x_2 \mathscr{H} x_1 t_2 x_2$ in T.

Give J a Rees matrix representation $\mathscr{M}^0(G; A, B; C)$ and let $x_1 t_i x_2 = (g_i, a, b)$, $i = 1, 2$. Since $x_1 t_1 x_2 \not\equiv_{N'} x_1 t_2 x_2$, we have $g_1 g_2^{-1} \notin N'$ which implies $g_1 g_2^{-1} \notin N$ since $g_1 g_2^{-1} \in G'$. Thus $x_1 t_1 x_2 \not\equiv_N x_1 t_2 x_2$, proving the assertion for πGM, i.e., $T \subseteq S$ implies $T^{\pi GM} | S^{\pi GM}$. The proof for $\alpha = \pi GGM$ is identical.

Let $\alpha = \pi RM$ and let $\bar{Q}_T$ and $\bar{Q}_S$ be the congruences associated with $T \twoheadrightarrow T^{\pi RM}$ and $S \twoheadrightarrow S^{\pi RM}$, respectively. Then we must show that $t_1, t_2 \in T$ and $t_1 \not\equiv t_2 \pmod{\bar{Q}_T}$ implies $t_1 \not\equiv t_2 \pmod{\bar{Q}_S}$. Suppose $t_1 \not\equiv t_2 \pmod{\bar{Q}_T}$. Then there exists a regular $\mathscr{J}$ class J' of T and $x \in J'$ such that $xt_1 \not\equiv_{N'} xt_2$. One of xt_1 and xt_2 must belong to J', so let $xt_1 \in J'$. If xt_1 is not $\mathscr{H}$ equivalent to xt_2 in T, then xt_1 is not $\mathscr{H}$ equivalent to xt_2 in S by Lemma 4.6, since xt_1 is regular in T, so $xt_1 \not\equiv_N xt_2$ in S. If $xt_1 \mathscr{H} xt_2$ in T, then the case is handled as in the proof for $\alpha = \pi GM$. Thus $T \subseteq S$ implies $T^{\pi RM} | S^{\pi RM}$. The assertion for $\alpha = \pi LM$ is proved dually.

(c) The proof of (c) follows from (a) and (b). ▌

4.8 Definition. Let $\mathscr{P}(S, \pi)$ be a property of homomorphisms defined by $(\varphi, T) \in \mathscr{P}(S, \pi)$ if and only if $\varphi\colon S \twoheadrightarrow T$ is a π homomorphism.

We now proceed to prove that S has a minimal homomorphic image with respect to $\mathscr{P}(S, \pi)$, denoted S^π. If G is a group with N the largest normal π' group, then $G/N \cong G^\pi$. If $\varphi\colon G \twoheadrightarrow H$ is a π homomorphism, then $G^\pi \cong H^\pi$.

4.9 Lemma. Let I be a maximal ideal of S and suppose there exists $\varphi \in \mathscr{P}(S, \pi)$ such that $\varphi(S) = \varphi(I)$. Let ψ be any homomorphism on S. Then ψ is a π homomorphism if and only if ψ restricted to I is a π homomorphism.

PROOF. Assume ψ restricted to I is a π homomorphism. If the $\mathscr{J}$ class $S–I$ is not π regular, we are done, so assume that G is a maximal subgroup of $S–I$ and $N \lhd G$ is the maximal normal π' subgroup of G, where $N \neq G$. Let $H = \varphi(G)$, let S_1' be the subsemigroup $\varphi^{-1}(H)$, and let $S_1 = eS_1'e$, where e is the identity of G. Then $\varphi(S_1) = H$, and since $\varphi(I) = \varphi(S)$, we have $\varphi(S_1 \cap I) = H$; $S_1 \cap I$ is a nonempty ideal of S_1. Consider φ as the restriction of φ to S_1 from this point on. Let $K(S_1)$ denote the kernel of S_1. $K(S_1) \subseteq I$, and since semigroup kernels go onto semigroup kernels under epimorphisms, and a group is its own (semigroup) kernel, $\varphi[K(S_1)] = H$. Proposition 7.2.5 of Krohn *et al.* [*1*] now tells us that each maximal subgroup of $K(S_1)$ is mapped onto H by φ. Let G_1 be a maximal subgroup of $K(S_1)$ and let e_1 be the identity of G_1.

Now let $\hat{\varphi}: H \twoheadrightarrow H^\pi$, the minimal homomorphism image with respect to π of H. But $\varphi|G$ and $\varphi|G_1$ are π homomorphisms, so $H^\pi = G^\pi = G_1{}^\pi$. Thus $\ker(\hat{\varphi}\varphi|G) = N$ and $\ker(\hat{\varphi}\varphi|G_1) = N_1$, the largest normal π' subgroup of G_1.

Define the *map* $\theta: G \to G_1$ by $\theta(g) = e_1 g e_1$. θ is not a homomorphism and is not onto. However

$$\begin{aligned}\varphi[\theta(g)] &= \varphi(e_1 g e_1)\\ &= \varphi(e_1)\,\varphi(g)\,\varphi(e_1)\\ &= \varphi(g).\end{aligned}$$

Then if $g \in G$ and $\theta(g) \in N_1$, then $\hat{\varphi}\varphi(\theta(g)) = 1 \in H^\pi$. But

$$\hat{\varphi}\varphi(g) = \hat{\varphi}\varphi[\theta(g)] = 1 \in H^\pi,$$

so $g \in N$. Thus we have shown that if $\theta(g) \in N_1$, then $g \in N$.

Now let $g \in G$ and suppose $\psi(g) = \psi(e)$. This implies

$$\psi(e_1 g e_1) = \psi(e_1 e e_1) = \psi(e_1),$$

since e is the identity of S_1. Then $e_1 g e_1 \in N_1$, i.e., $\theta(g) \in N_1$, so $g \in N$. Thus $\ker(\psi|G) \subseteq N$, so ψ is a π homomorphism. The converse is obvious. ▌

4.10 Proposition. A π-solvable semigroup S has a minimal homomorphic image with respect to $\mathscr{P}(S, \pi)$, denoted S^π. S^π is constructed as follows. If S is a π' semigroup, then $S^\pi = \{0\}$. If S is not a π' semigroup, let $J_1, \ldots, J_k$ be the k distinct π-regular $\mathscr{J}$ classes of S, ordered so that $i < j$ implies $J_j \nleqslant J_i$. For each i, let G_i be a maximal subgroup of J_i and let $N_i \lhd G_i$ be the maximal normal π' subgroup of G_i. Then we define a homomorphism ψ on S inductively. Let $\psi_1 = \pi GM_{J_1}$. Assume that ψ_j has been defined. If $\ker \psi_j | G_{j+1} \subseteq N_{j+1}$, then let $\psi_{j+1} = \psi_j$. Otherwise let $\psi_{j+1} = (\psi_j \times \pi GM_{J_{i+1}})\Delta$. Let $\psi = \psi_k$. Then $\psi(S) = S^\pi$.

PROOF. Let $\theta = (\theta_1 \times \theta_2)\Delta$ be a homomorphism on a semigroup S. Let G be a subgroup of S. Then

$$\ker \theta | G = (\ker \theta_1 | G) \cap (\ker \theta_2 | G).$$

Using this fact, it is easy to verify that ψ is a π homomorphism.

Let $\varphi\colon S \twoheadrightarrow T$ be any π homomorphism. We must show that there exists $T \underset{\pi}{\twoheadrightarrow} S^\pi$. Or equivalently, we must show that $\varphi(s_1) = \varphi(s_2)$ implies $\psi(s_1) = \psi(s_2)$. We do this inductively by showing that $\varphi(s_1) = \varphi(s_2)$ implies $\psi_j(s_1) = \psi_j(s_2)$ for $1 \leqslant j \leqslant k$.

Let $\varphi(s_1) = \varphi(s_2)$ and let $x_1, x_2 \in J_1$. We first show that $x_1 s_1 x_2 \in J_1$ if and only if $x_1 s_2 x_2 \in J_1$. If $x_1 s_1 x_2 \in J_1$ and $x_1 s_2 x_2 \notin J_1$, then $x_1 s_2 x_2 \in B(J_1)$, and since $\varphi(x_1 s_1 x_2) = \varphi(x_1 s_2 x_2)$, this implies $\varphi(J_1) \subseteq \varphi(B(J_1))$, i.e., $\varphi(J_1 \cup B(J_1)) = \varphi(B(J_1))$. But then by Lemma 4.9, a homomorphism which is a π homomorphism on $B(J_1)$ is a π homomorphism on $J_1 \cup B(J_1)$. The zero homomorphism is a π homomorphism on $B(J_1)$, hence a π homomorphism on J_1. But J_1 is π regular, a contradiction. Thus $x_1 s_1 x_2 \in J_1$ if and only if $x_1 s_2 x_2 \in J_1$ for all $x_1, x_2 \in J_1$.

We next show that if $x_1 s_1 x_2 \in J_1$ (and $x_1 s_2 x_2 \in J_1$), then $x_1 s_1 x_2 \equiv_{N_1} x_1 s_2 x_2$, which implies $\psi_1(s_1) = \psi_1(s_2)$. Clearly $x_1 s_1 x_2 \mathscr{H} x_1 s_2 x_2$. Give J_1 a Rees matrix representation with respect to the group G_1, so that $\varphi(g, a, b)$ can be written $(\omega(g), \psi_L(a), \psi_R(b))$ where $\omega = \varphi | G_1$ and ψ_L and ψ_R are functions. Let $x_1 s_i x_2 = (g_i, a, b)$, $i = 1, 2$. Then since $\varphi(x_1 s_1 x_2) = \varphi(x_1 s_2 x_2)$, we have $\omega(g_1) = \omega(g_2)$. Therefore $g_1 g_2^{-1} \in N_1$, since φ is a π homomorphism, and $(g_1, a, b) \equiv_{N_1} (g_2, a, b)$, proving the assertion.

Now by induction assume that $\varphi(s_1) = \varphi(s_2)$ implies $\psi_i(s_1) = \psi_i(s_2)$ for all $i \leqslant j$. We must show that $\varphi(s_1) = \varphi(s_2)$ implies $\psi_{j+1}(s_1) = \psi_{j+1}(s_2)$. If ψ_j is a π homomorphism when restricted to groups of J_{j+1}, then $\psi_j = \psi_{j+1}$ and the induction step proceeds trivially.

Hence assume ψ_j is not a π homomorphism on J_{j+1}, so

$$\psi_{j+1} = [\psi_j \times \pi GM_{J_{j+1}}]\, \Delta.$$

We again show that $x_1 s_1 x_2 \in J_{j+1}$ if and only if $x_1 s_2 x_2 \in J_{j+1}$ for all $x_1, x_2 \in J_{j+1}$. Assuming otherwise leads one, as before, to the conclusion that $\varphi[B(J_{j+1})] = \varphi[B(J_{j+1}) \cup J_{j+1}]$. Since ψ_j is a π homomorphism on $B(J_{j+1})$, by Lemma 4.9 ψ_j is a π homomorphism on J_{j+1}, a contradiction. Then we can proceed as before to prove that $\psi_{j+1}(s_1) = \psi_{j+1}(s_2)$. ▮

4.11 Corollary. (a) $S \underset{\pi}{\twoheadrightarrow} T$ implies $S^\pi \cong T^\pi$.

(b) Let S be 0-simple. Then $S^\pi = \pi GM(S)$.

(c) Let S be a πGM semigroup. Then $S = S^\pi$.

(d) Let $T \subseteq S$ and let φ be a π homomorphism on S. Then φ restricted to T is a π homomorphism and $T^\pi | S^\pi$.

(e) $S \twoheadrightarrow T$ does not in general imply $T^\pi | S^\pi$, so it is *false* that $T|S$ implies $T^\pi | S^\pi$.

PROOF. (a) We have

$$S \underset{\pi}{\twoheadrightarrow} T \underset{\pi}{\twoheadrightarrow} S^\pi \underset{\pi}{\twoheadrightarrow} T^\pi \qquad \text{and} \qquad S \underset{\pi}{\twoheadrightarrow} T \underset{\pi}{\twoheadrightarrow} T^\pi \underset{\pi}{\twoheadrightarrow} S^\pi$$

by the definition of minimal π-homomorphic image, so $S^\pi \cong T^\pi$.

(b) This follows from the construction of S^π.

(c) $\pi GM(S) = S$ by assumption [see Fact 2.6(b)], so by the construction of S^π, $S = S^\pi$.

(d) Let G' be a maximal subgroup of T, let G be the maximal subgroup of S containing G'. Clearly,

$$\ker(\varphi|G') \cong G' \cap \ker(\varphi|G) \subseteq \ker(\varphi|G),$$

a π' group. Therefore $\varphi|T$ is a π homomorphism. Now let $\varphi\colon S \underset{\pi}{\twoheadrightarrow} S^\pi$. Then $\varphi(T) \subseteq S^\pi$ and $\varphi(T) \underset{\pi}{\twoheadrightarrow} T^\pi$, since $\varphi\colon T \underset{\pi}{\twoheadrightarrow} \varphi(T) \underset{\pi}{\twoheadrightarrow} T^\pi$. Thus $T^\pi | S^\pi$.

(e) Let G be a nontrivial π group and let $S = G \times \{0\}^l$. $G \times \{0\}$ is an ideal of S, so let $S \twoheadrightarrow S/G \times \{0\} = T$. $T \cong G^0$ and $T^\pi \cong T \cong G^0$. However $S^\pi \cong G$, so T^π does not divide S^π. ▮

Recall the definition of a $\mathscr{J}'$ homomorphism (Definition 8.2.8 of Krohn *et al.* [*1*]). In Fact 8.39 [*1*], it is shown that $\mathscr{L}'$, $\mathscr{R}'$, and $\mathscr{H}'$ homomorphisms go under restriction and the minimal homomorphic images $S^{\mathscr{L}'}$, $S^{\mathscr{R}'}$, and $S^{\mathscr{H}'}$ exist. We now extend these results to $\mathscr{J}'$.

4.12 Lemma. Let T be a subsemigroup of S with J' a $\mathscr{J}$ class of T. Let J be the $\mathscr{J}$ class of S containing J'. Then no element of $B(J') \cap J$ is regular in T.

PROOF. If J is a null $\mathscr{J}$ class of S, then the assertion holds. So assume J is regular. Now suppose $B(J') \cap J$ has a regular element. Then there exists an idempotent $e \in B(J') \cap J$. Let $s \in J'$. Since $e \in B(J')$, there exist $x, y \in T$ such that $xsy = e$. Represent J by the regular Rees matrix semigroup $\mathscr{M}^0(G; A, B; C)$, where $G = H_{11}$, the $\mathscr{H}$ class of S containing e. Let H_{ij} be the $\mathscr{H}$ class of S containing s. Then $xs \in H_{1j}$ and $sy \in H_{i1}$, and since $C(1, 1) \neq 0$, $syxs \in H_{ij}$. Now we know that the map $s \to xsy$ is a $1 : 1$ onto a map of H_{ij} onto H_{11}. But $e = e^2 = xsyxsy = x(syxs)y = x(s)y$, so $s = syxs$. Furthermore, $e \mathscr{R} xs$ in S, so $exs = xs$, and $s = syexs$. Thus $s \mathscr{J} e$ in T, a contradiction. ▌

4.13 Proposition. $\mathscr{J}'$ goes under restriction, i.e., if $\varphi: S \twoheadrightarrow T$ is a $\mathscr{J}'$ homomorphism and $S_1 \subseteq S$, then φ restricted to S_1 is a $\mathscr{J}'$ homomorphism.

PROOF. Let s_1, s_2 be regular in S_1 and suppose $\varphi(s_1) = \varphi(s_2)$. Suppose s_1 is not $\mathscr{J}$ equivalent to s_2 in S_1. Since φ is a $\mathscr{J}'$ map on S, and s_1, s_2 are regular in S, $s_1 \mathscr{J} s_2$ in S. Let J_1, J_2 be the $\mathscr{J}$ classes of s_1, s_2, respectively, in S_1. By Lemma 4.12, J_1 and J_2 are not comparable in S_1, since J_1 and $J_2 \subseteq J$, a regular $\mathscr{J}$ class of S and J_1, J_2 are regular $\mathscr{J}$ classes. Let J' be the $\mathscr{J}$ class of $\varphi(S_1)$ containing $\varphi(s_1)$ and let J'' be the unique regular $\mathscr{J}$ class of S_1 such that $\varphi(J'') = J'$. Then $J'' \leqslant J_1$ and $J'' \leqslant J_2$ so $J'' \subseteq B(J)$. But φ is a $\mathscr{J}'$ map so J is the unique minimal $\mathscr{J}$ class of S such that $\varphi(J) = \bar{J}'$ the $\mathscr{J}$ class of T containing J'. This implies $J'' \subseteq J$, a contradiction. Therefore, $s_1 \mathscr{J} s_2$ in S_1. ▌

4.14 Proposition. (a) S has a minimal homomorphic image with respect to $\mathscr{P}(S, \mathscr{J}')$, written $S^{\mathscr{J}'}$, and if π is chosen to be the empty set of primes, then $S^{\mathscr{J}'} \cong S^{\pi GGM}$. Equivalently, if $J_1, \ldots, J_n$ are the regular $\mathscr{J}$ classes of S, then $S^{\mathscr{J}'}$ is a subdirect product of the semigroups $\{LM[RLM_{J_i}(S)]: i = 1, \ldots, n\}$, or equivalently $\{RM[LLM_{J_i}(S)]: i = 1, \ldots, n\}$.

(b) If $S \twoheadrightarrow T$, then $S^{\mathscr{J}'} \twoheadrightarrow T^{\mathscr{J}'}$.

(c) If $S|T$, then $S^{\mathscr{J}'}|T^{\mathscr{J}'}$.

PROOF. (a) Let $G_1, \ldots, G_n$ be maximal subgroups of the regular $\mathscr{J}$ classes $J_1, \ldots, J_n$, respectively. Then $\varphi: S \twoheadrightarrow S^{\pi GGM}$ is given by $\varphi = (GGM_{G_1} \times \cdots \times GGM_{G_n})\Delta$, and $GGM_{G_i}(S) \cong LM[RLM_{J_i}(S)]$, so

$$S^{\pi GGM} \leqslant\leqslant LM[RLM_{J_1}(S)] \times \cdots \times LM[RLM_{J_n}(S)]$$

$$\cong RM[LLM_{J_1}(S)] \times \cdots \times RM[LLM_{J_n}(S)].$$

See Definition 2.2(c).

We now show that $\varphi: S \twoheadrightarrow S^{\pi GGM}$ is a $\mathscr{J}'$ homomorphism. Let $s_1, s_2 \in S$ be regular and suppose s_1 is not $\mathscr{J}$ equivalent to s_2. Then for some $i \in \{1, \ldots, n\}$, $GGM_{G_i}(s_1) \neq 0$ and $GGM_{G_i}(s_2) = 0$, or vice versa. Thus $\varphi(s_1) \neq \varphi(s_2)$ and φ is $\mathscr{J}'$.

Now to show that $S^{\pi GGM}$ is the minimal $\mathscr{J}'$ homomorphic image, we must show that if $\psi: S \twoheadrightarrow T$ is a $\mathscr{J}'$ homomorphism and $\varphi(s_1) \neq \varphi(s_2)$, then $\psi(s_1) \neq \psi(s_2)$. Suppose $\varphi(s_1) \neq \varphi(s_2)$. Then there exists some regular $\mathscr{J}$ class J_i and $x_1, x_2 \in J_i$ such that $x_1 s_1 x_2 \not\equiv_{G_i} x_1 s_2 x_2$. Then one of the $x_1 s_i x_2$ must be in J_i, but both cannot be in J_i, for then $x_1 s_1 x_2 \mathscr{H} x_1 s_2 x_2$ which implies $x_1 s_1 x_2 \equiv_{G_i} x_1 s_2 x_2$. Therefore the other belongs to $B(J_i)$. By Fact 8.3.9(b) of Krohn *et al.* [*1*], a $\mathscr{J}'$ homomorphism separates J_i and $B(J_i)$, so $\psi(x_1 s_1 x_2) \neq \psi(x_1 s_2 x_2)$, which implies $\psi(s_1) \neq \psi(s_2)$. Thus $S^{\pi GGM} \cong S^{\mathscr{J}'}$, when $\pi = \{\emptyset\}$.

Proofs (b) and (c) follow from Proposition 4.7. ∎

4.15 Definition. Let $\mathscr{P}(S, \alpha)$ and $\mathscr{P}(S, \beta)$ be two properties of homomorphisms. Define an $\alpha + \beta$ *homomorphism* to be a homomorphism which is both an α homomorphism and a β homomorphism, i.e., define the properties of homomorphisms

$$\mathscr{P}(S, \alpha + \beta) = \mathscr{P}(S, \alpha) \cap \mathscr{P}(S, \beta).$$

4.16 Fact. Let $\mathscr{P}(S, \alpha)$ and $\mathscr{P}(S, \beta)$ be two properties of homomorphisms satisfying the following conditions:

(1) S^α and S^β exist, and

(2) if $\varphi \in \mathscr{P}(S, \alpha)$ or $\varphi \in \mathscr{P}(S, \beta)$ and $\varphi = \varphi_2 \varphi_1$, then $\varphi_1 \in \mathscr{P}(S, \alpha)$ or $\mathscr{P}(S, \beta)$, respectively.

Then $S^{\alpha+\beta}$ exists. Further, if $\varphi_\alpha: S \twoheadrightarrow S^\alpha$ and $\varphi_\beta: S \twoheadrightarrow S^\beta$, then $(\varphi_\alpha \times \varphi_\beta)\Delta(S) \cong S^{\alpha+\beta}$, so $S^{\alpha+\beta} \leqslant\leqslant S^\alpha \times S^\beta$.

Proof. Let Q_α and Q_β be the congruences associated with φ_α and φ_β, respectively. Then $(\varphi_\alpha \times \varphi_\beta)\Delta$ induces the congruence $Q_\alpha \cap Q_\beta$. Since $Q_\alpha \cap Q_\beta \subseteq Q_\alpha$, by condition (2), $(\varphi_\alpha \times \varphi_\beta)\Delta$ is an α homomorphism. Similarly $(\varphi_\alpha \times \varphi_\beta)\Delta$ is a β homomorphism, so $(\varphi_\alpha \times \varphi_\beta)\Delta \in \mathscr{P}(S, \alpha + \beta)$. Conversely, if $\theta: S \twoheadrightarrow S/Q$ is any $\alpha + \beta$ homomorphism, then $Q \subseteq Q_\alpha$ and $Q \subseteq Q_\beta$, so $Q \subseteq Q_\alpha \cap Q_\beta$. Thus $(\varphi_\alpha \times \varphi_\beta)\Delta(S)$ is the minimal homomorphic image with respect to $\mathscr{P}(S, \alpha + \beta)$, written $S^{\alpha+\beta}$. Clearly, $S^{\alpha+\beta} \leqslant\leqslant S^\alpha \times S^\beta$. ∎

4.17 Remark. The properties $\mathscr{J}$, $\mathscr{R}$, $\mathscr{L}$, $\mathscr{H}$, $\mathscr{J}'$, $\mathscr{R}'$, $\mathscr{L}'$, $\mathscr{H}'$, γ, π, and π' all satisfy conditions (1) and (2) of the previous fact.

4.18 Proposition. Let S be a semigroup.

(a) $S^{\pi GGM} \cong S^{\pi+\mathscr{J}'} \leqslant\leqslant S^\pi \times S^{\mathscr{J}'}$.

(b) $S^{\pi RM} \cong S^{\pi+\mathscr{L}'} \leqslant\leqslant S^{\pi} \times S^{\mathscr{L}'}$.

(c) $S^{\pi LM} \cong S^{\pi+\mathscr{R}'} \leqslant\leqslant S^{\pi} \times S^{\mathscr{R}'}$.

PROOF. (a) We first show that $\psi: S \twoheadrightarrow S^{\pi GGM}$ is a $\pi + \mathscr{J}'$ homomorphism. Let $s_1, s_2 \in S$ be regular and suppose $\psi(s_1) = \psi(s_2)$. Let $J_1, \ldots, J_n$ be the regular classes of S; $G_1, \ldots, G_n$, maximal subgroups of $J_1, \ldots, J_n$, respectively; and $N_1, \ldots, N_n$ the maximal normal π' subgroups of $G_1, \ldots, G_n$, respectively. Then

$$\psi = (GGM_{N_1} \times \cdots \times GGM_{N_n})\,\Delta$$

by Fact 4.3. If s_1 is not $\mathscr{J}$ equivalent to s_2, then there exists $j \in \{1, \ldots, n\}$ such that $GGM_{J_j}(s_1) = 0$ and $GGM_{J_j}(s_2) \neq 0$, or vice versa. Thus $s_1 \mathscr{J} s_2$ and ψ is a $\mathscr{J}'$ homomorphism. To show that ψ is a π homomorphism, we must show that $\ker \psi|G_i$ is a π' subgroup for each $i \in \{1, \ldots, n\}$. But

$$\ker(\psi|G) = \ker(GGM_{N_1}|G) \cap \cdots \cap \ker(GGM_{N_n}|G),$$

and $\ker(GGM_{N_i}|G_i) = N_i$. Thus

$$\ker(\psi|G_i) \subseteq \ker(GGM_{N_i}|G_i) = N_i,$$

so ψ is a π homomorphism.

Now to show that $S^{\pi GGM}$ is the minimal $\pi + \mathscr{J}'$ homomorphic image, we must show that if $\varphi: S \twoheadrightarrow T$ is a $\pi + \mathscr{J}'$ homomorphism, then there exists $\theta: T \twoheadrightarrow S^{\pi GGM}$ such that $\psi = \theta\varphi$. Equivalently, we must show that $\psi(s_1) \neq \psi(s_2)$ implies $\varphi(s_1) \neq \varphi(s_2)$. Suppose $\psi(s_1) \neq \psi(s_2)$. Then there exists some regular $\mathscr{J}$ class J_i and $x_1, x_2 \in J_i$ such that $x_1 s_1 x_2 \not\equiv_{N_i} x_1 s_2 x_2$ in S. Then one of the two elements must be in J_i, so let $x_1 s_1 x_2 \in J_i$.

(1) Suppose $x_1 s_2 x_2 \notin J_i$, i.e., $x_1 s_2 x_2 \in B(J_i)$. By Fact 8.3.9(b) of Krohn *et al.* [*1*], a $\mathscr{J}'$ homomorphism separates J and $B(J)$ if J is regular, i.e., $\varphi(J_i) \cap \varphi(B(J_i)) = \emptyset$, and so $\varphi(x_1 s_1 x_2) \neq \varphi(x_1 s_2 x_2)$ which implies $\varphi(s_1) \neq \varphi(s_2)$.

(2) Suppose $x_1 s_2 x_2 \in J_i$. Then $x_1 s_1 x_2 \mathscr{H} x_1 s_2 x_2$. Give J_i a Rees matrix representation with respect to G_i such that $\varphi(g, a, b) = (\varphi(g), \psi_L(a), \psi_R(b))$. Let $x_1 s_i x_2 = (g_i, a, b)$, $i = 1, 2$. Then $g_1 g_2^{-1} \notin N_i$ by assumption. Since φ is a π homomorphism, $\ker \varphi|G_i \subseteq N_i$. Therefore $\varphi(g_1) \neq \varphi(g_2)$, so $\varphi(x_1 s_1 x_2) \neq \varphi(x_1 s_2 x_2)$ which implies $\varphi(s_1) \neq \varphi(s_2)$. Thus $S^{\pi GGM} \cong S^{\pi+\mathscr{J}'}$, and $S^{\pi GGM} \leqslant\leqslant S^{\pi} \times S^{\mathscr{J}'}$.

(b) Let $\psi: S \twoheadrightarrow S^{\pi RM}$. Then $\psi = (RM_{N_1} \times \cdots \times RM_{N_n})\Delta$ by Fact 4.3. We show ψ is a $\pi + \mathscr{L}'$ homomorphism. By an argument similar to the above, ψ is a π homomorphism. Let $s_1, s_2 \in S$ be regular and let $\psi(s_1) = \psi(s_2)$. Then $s_1 \mathscr{J} s_2$, as above. Let $s_1, s_2 \in J_i$. If s_1 is not $\mathscr{L}$ equivalent to s_2, then clearly $RM_{N_i}(s_1) \neq RM_{N_i}(s_2)$, so $s_1 \mathscr{L} s_2$ and ψ is a $\pi + \mathscr{L}'$ homomorphism.

Now let $\varphi: S \twoheadrightarrow T$ be any $\pi + \mathscr{L}'$ homomorphism, and suppose $\psi(s_1) \neq \psi(s_2)$, $s_1, s_2 \in S$. Then there exists a $\mathscr{J}$ class J_i and $x \in J_i$ such that $xs_1 \neq_{N_i} xs_2$. One of the two must belong to J_i, say xs_1.

(1) If $xs_2 \notin J_i$, i.e., $xs_2 \in B(J_i)$, then $\varphi(xs_1) \neq \varphi(xs_2)$ by Fact 8.3.9(b) of Krohn *et al.* [*1*]. Thus $\varphi(s_1) \neq \varphi(s_2)$.

(2) If $xs_2 \in J_i$ but xs_1 is not $\mathscr{H}$ equivalent to xs_2, then xs_1 is not $\mathscr{L}$ equivalent to xs_2. Then since both xs_1 and xs_2 are regular and φ is an $\mathscr{L}'$ homomorphism, $\varphi(xs_1) \neq \varphi(xs_2)$ and $\varphi(s_1) \neq \varphi(s_2)$.

(3) If $xs_1 \mathscr{H} xs_2$, the argument used in (a) suffices here.

Thus $S^{\pi RM} \cong S^{\pi+\mathscr{L}'} \leqslant\leqslant S^{\pi} \times S^{L'}$.

(c) This is proven by the argument dual to (b). ∎

4.19 Proposition. Let S be a πRM semigroup. Then

$$\pi' RM(S) \cong S^{\pi'+\mathscr{L}'} \cong S^{\pi' RM}$$

PROOF. First $\pi' RM(S) \cong \pi' RM(S)^{\pi' RM} = \pi' RM(S)^{\pi'+\mathscr{L}'}$ by definition of $T^{\pi' RM}$ and Proposition 4.18. Thus it will suffice to prove that $S \twoheadrightarrow \pi' RM(S)$ is a $\pi' + \mathscr{L}'$ homomorphism, for $S \xrightarrow[\pi'+\mathscr{L}']{} T$ implies $S^{\pi'+\mathscr{L}'} \cong T^{\pi'+\mathscr{L}'}$. This follows because

$$S^{\pi'+\mathscr{L}'} \twoheadrightarrow T^{\pi'+\mathscr{L}'} \quad \text{and} \quad S \xrightarrow[\pi'+\mathscr{L}']{} T \xrightarrow[\pi'+\mathscr{L}']{} T^{\pi'+\mathscr{L}'} \twoheadrightarrow S^{\pi'+\mathscr{L}'}.$$

Let P be a largest π subgroup of the distinguished $\mathscr{J}$ class of S. By Proposition 2.13

$$\begin{aligned} S &\subseteq (P^0, P^0) \text{ w } ((G/P)^0 \times B^0, \pi' RM(S)) \\ &\subseteq (P^0, P^0) \text{ w } ((G/P)^0 \times B^0, F_R((G/P)^0 \times B^0)) \\ &\cong F((G/P)^0 \times B^0, P^0) \times_Y F_R((G/P)^0 \times B^0). \end{aligned}$$

Furthermore, the projection map

$$p_1: F((G/P)^0 \times B^0, P^0) \times_Y F_R((G/P)^0 \times B^0) \twoheadrightarrow F_R((G/P)^0 \times B^0)$$

when restricted to S yields $\pi' RM(S)$.

Define the subsemigroup

$$T = \{(f_2, f_1) \in F((G/P)^0 \times B^0, P^0) \times_Y F_R((G/P)^0 \times B^0) : (h, b) f_1 = (0, 0) \text{ if and only if } f_2(h, b) = 0\}.$$

Clearly $S \subseteq T$. We will show that p_1 restricted to T is an $\mathscr{L}$ homomorphism as well as a π' homomorphism, so p_1 restricted to S is a $\pi' + \mathscr{L}'$ homomorphism.

We must show that any two elements of T with the same first coordinate are $\mathscr{L}$ equivalent. Let $(f_2, f_1), (g_2, f_1) \in T$. Let $X = (G/P)^0 \times B^0$ and define $X_1 = \{x \in X: (x) f_1 \neq (0, 0)\}$. Define (h_1, e) and $(h_2, e) \in T$ by

$$(x)\, e = \begin{cases} x & \text{if } x \in X_1 \\ (0, 0) & \text{if } x \notin X_1 \end{cases}$$

$$h_1(x) = \begin{cases} g_2(x) f_2(x)^{-1} & \text{if } x \in X_1 \\ 0 & \text{if } x \notin X_1 \end{cases}$$

$$h_2(x) = \begin{cases} f_2(x) g_2(x)^{-1} & \text{if } x \in X_1 \\ 0 & \text{if } x \notin X_1 . \end{cases}$$

Then $(h_1, e)(f_2, f_1) = (g_2, f_1)$ and $(h_2, e)(g_2, f_1) = (f_2, f_1)$ so $(f_2, f_1) \mathscr{L} (g_2, f_1)$ in T, and $p_1: S \twoheadrightarrow \pi'RM(S)$ is an $\mathscr{L}'$ homomorphism.

Finally, let G be a subgroup of S. The kernel of p_1 restricted to G is isomorphic to a subgroup of $F((G/P)^0 \times B^0, P^0)$, a π semigroup (see Remark 1.16(b)). Hence the kernel is a π group and $p_1: S \twoheadrightarrow \pi'RM(S)$ is a π' homomorphism. Thus $S \underset{\pi'+\mathscr{L}'}{\twoheadrightarrow} \pi'RM(S)$, and $\pi'RM(S) \cong S^{\pi'+\mathscr{L}'}$. ∎

4.20 Definition. Let $\alpha = \gamma, \pi, \pi', \pi + \mathscr{J}', \pi RM$, etc. We say S is α *stable* if and only if $S \cong S^\alpha$.

4.21 Fact. (a) S^α is α-stable.

(b) If S is a πRM semigroup, then S is $\pi + \mathscr{L}'$ stable.

(c) If S is a πLM semigroup, then S is $\pi + \mathscr{R}'$ stable.

(d) If S is a πGGM or πGM semigroup, then S is $\pi + \mathscr{J}'$ stable.

PROOF. (a) Clear.

(b) By the definition of $S^{\pi RM}$, $S^{\pi RM} \twoheadrightarrow S$ since S is πRM. Thus $S \cong S^{\pi RM} \cong S^{\pi+\mathscr{L}'}$.

(c) and (d) are proved in the same manner. ∎

4.22 Lemma. Suppose a semigroup S is both π stable and either $\pi', \alpha, \alpha', \pi' + \alpha$, or $\pi' + \alpha'$ stable, where $\alpha = \mathscr{J}, \mathscr{R}, \mathscr{L}$, or $\mathscr{H}$. Then $S = \{0\}$.

PROOF. Consider the diagram below.

$$\begin{array}{ccccccc} S & \twoheadrightarrow & S^{\pi'+\alpha} & \twoheadrightarrow & S^{\pi'+\alpha'} & \twoheadrightarrow & S^{\pi'}. \\ & & \downarrow & & \downarrow & & \\ & & S^{\alpha} & & S^{\alpha'} & & \end{array}$$

If S is isomorphic to either $S^{\pi'}$, S^{α}, $S^{\alpha'}$, or $S^{\pi'+\alpha'}$, then $S \cong S^{\pi'+\alpha}$. Thus it suffices to consider the case when S is both π and $\pi' + \alpha$ stable.

Suppose S has a 0-minimal ideal I. If I is a π' semigroup, then $S \twoheadrightarrow S/I$ is a proper π homomorphism, so by the assumption that S is π-stable, I must be regular and $J = I^{\#}$ must be π regular. Let G be a maximal subgroup of J. Then $G \neq \{1\}$ and G can have no nontrivial π' subgroup, N, for otherwise $S \twoheadrightarrow S/N$ would be a proper π homomorphism. Then G must have a nontrivial normal π group P. But $S \twoheadrightarrow S/P$ is a proper $\pi' + \mathscr{H}$ homomorphism, hence a proper $\pi' + \alpha$ homomorphism, a contradiction. Thus S has no 0-minimal ideal, so $S = \{0\}$. ∎

4.23 Corollary. Let S be both a πGM semigroup and a $\pi' RM$ semigroup. Then $S = \{0\}$.

PROOF. S is both π and $\pi' + \mathscr{L}'$ stable. ∎

4.24 Lemma. Let $\alpha = \mathscr{J}, \mathscr{R}, \mathscr{L}$, or $\mathscr{H}$. Let φ_i: $S_i \twoheadrightarrow T_i$, $i = 1, 2$ be a π, α, or an α' homomorphism. Then

$$\varphi_1 \times \varphi_2 \colon S_1 \times S_2 \twoheadrightarrow T_1 \times T_2$$

is a π, α, or an α' homomorphism, respectively.

PROOF. The following statements are easily verified.

(1) $(s_1, s_2) \, \alpha \, (t_1, t_2)$ in $S_1 \times S_2$ if and only if $s_1 \, \alpha \, t_1$ in S_1 and $s_2 \, \alpha \, t_2$ in S_2.

(2) (s_1, s_2) is regular in $S_1 \times S_2$ if and only if s_1 is regular in S_1 and s_2 is regular in S_2.

Using (1) and (2), it is simple to verify the assertion for α and α'. For the π case, let G be a subgroup of $S_1 \times S_2$ and let

$$p_i \colon S_1 \times S_2 \twoheadrightarrow S_i, \qquad i = 1, 2$$

be the projection maps. Let $p_i(G) = G_i$, so $G \subseteq G_1 \times G_2 \subseteq S_1 \times S_2$. Then

$$\ker(\varphi_1 \times \varphi_2 | G) \subseteq \ker(\varphi_1 \times \varphi_2 | G_1 \times G_2) = \ker(\varphi_1 | G_1) \times \ker(\psi_1 | G_2),$$

a π' group. Then $\varphi_1 \times \varphi_2$ is a π homomorphism. ∎

4.25 Corollary. If φ_i, $i = 1, 2$ are $\pi + \alpha$ or $\pi + \alpha'$ homomorphisms, where $\alpha = \mathscr{J}$, $\mathscr{R}$, $\mathscr{L}$, or $\mathscr{H}$, then $\varphi_1 \times \varphi_2$ is a $\pi + \alpha$ or $\pi + \alpha'$ homomorphism, respectively. ∎

4.26 Proposition. Let φ: $S \twoheadrightarrow T$ be an epimorphism. Let $\alpha = \mathscr{J}'$,

$\mathscr{R}'$, $\mathscr{L}'$, $\mathscr{H}'$, $\pi' + \mathscr{J}'$, $\pi' + \mathscr{R}'$, $\pi' + \mathscr{L}'$, or $\pi' + \mathscr{H}'$. Then $\varphi = \varphi_n \cdots \varphi_1$, where the φ_i are alternately π epimorphisms and α epimorphisms.

PROOF. Consider the series

$$S \twoheadrightarrow S^{\pi} \twoheadrightarrow (S^{\pi})^{\alpha} \twoheadrightarrow (S^{\pi\alpha})^{\pi} \twoheadrightarrow \cdots \twoheadrightarrow \{0\}. \tag{4.1}$$

Lemma 4.22 assures that this series reaches $\{0\}$. Let $\psi: S \to S \times T$ be given by $\psi(s) = (s, \varphi(s))$, and consider

$$S \underset{1:1}{\overset{\psi}{\twoheadrightarrow}} S \times T \underset{\pi}{\twoheadrightarrow} S^{\pi} \times T \underset{\alpha}{\twoheadrightarrow} S^{\pi\alpha} \times T \underset{\pi}{\twoheadrightarrow} \cdots$$
$$\twoheadrightarrow \{0\} \times T \cong T \tag{4.2}$$

where the maps on T are the identity maps and the maps on the first coordinate are given by series (4.1). The maps of (4.2) are alternately π and α homomorphisms by virtue of Lemma 4.24. Then the restriction of series (4.2) to the images of S is

$$S \twoheadrightarrow S \underset{\pi}{\twoheadrightarrow} S_1 \underset{\alpha}{\twoheadrightarrow} S_2 \underset{\pi}{\twoheadrightarrow} \cdots \twoheadrightarrow T \tag{4.3}$$

since the restriction to subsemigroups of a π or α homomorphism is a π or α homomorphism, respectively. The composed homomorphism of (4.3) is $\varphi: S \twoheadrightarrow T$. ∎

4.27 Corollary. If φ is a MPE, then φ is either a π or a $\pi' + \mathscr{H}'$ homomorphism. ∎

This result can be improved to π and $\pi' + \mathscr{H}$ if needed.

4.28 Theorem.† Let S be π solvable and consider all homomorphism series of the form

$$S \twoheadrightarrow \pi PGM_1 \twoheadrightarrow \pi' RM_1 \twoheadrightarrow \pi PGM_2 \twoheadrightarrow \cdots \twoheadrightarrow \pi PGM_n$$
$$\twoheadrightarrow \pi' RM_n \twoheadrightarrow \{0\}, \tag{4.4}$$

where the πPGM_i are π-pure group mapping, the $\pi' RM_i$ are π'-right mapping, and $\pi PGM_n \neq \{0\}$. Let the *length* of such a series be *n*. Let $\alpha_\pi(S) = \max\{\text{length of all such series for } S\}$. Then $l_\pi(S) = \alpha_\pi(S)$.

PROOF. By virtue of Corollary 4.23, every epimorphism in these series is proper except possibly the first and last. Furthermore, every series of type (4.4) can be replaced by the following series of the same length:

$$S \twoheadrightarrow \pi PGM_1 \twoheadrightarrow \pi' RM[\pi PGM_1] \twoheadrightarrow \pi PGM_2 \twoheadrightarrow \cdots \twoheadrightarrow \pi PGM_n$$
$$\twoheadrightarrow \pi' RM[\pi PGM_n] \twoheadrightarrow \{0\}.$$

† See Note Added in Proof, page 208.

To prove this, let T be a πGM semigroup and consider $T \twoheadrightarrow \pi' RM_i$. By Proposition 4.19, $\pi' RM(T) \cong T^{\pi'+\mathscr{L}'}$ and $T^{\pi'+\mathscr{L}'} \cong T^{\pi' RM}$ and by definition $T^{\pi' RM} \twoheadrightarrow \pi' RM_i$. Therefore $T \twoheadrightarrow \pi' RM_i$ can be factored to $T \twoheadrightarrow \pi' RM(T) \twoheadrightarrow \pi' RM_i$, proving the assertion.

Now it is easy to see that $\alpha_\pi(S) \leqslant l_\pi(S)$, for by the definition of πPGM, the π length must drop exactly one from πPGM_i to $\pi' RM[\pi PGM_i]$.

We prove the reverse inequality, $l_\pi(S) \leqslant \alpha_\pi(S)$, by induction on the order of S. Assume the inequality true for all semigroups of order less than $|S|$. Let $l_\pi(S) = n$. If S is not subdirectly indecomposable, then by Axiom I (Definition 3.4), there exists a proper homomorphic image T of S with $l_\pi(S) = l_\pi(T)$. But by induction $l_\pi(T) = \alpha_\pi(T)$, so T, hence S, has a chain of type (4.4) of length n, so $\alpha_\pi(S) \geqslant n = l_\pi(S)$.

Let S be subdirectly indecomposable; then S is either a πGM, $\pi' RM$, LLM semigroup or a semigroup with a null ideal (Theorem 2.9(b)). In the last three cases, S has a proper π-homomorphic image whose π length is the same as $l_\pi(S)$, so again by induction, $\alpha_\pi(S) \geqslant n = l_\pi(S)$.

Let S be a non-πPGM semigroup. Then $l_\pi(S) = l_\pi(\pi' RM(S))$, so using the same argument as above, $\alpha_\pi(S) \geqslant l_\pi(S)$. If S is a πPGM, then $l_\pi(\pi' RM(S)) = n - 1$, $n \geqslant 1$. If $n = 1$, then $S \twoheadrightarrow \pi' RM(S)$ is a series of type (4.4) of length 1, so $\alpha_\pi(S) \geqslant 1 = l_\pi(S)$. If $n > 1$, then $\pi' RM(S)$ has a series of length $n - 1$, so the series $S \twoheadrightarrow \pi' RM(S)$ followed by this longest series for $\pi' RM(S)$ has length n, because $\pi' RM(S)$ is not a πPGM semigroup. Thus again $\alpha_\pi(S) \geqslant l_\pi(S)$, and then $\alpha_\pi(S) = l_\pi(S)$. ∎

4.29 Corollary.† (Continuity of π Length with Respect to Homomorphisms). (a) $\varphi: S \xrightarrow[\pi'+\mathscr{L}']{} T$ implies

$$l_\pi(T) \leqslant l_\pi(S) \leqslant l_\pi(T) + 1.$$

(b) Let $\varphi: S \twoheadrightarrow T$ be an epimorphism and let $l_\pi(S) = n$ and $l_\pi(T) = k$. Then there exist epimorphisms

$$S = S_n \twoheadrightarrow S_{n-1} \twoheadrightarrow \cdots \twoheadrightarrow S_k = T$$

so that the composite epimorphism is φ and $l_\pi(S_j) = j$ for $j = k, \ldots, n$.

Proof. (a) Let

$$S \twoheadrightarrow \pi PGM_1 \twoheadrightarrow \pi' RM_1 \twoheadrightarrow \pi PGM_2 \twoheadrightarrow \cdots \tag{4.4}$$

be a longest series of this type for S. Now since $S \xrightarrow[\pi'+\mathscr{L}']{} T$ we have

$$T \twoheadrightarrow T^{\pi'+\mathscr{L}'} \cong S^{\pi'+\mathscr{L}'} \cong S^{\pi' RM} \twoheadrightarrow \pi' RM_1$$

so

$$T \twoheadrightarrow \pi' RM_1 \twoheadrightarrow \pi PGM_2 \twoheadrightarrow \cdots$$

† See Note Added in Proof, page 208.

is a series of type (4.4) for T. Then $l_\pi(T) \geqslant l_\pi(S) - 1$. On the other hand, $l_\pi(T) \leqslant l_\pi(S)$.

(b) Since $\varphi: S \twoheadrightarrow T$ can be decomposed into alternating π homomorphisms and $\pi' + \mathscr{L}'$ homomorphisms (Proposition 4.26), the assertion follows immediately from (a) and Axiom II. ∎

This theorem gives (in theory) a method for computing the π length of an arbitrary finite π-solvable semigroup. However, in practice, it is not useful, for it is not known, in general, which πGM semigroups are pure and which are not. Some conditions are known, but the results are very incomplete. However, there is a class of semigroups (which includes union of groups semigroups) closed under division in which every nonzero πGM semigroup is pure. In this case, Theorem 4.28 is very useful, for given a semigroup in a concrete representation it is not particularly difficult to find a longest πGM–$\pi' RM$ chain for it. (The longest such chain, in general, gives an upper bound to $l_\pi(S)$.) This class of semigroups is all semigroups S such that $S^{\mathscr{I}'}$ is a π' semigroup, denoted $\mathscr{S}_\pi^0$. Assuming for the moment that every nonzero πGM semigroup in $\mathscr{S}_\pi^0$ is pure, we have the following corollary.

4.30 Corollary.† Let S be a π-solvable semigroup and consider all homomorphism series of the form

$$S \twoheadrightarrow \pi GM_1 \twoheadrightarrow \pi' RM_1 \twoheadrightarrow \cdots \twoheadrightarrow \pi GM_n \twoheadrightarrow \pi' RM_n \twoheadrightarrow \{0\} \tag{4.5}$$

where $\pi GM_n \neq \{0\}$. Let the length of such a series be n, and define $\pi_a(S) = \max\{\text{length of all such series for } S\}$. Then $\pi_a(S) \geqslant l_\pi(S)$, and if $S \in \mathscr{S}_\pi^0$, then $\pi_a(S) = l_\pi(S)$. ∎

In the next section we restrict our attention to the class $\mathscr{S}_\pi^0$.

5. π Length and Homomorphisms for a Restricted Class of Semigroups

This section proves several theorems relating π length to homomorphism chains for a restricted class of semigroups which includes π-solvable union of groups semigroups. We first show that the class $\mathscr{S}_\pi^0$, defined before Corollary 4.30, has the property ascribed to it there —that every nonzero πGM semigroup in $\mathscr{S}_\pi^0$ is pure.

5.1 Notation. Recall the definition of the π complexity of a π-solvable semigroup S. In that notation $C_\pi(S) = (n, \mathbf{\Pi})$, for example, meant that all minimal π, π' wreath product decompositions of S were

† See Note Added in Proof, page 208.

of length n and had a π group as the first coordinate (on the right). Suppose n is even. Then an equivalent notation for $C_\pi(S)$ would be $(\mathbf{\Pi}', n)$; if n is odd, $C_\pi(S) = (\mathbf{\Pi}, n)$. Thus we introduce $(\mathbf{\Pi}', n)$, $(\mathbf{\Pi}, n)$ and $(\mathbf{\Pi}' \vee \mathbf{\Pi}, n)$ as follows:

$$(\mathbf{\Pi}' \vee \mathbf{\Pi}, n) \equiv (n, \mathbf{\Pi}' \vee \mathbf{\Pi}) \qquad \text{for every } n \geqslant 1$$

$$(\mathbf{\Pi}', n) \equiv \begin{cases} (n, \mathbf{\Pi}) & \text{if } n \text{ is even} \\ (n, \mathbf{\Pi}') & \text{if } n \text{ is odd} \end{cases}$$

$$(\mathbf{\Pi}, n) \equiv \begin{cases} (n, \mathbf{\Pi}') & \text{if } n \text{ is even} \\ (n, \mathbf{\Pi}) & \text{if } n \text{ is odd.} \end{cases}$$

The change of notation carries with it the partial ordering previously defined.

Finally, we transfer the notion of addition of complexities to the new notation. Thus, for example,

$$(\mathbf{\Pi}', 1) \oplus (\mathbf{\Pi}, n) = (\mathbf{\Pi}', n + 1)$$
$$(\mathbf{\Pi}', 1) \oplus (\mathbf{\Pi}', n) = (\mathbf{\Pi}', 1) \oplus (\mathbf{\Pi}' \vee \mathbf{\Pi}, n) = (\mathbf{\Pi}', n)$$
$$(\mathbf{\Pi}, 1) \oplus (\mathbf{\Pi}', n) = (\mathbf{\Pi}, n + 1)$$
$$(\mathbf{\Pi}, 1) \oplus (\mathbf{\Pi}, n) = (\mathbf{\Pi}, 1) \oplus (\mathbf{\Pi}' \vee \mathbf{\Pi}, n) = (\mathbf{\Pi}, n).$$

5.2 Proposition. (a) Consider $(X_2, P) \text{ w } (X_1, S)$, where P is a left simple π semigroup (e.g., a π group) and S is arbitrary. Let p_1: $(X_2, P) \text{ w } (X_1, S) \twoheadrightarrow S$ be the natural projection map. Then p_1 is a $\pi' + \mathscr{L}'$ homomorphism. If S is a monoid, then p_1 is a $\pi' + \mathscr{L}$ homomorphism.

(b) Consider p_1: $(Y_2, N) \text{ w } (Y_1, T) \twoheadrightarrow T$, where N is a π' semigroup and T is arbitrary. Then p_1 is a π homomorphism.

Proof. (a) $(X_2, P) \text{ w } (X_1, S) \subseteq (X_2, P) \text{ w } (X_1, S^1)$, and by Proposition 8.3.24(a) of Krohn *et al.* [*1*],

$$p_1\colon (X_2, P) \text{ w } (X_1, S^1) \twoheadrightarrow S^1$$

is an $\mathscr{L}$ map. Hence p_1: $(X_2, P) \text{ w } (X_1, S) \twoheadrightarrow S$ is an $\mathscr{L}'$ map.

Let G be a subgroup of $(X_2, P) \text{ w } (X_1, S)$. Then $N = \ker(p_1|G)$ is isomorphic to a subgroup of $F(X_1, P)$, a π semigroup (Remark 1.16(b)). Hence N is a π group and p_1 is a π' homomorphism. Thus p_1 is a $\pi' + \mathscr{L}'$ homomorphism.

(b) Use the same group argument as in (a) to prove that p_1: $(Y_2, N) \text{ w } (Y_1, S) \twoheadrightarrow S$ is a π homomorphism. ∎

5.3 Proposition. If S is a nontrivial $\pi' RM$ semigroup, then $C_\pi(S) = (\mathbf{\Pi}', n)$ for some $n \geqslant 1$.

Proof. By 4.18 and 4.21, $S \cong S^{\pi' RM} \cong S^{\pi'+\mathscr{L}'}$, and by Proposition 4.7, if $S|T$, then $S^{\pi'+\mathscr{L}'}|T^{\pi'+\mathscr{L}'}$.

Suppose $C_\pi(S) = (\mathbf{\Pi}, n)$ or $(\mathbf{\Pi} \vee \mathbf{\Pi}', n)$, $n \geqslant 1$. If $n = 1$, S would either be a π group or trivial, a contradiction. So assume $n \geqslant 2$. Then there exists a π transformation group (X_2, P) and a semigroup T such that

$$S|(X_2, P) \text{ w } (X_1, T)$$

where $C_\pi(T) = (\mathbf{\Pi}', n - 1)$. But by Proposition 5.2

$$p_1 \colon (X_2, P) \text{ w } (X_1, T) \twoheadrightarrow T$$

is a $\pi' + \mathscr{L}'$ homomorphism, so $[(X_2, P) \text{ w } (X_1, T)]^{\pi'+\mathscr{L}'} \cong T^{\pi'+\mathscr{L}'}$. So $S \cong S^{\pi'+\mathscr{L}'}|[(X_2, P) \text{ w } (X_1, T)]^{\pi'+\mathscr{L}'} \cong T^{\pi'+\mathscr{L}'}|T$ and

$$C_\pi(S) \leqslant C_\pi(T) = (\mathbf{\Pi}', n - 1),$$

a contradiction. Thus $C_\pi(S) = (\mathbf{\Pi}', n)$ for some $n \geqslant 1$. ∎

5.4 Lemma. Let S be a πGM semigroup and suppose

$$C_\pi(S) = (\mathbf{\Pi}, m) \qquad \text{for some} \quad m \geqslant 1.$$

Then S is a πPGM semigroup.

Proof. Let $I^0 = \mathscr{M}^0(G; A, B; C)$ be the distinguished ideal of S and let P be the largest normal π subgroup of G.

Since S is an RM semigroup, we know that

$$S \subseteq (P^0, P^0) \text{ w } ((G/P)^0 \times B_0, RM_P(S))$$

so

$$C_\pi[RM_P(S)] \leqslant C_\pi(S) \leqslant (\mathbf{\Pi} \vee \mathbf{\Pi}', 2) \oplus C_\pi[RM_P(S)].$$

But $RM_P(S)$ is a $\pi' RM$ semigroup, so $C_\pi[RM_P(S)] = (\mathbf{\Pi}', n)$ for some n. Then

$$(\mathbf{\Pi}', n) \leqslant C_\pi(S) \leqslant (\mathbf{\Pi}, n + 1). \tag{5.1}$$

But $C_\pi(S) = (\mathbf{\Pi}, m)$ for some m. Thus by (5.1), $m = n + 1$ and $C_\pi(S) = (\mathbf{\Pi}, n + 1)$. Passing to l_π, this implies

$$l_\pi(S) = 1 + l_\pi(RM_P(S)). \quad ∎$$

5.5 Proposition. Let S be a nontrivial πGM semigroup with $\#_\pi(S) = n \geqslant 1$. Let $\bar{S} = LM[RLM(S)]$. Then $\#_\pi(\bar{S}) \leqslant n - 2$, $n \geqslant 2$, implies $C_\pi(S) = (\mathbf{\Pi}, n)$. If $n = 1$, $C_\pi(S) = (\mathbf{\Pi}, 1)$.

PROOF. The case $n = 1$ is trivial. Assume $C_\pi(S) = (\mathbf{\Pi}', n)$ [case (a)], or $(\mathbf{\Pi} \vee \mathbf{\Pi}', n)$ [case (b)] for some $n \geqslant 2$. Then there exists a π' semigroup N and a semigroup T such that $S \overset{\varphi}{\twoheadleftarrow} S_1 \subseteq (X_2, N) \le (X_1, T)$ where $C_\pi(T) = (\mathbf{\Pi}, n - 1)$. Further, T can be chosen so that if

$$p_1\colon (X_2, N) \mathrm{w} (X_1, T) \twoheadrightarrow T$$

is the projection map, then $p_1(S_1) = T$. We know that p_1 is a π homomorphism.

Define $\bar{S} = LM[RLM(S)]$ or equivalently, if G is a maximal subgroup of the distinguished $\mathscr{J}$ class J of S, then define $\bar{S} = GGM_G(S)$. Let J_1 be the unique minimal $\mathscr{J}$ class of S_1 such that $\varphi(J_1) = J$. The congruence induced on S_1 by $\psi\colon S_1 \twoheadrightarrow S \twoheadrightarrow \bar{S}$ separates J_1 and $F(J_1)$. Let $\theta = (p_1 \times \psi)\Delta$ and define $T_1 = \theta(S_1)$, so $T_1 \leqslant\leqslant T \times \bar{S}$. We will show that there exists an epimorphism from T_1 onto S.

Notice that θ separates J_1 and $F(J_1)$. Further, let G_1 be a maximal subgroup of J_1 and let N_1 be the largest normal π' subgroup of G_1. θ is a π homomorphism since p_1 is, so $\ker \theta | G_1 \subseteq N_1$. Now since S is a πGM semigroup, its distinguished maximal subgroup G contains no nontrivial normal π' subgroups. Let $K = \ker \varphi | G_1$. If $N_1 \not\subseteq K$, then N_1K/K is a nontrivial normal subgroup of $G_1/K \cong G$. But $N_1K/K \cong N_1/(N_1 \cap K)$, a π' subgroup. Thus N_1 must be contained in K, and we conclude that $\ker \theta | G_1 \subseteq \ker \varphi | G_1$. Now applying Proposition 2.15(a), we find that there exists an epimorphism $\theta_1\colon T_1 \twoheadrightarrow S$.

Thus by Axiom I,

$$\begin{aligned} C_\pi(S) \leqslant C_\pi(T_1) &\leqslant \mathrm{LUB}\{C_\pi(T), C_\pi(\bar{S})\} \\ &= \mathrm{LUB}\{(\mathbf{\Pi}, n - 1), C_\pi(\bar{S})\} \end{aligned} \tag{5.2}$$

To avoid a contradiction, $C_\pi(\bar{S})$ must equal in case (a) $(\mathbf{\Pi}', n)$ and in case (b) $(\mathbf{\Pi}', n - 1)$. Since $\bar{S}$ is a $\pi' RM$ semigroup, $C_\pi(\bar{S}) = (\mathbf{\Pi}', k)$ for some k, so $C_\pi(\bar{S})$ can take on no other values associated with $\#_\pi(\bar{S}) = n$ or $n - 1$. Thus $\#_\pi(\bar{S}) \leqslant n - 2$ implies $C_\pi(S) = (\mathbf{\Pi}, n)$. ∎

5.6 Definition. Let n be a nonnegative integer. Define $\mathscr{S}_\pi{}^n$ to be the collection of all finite π-solvable semigroups with the property that $S \in \mathscr{S}_\pi{}^n$ implies $l_\pi(S^{\mathscr{I}'}) \leqslant n$. Notice that $\mathscr{S}_\pi{}^n$ is closed under division. All π-solvable union of group semigroups are contained in $\mathscr{S}_\pi{}^0$. See 7.2.24 in Krohn *et al.* [*1*].

5.7 Proposition. Let $S \in \mathscr{S}_\pi^k$, $k \geqslant 0$, be a πGM semigroup. If $l_\pi(S) > k$, then S is a πPGM semigroup.

Proof. $S \in \mathscr{S}_\pi^k$ implies $l_\pi(S^{\mathscr{I}'}) \leqslant k$ which implies

$$C_\pi(S^{\mathscr{I}'}) \leqslant (\mathbf{\Pi}', 2k + 1).$$

Assume $l_\pi(S) > k$. If $C_\pi(S) = (\mathbf{\Pi}', n)$, then by (5.2) we have $C_\pi(\bar{S}) = (\mathbf{\Pi}', n)$. Since $S^{\mathscr{I}'} \twoheadrightarrow \bar{S}$, we have $(\mathbf{\Pi}', n) \leqslant (\mathbf{\Pi}', 2k + 1)$ or $n \leqslant 2k + 1$. Hence $l_\pi(S) \leqslant k$, a contradiction. Thus S cannot "end" in $\mathbf{\Pi}'$.

If $C_\pi(S) = (\mathbf{\Pi} \vee \mathbf{\Pi}', n)$, then by (5.2) $C_\pi(\bar{S}) = (\mathbf{\Pi}', n - 1)$. Thus $(\mathbf{\Pi}', n - 1) \leqslant (\mathbf{\Pi}', 2k + 1)$, so $n \leqslant 2(k + 1)$ and $l_\pi(S) \leqslant k + 1$. So we have shown that if $l_\pi(S) > k$, either S "ends" in a $\mathbf{\Pi}$ (and hence is πPGM) or $C_\pi(S) = (\mathbf{\Pi} \vee \mathbf{\Pi}', 2(k + 1))$. In this case $l_\pi(S) = k + 1$. Now $C_\pi(\pi' RM(S)) = (\mathbf{\Pi}', q) \leqslant (\mathbf{\Pi} \vee \mathbf{\Pi}', 2(k + 1))$, so $q < 2(k + 1)$. If q is even, $l_\pi(\pi' RM(S)) = q/2 < k + 1 = l_\pi(S)$. If q is odd, $l_\pi(\pi' RM(S)) = (q - 1)/2 < l_\pi(S)$. This is sufficient to prove that S is a πPGM semigroup in this case. ▌

Letting $k = 0$, we obtain the following.

5.8 Corollary. Let $S \in \mathscr{S}_\pi^0$ be a nontrivial πGM semigroup. Then S is a πPGM semigroup. ▌

5.9 Remark. Now for the collection of semigroups $\mathscr{S}_\pi^0$, which includes union of groups semigroups, we can alter the Axioms for π length as follows: Leave Axioms I and II unaltered and let Axiom III read as follows:

Axiom III. Let S be a nontrivial πGM semigroup. Then

$$\theta(S) = 1 + \theta(\pi' RM(S)).$$

Restricting the axioms to $\mathscr{S}_\pi^0$ makes sense because $\mathscr{S}_\pi^0$ is closed under homomorphisms.

The balance of this section is devoted to finding functions from $\mathscr{S}_\pi^0$ into the nonnegative integers that satisfy the π-length axioms. Then, of course, the functions *will be* l_π.†

5.10 Definition. Let α be any of the types of homomorphisms that are preserved under direct products and under restriction to subsemigroups such as π, $\mathscr{J}'$, $\mathscr{L}'$, $\mathscr{R}'$, $\mathscr{H}'$, $\pi + \mathscr{J}'$, $\pi + \mathscr{L}'$, etc. Given $\varphi: S \twoheadrightarrow T$, let $\{T_i: i = 1, \ldots, n\}$ be the set of all semigroups (up to isomorphism) such that there exists $\psi_i: S \twoheadrightarrow T_i$ and $\theta_i: T_i \underset{\alpha}{\twoheadrightarrow} T$, where $\varphi = \theta_i \psi_i$, $i = 1, \ldots, n$. Define the semigroup $T^{\alpha^{-1}}$ by

$$T^{\alpha^{-1}} = (\psi_1 \times \cdots \times \psi_n)\, \Delta(S).$$

† See Note Added in Proof, page 208.

5.11 Fact. Let α be as above.

(a) $T \twoheadrightarrow T^{\alpha^{-1}}$ is an α homomorphism.

(b) Let T' be any semigroup such that $\varphi\colon S \twoheadrightarrow T' \underset{\alpha}{\twoheadrightarrow} T$. Then

$$T^{\alpha^{-1}} \underset{\alpha}{\twoheadrightarrow} T' \underset{\alpha}{\twoheadrightarrow} T$$

PROOF. (a) Define $\theta\colon T_1 \times \cdots \times T_n \twoheadrightarrow T \times \cdots \times T$ by

$$\theta = \theta_1 \times \cdots \times \theta_n .$$

θ is an α homomorphism since the θ_i are. $T^{\alpha^{-1}} \leqslant\leqslant T_1 \times \cdots \times T_n$, so θ restricted to $T^{\alpha^{-1}}$ is an α homomorphism. We show that $\theta(T^{\alpha^{-1}}) \cong T$, for

$$\begin{aligned}\theta(T^{\alpha^{-1}}) &= (\theta_1 \times \cdots \times \theta_n)(\psi_1 \times \cdots \times \psi_n)\, \Delta(S)\\ &= (\theta_1\psi_1 \times \cdots \times \theta_n\psi_n)\, \Delta(S)\\ &= (\varphi \times \cdots \times \varphi)\, \Delta(S)\\ &\cong \varphi(S) = T.\end{aligned}$$

(b) This is clear from the definition of $T^{\alpha^{-1}}$. ∎

We are now prepared to define six functions from the semigroups $\mathscr{S}_\pi{}^0$ to the nonnegative integers N, each of which will turn out to be the π length, l_π .†

5.12 Definition. Let $S \in \mathscr{S}_\pi{}^0$, the collection of all π-solvable semigroups S such that $S^{\mathscr{I}'}$ is a π' semigroup.

(a) Let πGM_i and $\pi' RM_i$ represent πGM and $\pi' RM$ semigroups, respectively. Consider all series for S of the form

$$S \twoheadrightarrow \pi GM_1 \twoheadrightarrow \pi' RM_1 \twoheadrightarrow \pi GM_2 \twoheadrightarrow \cdots . \tag{a}$$

Let the *length* of each such series be the largest integer n such that $\pi GM_n \neq \{0\}$. Define $\pi_a\colon \mathscr{S}_\pi{}^0 \to N$ by letting $\pi_a(S) =$ the maximum of the lengths of all such series.

(a′) Let πGGM_i and $\pi' RM_i$ represent πGGM and $\pi' RM$ semigroups, respectively. Consider all series for S of the form

$$S \twoheadrightarrow \pi GGM_1 \twoheadrightarrow \pi' RM_1 \twoheadrightarrow \pi GGM_2 \twoheadrightarrow \cdots . \tag{a′}$$

Let the *length* of each such series be the largest integer n such that πGGM_n is not a π' semigroup. Define $\pi_{a'}\colon \mathscr{S}_\pi{}^0 \to N$ by letting $\pi_{a'}(S) =$ the maximum of the lengths of all such series.

† See Note Added in Proof, page 208.

(b) Consider the series

$$\{0\} \twoheadleftarrow \{0\}^{\pi^{-1}} \twoheadleftarrow (\{0\}^{\pi^{-1}})^{(\pi'+\mathscr{L}')^{-1}} \twoheadleftarrow \cdots \twoheadleftarrow S. \qquad \text{(b)}$$

Starting from $\{0\}$, this series must reach S by virtue of Proposition 4.26. For at each stage T, the homomorphism $\varphi: S \twoheadrightarrow T$, if proper, can be broken into π and $\pi' + \mathscr{L}'$ homomorphisms, $\varphi = \varphi_n \cdots \varphi_1$, and φ_n can be only one of the two possibilities by the definition of T. Thus the series can be continued.

Define $\pi_b: \mathscr{S}_\pi^0 \to N$ by letting $\pi_b(S)$ = the number of proper homomorphisms of the form $T^{(\pi'+\mathscr{L}')^{-1}} \twoheadrightarrow T$ in the series.

(c) Consider the series

$$\begin{aligned} S &\twoheadrightarrow S^{(\pi+\mathscr{J}')} \twoheadrightarrow S^{(\pi+\mathscr{J}')(\pi'+\mathscr{L}')} \\ &\twoheadrightarrow S^{(\pi+\mathscr{J}')(\pi'+\mathscr{L}')(\pi+\mathscr{J}')} \twoheadrightarrow \cdots. \end{aligned} \qquad \text{(c)}$$

Define $\pi_c: \mathscr{S}_\pi^0 \to N$ by letting $\pi_c(S)$ = the number of proper $\pi' + \mathscr{L}'$ homomorphisms in the series.

(d) Consider the series

$$S \twoheadrightarrow S^{\pi GM} \twoheadrightarrow S^{(\pi GM)\pi' RM} \twoheadrightarrow S^{(\pi GM)(\pi' RM)(\pi GM)} \twoheadrightarrow \cdots. \qquad \text{(d)}$$

Define $\pi_d: \mathscr{S}_\pi^0 \to N$ by letting $\pi_d(S)$ = the number of proper homomorphisms of the form $T \twoheadrightarrow T^{\pi' RM}$.

(e) Consider the series

$$S \twoheadrightarrow S^{\pi} \twoheadrightarrow S^{\pi(\pi'+\mathscr{L}')} \twoheadrightarrow S^{\pi(\pi'+\mathscr{L}')\pi} \twoheadrightarrow \cdots. \qquad \text{(e)}$$

Define $\pi_e: \mathscr{S}_\pi^0 \to N$ by letting $\pi_e(S)$ = the number of proper $\pi' + \mathscr{L}'$ homomorphisms in the series.

5.13 Theorem.† Let $S \in \mathscr{S}_\pi^0$. Then

$$l_\pi(S) = \pi_a(S) = \pi_{a'}(S) = \pi_b(S) = \pi_c(S) = \pi_d(S) = \pi_e(S).$$

PROOF. We proceed by a series of lemmas.

5.14 Lemma.† Let $S \in \mathscr{S}_\pi^0$. Then $l_\pi(S) = \pi_a(S) = \pi_{a'}(S)$.

PROOF. We have already proved $l_\pi(S) = \pi_a(S)$ in Theorem 4.28 and Corollary 5.8. So we will show that $\pi_a(S) = \pi_{a'}(S)$.

A πGM semigroup that is a π' semigroup is $\{0\}$. Furthermore, a πGM semigroup is a πGGM semigroup. Then a series of type (a) is

† See Note Added in Proof, page 208.

a series of type (a′) and $\pi_a(S) \leqslant \pi_{a'}(S)$. Now take a longest series of type (a′). Let $\pi_{a'}(S) = n$, so πGGM_i is not a π' semigroup for $i = 1, \ldots, n$. But a πGGM semigroup that is not a π' semigroup is a πGM semigroup. For suppose $S \twoheadrightarrow T$ and T is a πGGM semigroup but not a πGM semigroup. We have shown that $S^{\mathscr{I}'}$ is a subdirect product of all homomorphic images of S that are GGM but not GM semigroups. Since $S^{\mathscr{I}'}$ is a π' semigroup by assumption, T is a π' semigroup. Thus the πGGM_i of series (a′), $i = 1, \ldots, n$ are πGM semigroups, so $\pi_{a'}(S) = n \leqslant \pi_a(S)$ and $\pi_a(S) = \pi_{a'}(S)$ for all $S \in \mathscr{S}_\pi^0$. ▌

5.15 Lemma. $\pi_b(S) = \pi_c(S) = \pi_d(S) = \pi_e(S)$ for all $S \in \mathscr{S}_\pi^0$.

PROOF. First consider series (b). Let

$$S_{-1} = \{0\}^{\pi^{-1}}, \qquad S_{-2} = (\{0\}^{\pi^{-1}})^{(\pi'+\mathscr{L}')^{-1}}, \text{ etc.}$$

Then series (b) is written

$$S = S_{-k} \twoheadrightarrow S_{-k+1} \twoheadrightarrow \cdots \twoheadrightarrow S_{-2} \xrightarrow[\pi'+\mathscr{L}']{} S_{-1} \xrightarrow[\pi]{} \{0\}. \tag{b}$$

We claim that $S_{-1} = (\Pi\theta_j^{(1)})(S)$, where j runs over the collection of all epimorphisms such that

$$\theta_j^{(1)}\colon S \twoheadrightarrow T_j \qquad \text{and} \qquad T_j \xrightarrow[\pi]{} \{0\},$$

$S_{-2} = (\Pi\theta_j^{(2)})(S)$, where j runs over the collection of all epimorphisms such that $\theta_j^{(2)}\colon S \twoheadrightarrow T_j$ and there exist epimorphisms so that $T_j \xrightarrow[\pi'+\mathscr{L}']{} T_j' \xrightarrow[\pi]{} \{0\}$, etc. To prove this let $U_{-k} = (\Pi\theta_j^{(k)})(S)$. By definition of S_{-1}, $U_{-1} = S_{-1} \cong \Pi_S'$, the maximal π' semigroup homomorphic image of S. Now,

$$S \twoheadrightarrow U_{-2} \xrightarrow[\pi'+\mathscr{L}']{} U_{-1} \xrightarrow[\pi]{} \{0\},$$

since direct sums and restrictions of $\pi' + \mathscr{L}'$ and π homomorphisms are $\pi' + \mathscr{L}'$ and π homomorphisms, respectively. Since $S_{-2} = (S_{-1})^{(\pi'+\mathscr{L}')^{-1}}$, we have $S_{-2} \twoheadrightarrow U_{-2}$. On the other hand,

$$S \twoheadrightarrow S_{-2} \xrightarrow[\pi'+\mathscr{L}']{} S_{-1} \xrightarrow[\pi]{} \{0\}$$

so $U_{-2} \twoheadrightarrow S_{-2}$. Thus $U_{-2} \cong S_{-2}$. Continuing in this way we prove $U_{-i} \cong S_{-i}$ for all $i = 1, 2, \ldots$. Let k be the smallest integer such that $S_{-k} \cong S$.

We now prove that the number of proper $\pi' + \mathscr{L}'$ homomorphisms in the series

$$S = S_{-k} \twoheadrightarrow S_{-k+1} \twoheadrightarrow \cdots \twoheadrightarrow S_{-2} \xrightarrow[\pi'+\mathscr{L}']{} \!\!\!\!\twoheadrightarrow S_{-1} \xrightarrow[\pi]{} \!\!\!\!\twoheadrightarrow \{0\} \tag{b}$$

(i.e., $\pi_b(S)$) is less than or equal to the number of proper $\pi' + \mathscr{L}'$ homomorphisms in *any* alternating π-($\pi' + \mathscr{L}'$) series of S starting with a π homomorphism and ending with $\{0\}$.

Let k be even. Then series (b) starts with an $\pi' + \mathscr{L}'$ homomorphism. Suppose an alternating π-($\pi' + \mathscr{L}'$) series of S starting with a π got to $\{0\}$ in $k - 1$ steps. Then by the above characterization of $S_{-(k-1)}$, we would have $S \cong S_{-(k-1)}$, a contradiction. If the series in question got to $\{0\}$ in $k - 2$ steps, then by adding on the trivial map $\{0\} \xrightarrow[\pi]{} \!\!\!\!\twoheadrightarrow \{0\}$ to the end we have a series of length $k - 1$, again giving a contradiction. Thus the series must have length k or greater, and the assertion is true for this case.

Let k be odd, so the series (b) starts with a π homomorphism. If the alternating series in question has length $k - 2$ or less, a contradiction again arises. So in this case, the length of the series must be at least $k - 1$. But it is easy to see that in this case that the number of $\pi' + \mathscr{L}'$ homomorphisms equals $\pi_b(S)$, so it is proved.

Now we apply the tools of Section 4 to get the commutative diagram in Figure 5.1 (page 206).

If (b) starts in an $\pi' + \mathscr{L}'$ homomorphism, add the identity homomorphism in the beginning so that it starts with a π. Then notice that $S_{-1} \cong \Pi'_S \twoheadrightarrow S^{\mathscr{I}'}$, since for our class of semigroups $S^{\mathscr{I}'}$ is a π' semigroup. Then every π map except the last one is a $\pi + \mathscr{I}'$ map. Thus square 1 commutes.

Since $S_{-n+1} \xrightarrow[\pi'+\mathscr{L}']{} \!\!\!\!\twoheadrightarrow S_{-n+2}$, we have $S_{-n+1} \twoheadrightarrow S_{-n+2} \twoheadrightarrow S^{\pi'+\mathscr{L}'}_{-n+1}$. Using Proposition 4.7(a), square 2 commutes.

Since $S_{-n+2} \xrightarrow[\pi+\mathscr{I}']{} \!\!\!\!\twoheadrightarrow S_{-n+3} \twoheadrightarrow S^{(\pi+\mathscr{I}')}_{-n+2}$, square 3 commutes by Proposition 4.7(a). Continue in this manner on out the (b)–(c) ladder.

Notice that by the definitions of $S^{\pi+\mathscr{I}'} \cong S^{\pi GGM}$, $S^{\pi GM}$, and S^{π}, the following diagram exists and commutes.

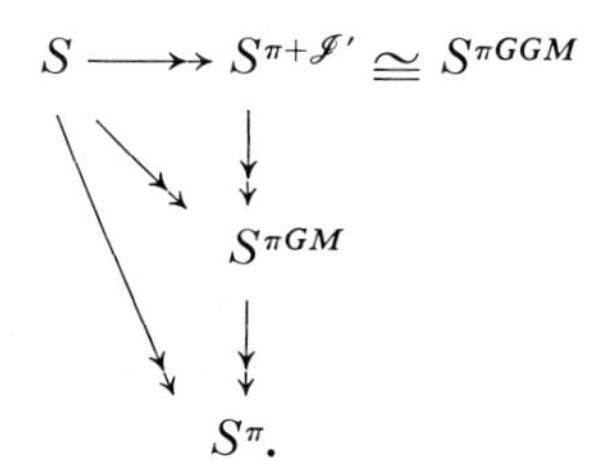

Thus, squares 4 and 7 commute. Since $S^{\pi'+\mathscr{L}'} \cong S^{\pi' RM}$, square 5 and 8 commute, by Proposition 4.7(a). For square 6 we have

$$\begin{array}{ccccc} S^{(\pi+\mathscr{I}')(\pi'+\mathscr{L}')} & \twoheadrightarrow & S^{(\pi+\mathscr{I}')(\pi'+\mathscr{L}')(\pi+\mathscr{I}')} & & \\ \downarrow & & \downarrow & & \\ S^{\pi GM(\pi' RM)} & \twoheadrightarrow & S^{\pi GM(\pi' RM)(\pi+\mathscr{I}')} & \twoheadrightarrow & S^{\pi GM(\pi' RM)\pi GM}. \end{array}$$

For square 9 we have (by Proposition 4.7(a))

$$\begin{array}{ccccc} S^{\pi GM(\pi' RM)} & \twoheadrightarrow & S^{\pi GM(\pi' RM)(\pi GM)} & & \\ \downarrow & & \downarrow & & \\ S^{\pi(\pi'+\mathscr{L}')} & \twoheadrightarrow & S^{\pi(\pi'+\mathscr{L}')\pi GM} & \twoheadrightarrow & S^{\pi(\pi'+\mathscr{L}')\pi}. \end{array}$$

Continue in the same manner on out the diagram.

Let $T_c = S^{(\pi+\mathscr{I}')\cdots(\pi'+\mathscr{L}')}$, $T_d = S^{\pi GM\cdots\pi' RM}$, and $T_e = S^{\pi\cdots(\pi'+\mathscr{L}')}$. Now since S_{-1} is a π' semigroup, so are T_c, T_d, and T_e. We show that if T is a π' semigroup, then $T^{(\pi+\mathscr{I}')} \cong T^{\mathscr{I}'}$, $T^{\pi GM} = \{0\}$, and $T^{\pi} = \{0\}$.

The last two are obvious. For the first, recall that

$$T^{\pi+\mathscr{I}'} \leqslant\leqslant T^{\pi} \times T^{\mathscr{I}'}.$$

But $T^{\pi} = \{0\}$. Hence $T^{(\pi+\mathscr{I}')} \leqslant T^{\mathscr{I}'}$ and $T^{(\pi+\mathscr{I}')} \twoheadrightarrow T^{\mathscr{I}'}$, so they are isomorphic.

Now $T_c^{(\pi+\mathscr{I}')} \cong T_c^{\mathscr{I}'}$ is isomorphic to $S^{\mathscr{I}'}$ since every map in (c) is a $\mathscr{I}'$ homomorphism. Clearly $S^{\mathscr{I}'(\pi'+\mathscr{L}')} \cong S^{\mathscr{I}'}$. Thus we have justified Figure 5.1 (page 206).

It is now clear that the number of proper $\pi' + \mathscr{L}'$ homomorphisms in (b) is greater than or equal to the number in (c), (d), or (e). That is,

$$\pi_b(S) \geqslant \pi_c(S), \quad \pi_d(S), \quad \text{and} \quad \pi_e(S).$$

But we have shown that $\pi_b(S)$ is less than or equal to the number of proper $\pi' + \mathscr{L}'$ homomorphisms in any alternating π-$(\pi' + \mathscr{L}')$ series of S starting with a π homomorphism and ending in $\{0\}$. (End (c) in zero by $S^{\mathscr{I}'} \underset{\pi}{\twoheadrightarrow} \{0\}$). Thus,

$$\pi_b(S) = \pi_c(S) = \pi_d(S) = \pi_e(S)$$

for all $S \in \mathscr{S}_{\pi}^{0}$. ∎

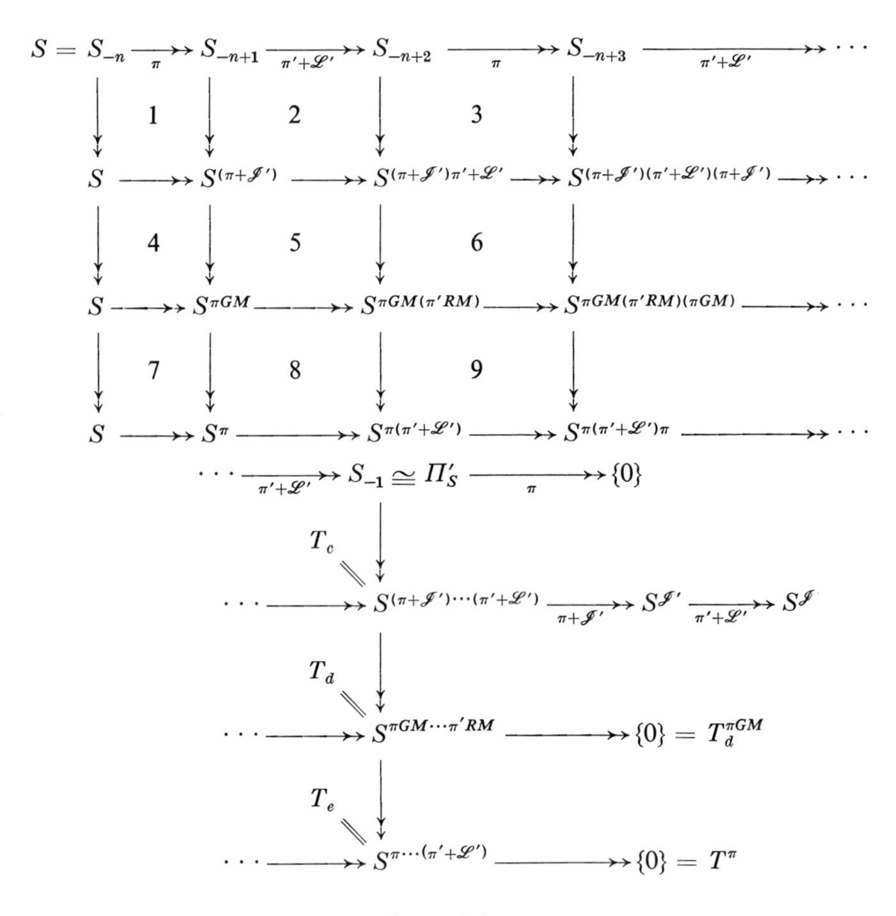

FIGURE 5.1.

5.16 Lemma. Let S and $T_1, \ldots, T_n$ be semigroups and let α be either π, $\pi + \mathscr{J}'$, $\pi + \mathscr{L}'$, $\pi + \mathscr{R}'$, or $\pi + \mathscr{H}'$. Then if

$$S \leqslant\leqslant T_1 \times \cdots \times T_n, \qquad \text{and} \qquad \theta_i\colon T_i \twoheadrightarrow T_i^{\alpha},$$

so that $\theta = \theta_1 \times \cdots \times \theta_n\colon T_1 \times \cdots \times T_n \twoheadrightarrow T_1^{\alpha} \times \cdots \times T_n^{\alpha}$, then $\theta(S) \cong S^{\alpha}$ and $S^{\alpha} \leqslant\leqslant T_1^{\alpha} \times \cdots \times T_n^{\alpha}$.

PROOF. θ restricted to S is an α homomorphism since α homomorphisms are preserved under direct product and restriction. Thus $\theta(S) \twoheadrightarrow S^{\alpha}$. On the other hand, let $p_i\colon S \twoheadrightarrow T_i$, so $\theta_i p_i\colon S \twoheadrightarrow T_i^{\alpha}$.

Now since $S \twoheadrightarrow T_i$, we have $S^\alpha \overset{\varphi_i}{\twoheadrightarrow} T_i^\alpha$, so if $\psi: S \twoheadrightarrow S^\alpha$, then $\varphi_i\psi = \theta_i p_i$. Now

$$\begin{aligned}\theta(S) &= (\theta_1 p_1 \times \cdots \times \theta_n p_n)\, \Delta(S)\\ &=(\varphi_1\psi \times \cdots \times \varphi_n\psi)\, \Delta(S)\\ &= (\varphi_1 \times \cdots \times \varphi_n)\, \Delta\psi(S)\\ &= (\varphi_1 \times \cdots \times \varphi_n)\, \Delta(S^\alpha).\end{aligned}$$

Therefore $S^\alpha \twoheadrightarrow \theta(S)$, so $\theta(S) \cong S^\alpha \leqslant\!\!\leqslant T_1^\alpha \times \cdots \times T_n^\alpha$. ▮

5.17 Lemma.† $l_\pi(S) = \pi_b(S) = \pi_c(S) = \pi_d(S) = \pi_e(S)$ for all $S \in \mathscr{S}_\pi^0$.

Proof. We first show that π_c satisfies Axiom I. Let

$$S \leqslant\!\!\leqslant S_1 \times \cdots \times S_n .$$

By virtue of Lemma 5.16,

$$S^{\pi+\mathscr{J}'} \leqslant\!\!\leqslant S_1^{\pi+\mathscr{J}'} \times \cdots \times S_n^{\pi+\mathscr{J}'},$$

$$S^{(\pi+\mathscr{J}')(\pi'+\mathscr{L}')} \leqslant\!\!\leqslant S_1^{(\pi+\mathscr{J}')(\pi'+\mathscr{L}')} \times \cdots \times S_n^{(\pi+\mathscr{J}')(\pi'+\mathscr{L}')},$$

etc. Now it is easy to prove that if $T \leqslant\!\!\leqslant T_1 \times \cdots \times T_n$, then T is a π' semigroup if and only if each T_i, $i = 1, \ldots, n$, is a π' semigroup. Further, let T be $\pi + \mathscr{J}'$ stable. Then T is a π' semigroup if and only if $T \cong T^{\mathscr{J}'}$. For assume T is a π' semigroup. Then

$$T \cong T^{\pi+\mathscr{J}'} \leqslant\!\!\leqslant T^\pi \times T^{\mathscr{J}'}.$$

But $T^\pi = \{0\}$, so $T \cong T^{\mathscr{J}'}$. The converse follows by the assumption that $T \in \mathscr{S}_\pi^0$.

Now let T be a $\pi + \mathscr{J}'$ stable term in series (c) for S. Then $T \leqslant\!\!\leqslant T_1 \times \cdots \times T_n$, and each T_i is $\pi + \mathscr{J}'$ stable. If $T = S^{\mathscr{J}'}$, then T is a π' semigroup and each T_i is a π' semigroup. Thus each $T_i = T_i^{\mathscr{J}'} \cong S_i^{\mathscr{J}'}$, and $\pi_c(S) \geqslant \max\{\pi_c(S_i): i = 1, \ldots, n\}$. On the other hand, if T is such that $T \twoheadrightarrow T_i^{\pi'+\mathscr{L}'}$ is proper, then T is not a π' semigroup (since $T \ncong T^{\mathscr{J}'}$). Then there exists at least one T_i which is not a π' semigroup. Hence $T_i \neq T_i^{\mathscr{J}'}$, so $T_i \twoheadrightarrow T_i^{\pi'+\mathscr{L}'}$ is proper. Therefore, for some $i = 1, \ldots, n$, $\pi_c(S_i) \geqslant \pi_c(S)$, and π_c satisfies Axiom I.

We now prove that π_e satisfies Axiom II. Clearly $\pi_e(\{0\}) = 0$. If $\varphi: S \twoheadrightarrow T$ is a π homomorphism, then $S^\pi \cong T^\pi$. Hence π_e for S and

† See Note Added in Proof, page 208.

T differ only in the first term and thus have the same length, that is $\pi_e(S) = \pi_e(T)$.

Finally we show that π_c satisfies Axiom III. Let S be a nontrivial πGM semigroup. Then $S \twoheadrightarrow \pi' RM(S)$ equals $S \twoheadrightarrow S^{\pi'+\mathscr{L}'}$ by Proposition 4.19. Also S is πGGM, so $S = S^{\pi GGM} \cong S^{\pi+\mathscr{J}'}$. Thus series (c) for S is

$$S \twoheadrightarrow S^{\pi+\mathscr{J}'} = S \twoheadrightarrow \pi' RM(S) \cong S^{\pi'+\mathscr{L}'} \twoheadrightarrow S^{\pi'+\mathscr{L}'(\pi+\mathscr{J}')} \twoheadrightarrow \cdots$$

and hence $\pi_c(S) = \pi_c(\pi' RM(S)) + 1$. This proves the lemma and completes the proof of Theorem 5.13. ∎

REFERENCES

1. K. Krohn, J. Rhodes and B. Tilson, "Lectures on the Algebraic Theory of Finite Semigroups and Finite State Machines," Chapters 1, 5–9 (Chapter 6 with M. A. Arbib) *in Algebraic Theory of Machines, Languages, and Semigroups* (M. A. Arbib, ed.), Academic Press, New York, 1968).
2. J. Rhodes and B. Tilson, "Lower Bounds for Complexity of Finite Semigroups," *Math. System Theory* (to be published).
3. P. Hall, and G. Higman, "On the p-Length of p-Solvable Groups and Reduction Theorems for Burnside's Problem," *Proc. London Math. Soc.* [3]**6**, 1–42 (1956).
4. J. Rhodes, "Proof of the Fundamental Lemma of Complexity for Arbitrary Finite Semigroups—Weak Version," *J. Combinatorial Theory* (to be published).

Note Added in Proof. John Rhodes has informed me that his paper [4] contained an error invalidating his proof that if $\varphi: S \twoheadrightarrow T$ is a γ homomorphism, then $\#_G(S) = \#_G(T)$. Whether this is true is still an open question. The theorem of Rhodes [4] has been weakened to the following: If $\varphi: S \twoheadrightarrow T$ is a $\gamma(\mathscr{H})$ homomorphism (1:1 on $\mathscr{H}$ classes of S), then $\#_G(S) = \#_G(T)$. When restricted to the class of *regular* semigroups, however, this theorem coincides with the original theorem, because a $\gamma(\mathscr{H})$ homomorphism is a γ homomorphism on a regular semigroup. This, then, forces me to restrict the statements of the following results to *regular π-solvable semigroups*: Theorems 3.6, 4.28, 5.13; Corollaries 4.29, 4.30; Lemmas 5.14, 5.17; Remark 5.9. All other results remain valid as stated. Also, in Theorem 5.13, $\pi_a(S) = \pi_{a'}(S) = \pi_b(S) = \pi_c(S) = \pi_d(S) = \pi_e(S)$ for all $S \in \mathscr{S}_\pi{}^0$ is still valid (regular is not needed). Regularity is needed to show $l_\pi(S) = \pi_a(S)$.

*Stationary Measures for Random Walks on Semigroups**

M. ROSENBLATT

Department of Mathematics
University of California, San Diego
La Jolla, California

I. Introduction

In recent years, there has been a certain amount of interest in random walks on semigroups. I will briefly consider one possible setting for such a concept. Let S be a sigma-compact Hausdorff semigroup. There is a distinguished Borel field of sets $\mathscr{B}$ generated by the topology on S. Consider a regular probability measure ν on the semigroup S. The convolution for two such measures ν, μ which we denote by $\nu * \mu$ can be defined in a natural way as follows. Let $\mathscr{L}$ be the class of real-valued continuous functions vanishing outside compact sets. Given any function $f \in \mathscr{L}$ let $\Lambda(f)$ be given by the iterated integral

$$\Lambda(f) = \int \left\{ \int f(vu)\, \nu(dv) \right\} \mu(du). \tag{1}$$

$\Lambda(f)$ is a positive linear functional on $\mathscr{L}$, that is, $\Lambda(f) \geqslant 0$ if $f \geqslant 0$. There is then a unique regular measure η such that

$$\Lambda(f) = \int f(u)\, \eta(du) \tag{2}$$

which we call the convolution $\eta = \nu * \mu$ of ν and μ [see Halmos (1958)]. Let $\nu^{(n)}$ denote the nth convolution of ν with itself. It is interesting to examine the asymptotic behavior of the sequence $\nu^{(n)}$ as $n \to \infty$ or of

* This research was supported by the Office of Naval Research.

averages of this convolution sequence. In order to do this it is convenient to introduce right or left random walks on the semigroup S induced by the measure ν. Given any set $B \in \mathscr{B}$ let

$$s^{-1}B = \{s' : ss' \in B\}, \qquad Bs^{-1} = \{s' : s's \in B\}. \tag{3}$$

The right (left) random walk on S induced by ν is the Markov process on S with transition probability function

$$P(s, B) = \nu(s^{-1}B)(= \nu(Bs^{-1})). \tag{4}$$

A straightforward modification of arguments given in Heble and Rosenblatt (1963) shows that for each set $B \in \mathscr{B}$, $\nu(Bs^{-1})$ is $\mathscr{B}$ measurable and that

$$\eta(B) = \nu * \mu(B) = \int \nu(Bs^{-1})\, \mu(ds) \tag{5}$$

for ν and μ regular probability measures.

The asymptotic behavior of convolution sequences and their averages has been studied most extensively on a compact topological semigroup. Some of the results for a compact semigroup will be briefly described in Section II. The asymptotic behavior of averages of convolution sequences is related to the existence and form of stationary measures π for the corresponding random walk on the semigroup

$$\int P(s, B)\, \pi(ds) = \int \nu(s^{-1}B)\, \pi(ds) = \pi(B). \tag{6}$$

If the semigroup is compact, the stationary measure π is a probability measure. If the semigroup is locally compact, the stationary measure (if it exists) may be properly sigmafinite. In Section III we shall consider radom walks on countable semigroups with at least one recurrent state. The results are new for random walks with null recurrent states. The fact that the semigroups are countable allows us to use elements of the theory of Markov chains. Such an investigation sheds a good deal of light on the corresponding problem for general sigma-compact semigroups with random walks having a conservative part.

II. Compact Semigroups

Let ν be a regular probability measure on the compact semigroup S. Consider the support $\sigma(\nu)$ of the measure ν. There is no loss in generality if *one assumes that S is generated by* $\sigma(\nu)$, that is, $S =$ closure $(\bigcup_{n=1}^{\infty} (\sigma(\nu))^n)$, and we shall assume that this is so.

A compact Hausdorff semigroup S has a minimal two-sided ideal $K \subset S$

$$KS = SK = K \tag{7}$$

which is a completely simple semigroup [see Wallace (1956)]. The probability mass of $\nu^{(n)}$ concentrates on K as $n \to \infty$ in the following sense. Given any open set O containing K

$$\nu^{(n)}(O) \to 1 \tag{8}$$

as $n \to \infty$ [see Rosenblatt (1960)]. It is also known that there is weak star convergence of the averages

$$n^{-1} \sum_{k=1}^{n} \nu^{(k)} \tag{9}$$

as $n \to \infty$ to an idempotent probability measure π

$$\pi^{(2)} = \pi \tag{10}$$

with its support K. The limiting idempotent probability measure is uniquely determined as the solution of

$$\int \pi(ds)\, \nu(s^{-1}B) = \pi(B), \qquad B \in \mathscr{B}. \tag{11}$$

The structure of any such idempotent probability measure can be given in terms of a representation of K. The completely simple (kernel) semigroup K can be represented as a product space

$$X \times G \times Y \tag{12}$$

of two compact spaces X, Y and a compact topological group G. Let the induced Borel fields on the spaces X, G, Y be $\mathscr{B}_1$, $\mathscr{B}_2$, $\mathscr{B}_3$ with the product space endowed with the product Borel field

$$\mathscr{B}_1 \times \mathscr{B}_2 \times \mathscr{B}_3 . \tag{13}$$

The typical element $k \in K$ is a triple $k = (x, g, y)$ with multiplication given by

$$kk' = (x, g, y)(x', g', y') = (x, gyx'g', y') \tag{14}$$

where yx is a continuous function on $X \times Y$ into G. Notice that $X(Y)$ is the space of right (left) ideal indicators of K. An idempotent measure

π on K is characterized by its form on product sets $B_1 \times B_2 \times B_3$, $B_i \in \mathscr{B}_i$,

$$\pi(B_1 \times B_2 \times B_3) = \alpha(B_1)\, \chi(B_2)\, \beta(B_3) \tag{15}$$

where α, β are regular probability measures on X and Y, respectively, and χ is the normalized Haar measure on G ($\chi(G) = 1$). This characterization of idempotent measures was obtained by Pym (1962) and Heble and Rosenblatt (1963) [see Grenander (1963)]. Some extensions of these results on idempotent measures have been obtained by Tortrat (1966). Related results on the special cases of left and right invariant measures ($\pi(s^{-1}B) = \pi(B)$ and $\pi(Bs^{-1}) = \pi(B)$ respectively for $B \in \mathscr{B}$) were obtained earlier by Rosen (1956). These results were obtained for semigroups with multiplication jointly continuous in the factors. De Leeuw and Glicksberg (1961) obtained corresponding results for semigroups with the multiplication continuous separately in each of the factors.

Necessary and sufficient conditions were obtained for the convergence of the unaveraged convolution sequence $\nu^{(n)}$ to an idempotent probability measure π as $n \to \infty$ on a compact topological semigroup by Rosenblatt (1964). Let ν be a regular probability measure on S whose support generates S. It is shown that the sequence of measures $\nu^{(n)}$ converges in the weak star topology to a probability measure (an idempotent measure) if and only if there is no proper closed normal subgroup G' (proper inclusion) of G such that $YX \subset G'$ with the support of ν contained in

$$(X \times G' \times Y)^{-1}(X \times gG' \times Y) \tag{16}$$

where $g \notin G'$. Martin-Löf (1965) considered the same problem of convergence of the unaveraged convolution sequence to an idempotent measure on a countable semigroup (which need not be compact). It is clear that if the averaged or unaveraged sequences of convolutions converge to a nontrivial measure on a countable semigroup, the limit measure must be an idempotent probability measure. However, we can still consider the asymptotic behavior of $\sum_{j=1}^{n} \nu^{(j)}$ as $n \to \infty$ on a countable semigroup even though $\nu^{(n)}(s) \to 0$ as $n \to \infty$ for every $s \in S$. We shall investigate this for measures ν and semigroups S for which there is an element $s \in S$ such that

$$\sum_{n=1}^{\infty} \nu^{(n)}(s) = \infty \tag{17}$$

in Section III. This means that the associated right and left random walks on S have at least one null recurrent state. The reader can refer to Ljapin (1963) for a discussion of the required algebraic results on semigroups.

III. Measures on Countable Semigroups

Let ν be a probability measure on the countable semigroup S. We *assume that S is generated by the support $\{s : \nu(s) > 0\}$ of the measure ν.* Assume there is an element $s \in S$ such that

$$\sum_{n=1}^{\infty} \nu^{(n)}(s) = \infty. \tag{17}$$

The element s is then a recurrent state for the right and left random walks on S induced by ν. But then sS and Ss are irreducible closed sets of states for the right and left random walks, respectively. This implies that sS and Ss are minimal right and left ideals of the semigroup S. The semigroup S must then contain a minimal two-sided ideal (the kernel semigroup of S) which is completely simple. The right (left) ideals of K are the sets of elements sS (Ss) determined by the elements s for which (17) holds. We therefore have the following simple lemma which was obtained by Martin-Löf (1965).

Lemma 1. *Let ν be a probability measure on the countable semigroup S. If S is generated by the support $\sigma(\nu)$ of ν and there is an $s \in S$ for which* (17) *holds, then S contains a minimal two-sided completely simple ideal K.*

We shall now try to obtain information about the form of the stationary (possibly sigma-finite) measures for the right and left random walks on S generated by ν since it will be useful in determining the asymptotic behavior of $\sum_{j=1}^{n} \nu^{(j)}$. For this it will be helpful to establish a small lemma on sigma-finite measures for Markov chains. Let $p_{i,j} \geqslant 0$, $\sum_j p_{i,j} \equiv 1$, be the transition probabilities for a Markov chain with a nonvacuous set R of recurrent states. If D is a set of states such that

$$P(z_n \in D \text{ infinitely often}, n \geqslant 1 \mid z_0 = i) \equiv 1 \tag{18}$$

for all $i \in D$, where z_n is a Markov chain with transition probability matrix $P = (p_{i,j})$, we can consider the chain "on the set D" with transition probabilities

$${}_D p_{i,j} = p_{i,j} + \sum_{k \notin D} p_{i,k} p_{k,j} + \sum_{k_i \notin D} p_{i,k_1} p_{k_1,k_2} p_{k_2,j} + \cdots$$

when $i, j \in D$. Notice that

$$\sum_{j \in D} {}_D p_{i,j} \equiv 1, \qquad {}_D p_{i,j} \geqslant 0. \tag{20}$$

Lemma 2. *Let $P = (p_{i,j})$ be a transition probability matrix with a non-vacuous set of recurrent states R. If*

$$\sum_{j \in R} p_{i,j}^{(n)} \to 1 \tag{21}$$

for all i, it follows that any sigma-finite stationary measure π for P ($\pi P = \pi$) has measure zero on the transient states.

Let π be a sigma-finite stationary measure for P. Assume that i is a transient state with $\pi_i > 0$. In each irreducible set of recurrent states C_α that i leads to with positive probability ($\sum_{j \in C_\alpha} p_{i,j}^{(n)} > 0$ for some integer $n \geqslant 1$) choose one state j_α. Let D consist of i and the recurrent states j_α. Then (18) holds for the set D. A simple argument indicates that

$$\pi_{j_\alpha} \geqslant \pi_i \; {}_D p_{i,j_\alpha} + \pi_{j_\alpha} \; {}_D p_{j_\alpha, j_\alpha} \tag{22}$$

[see Harris (1956)]. However, ${}_D p_{i,j_\alpha} > 0$ and ${}_D p_{j_\alpha, j_\alpha} = 1$. We have a contradiction since (22) can only hold if $\pi_i = 0$. The proof is complete and the following corollary is almost an immediate consequence.

Corollary. *Under the assumptions of Lemma* 1, *a sigma-finite stationary measure for the random walk with transition probabilities $\nu(s^{-1} s')$ ($\nu(s' s^{-1})$) on S has measure zero outside the kernel K.*

Now $\nu^{(n)}(K) \to 1$ as $n \to \infty$ [see Martin-Löf (1965)]. This implies that $\nu^{(n)}(s^{-1}K)$, $\nu^{(n)}(Ks^{-1}) \to 1$ as $n \to \infty$ for all s. On applying Lemma 2, the corollary follows.

A stationary measure for the right (left) random walk on S is uniquely determined except for multiplicative constants on each irreducible set of states sS (Ss) if (17) holds for the element s. First the stationary distribution will be determined for the right random walk under the assumptions of Lemma 1. A similar argument specifies the form of the stationary distribution for the left random walk. Consider the right random walk on the minimal right ideal kS with $k = (x, g, y) \in K$. It has already been remarked that the minimal right ideals are the irreducible closed sets of states for the right random walk. Let $H = \{x\} \times G \times \{y\}$ be a subgroup of the right ideal kS. If $z_0, z_1, \ldots$ is the right random walk on kS, almost all sequences will have infinitely many elements in H because of the irreducibility of the Markov chain on kS and the recurrence of the states. If $z_0 \in H$, let $w_0 = z_0, w_1, w_2, \ldots$ be the successive members of the sequence which belong to H. They form a Markov chain which we shall call the process on H or H process. The transition probability of the H process is

$$\tilde{\nu}((x, g, y), (x, g', y)) = \nu((x, g, y)^{-1}(x, g', y)) + \sum_{s \in kS-H} \nu((x, g, y)^{-1}s)\,\nu(s^{-1}(x, g', y)) + \cdots. \tag{23}$$

It is clear that

$$\sum_{g'} \tilde{\nu}((x, g, y), (x, g', y)) = 1 \tag{24}$$

but we wish to show that

$$\sum_{g} \tilde{\nu}((x, g, y), (x, g', y)) = 1. \tag{25}$$

This can be seen by means of the following argument. Let L be the set of elements of S which are taken into H on left multiplication by elements of H. L is a subsemigroup of S. L can now be partitioned into disjoint equivalence classes of elements. Two elements l, l' of L are in the same equivalence class if

$$hl = hl' \tag{26}$$

for each element $h \in H$. Every equivalence class of L contains precisely one element $h \in H$. For this reason it is appropriate to call the equivalence class containing h L_h. Notice that

$$hL_{h'} = hh' \tag{27}$$

and

$$L_h L_{h'} \subset L_{hh'} \tag{28}$$

The transition probability of the H process can be written in terms of the probability measure $\tilde{\nu}$ on L

$$\tilde{\nu}(l) - \nu(l) + \sum_{\substack{s_1 \notin L \\ s_1 s_2 = l}} \nu(s_1)\,\nu(s_2) + \sum_{\substack{s_1, s_1 s_2 \notin L \\ s_1 s_2 s_3 = l}} \nu(s_1)\,\nu(s_2)\,\nu(s_3) + \cdots \tag{29}$$

as

$$\tilde{\nu}(h, h') = \tilde{\nu}(h^{-1}h') = \tilde{\nu}(L_{h''}) \tag{30}$$

where h'' is the element of H such that $hh'' = h'$. Both (29) and (30) imply that (25) is valid for all $g' \in G$. But then the measure identically equal to one at each element of H is (except for a multiplicative constant) the unique sigma-finite stationary measure for the H process.

Lemma 3. *Assume the hypothesis of Lemma 1. Let $k = (x, g, y) \in K$. Consider the right random walk on kS induced by the probability measure ν. Then the unique stationary sigma-finite measure (exept for a multiplicative constant) for the process on $H = \{x\} \times G \times \{y\}$ is $p = (p_h)$ with $p_h \equiv 1$.*

The following simple lemma is helpful in obtaining further information about the form of stationary invariant measures for random walks on S.

Lemma 4. *The following equalities hold for elements $k = (x, g, y)$ of the kernel semigroup K*

$$(x, g, y)^{-1}(x, g', y') = (\bar{x}, g, y)^{-1}(\bar{x}, g', y') \tag{31}$$

$$(x', g', y)(x, g, y)^{-1} = (x', g', \bar{y})(x, g, \bar{y})^{-1}. \tag{31'}$$

We shall only derive (31) since the argument for (31′) is quite similar. Notice that if

$$(x, g, y)\, s = (x, g', y'), \tag{32}$$

then

$$\begin{aligned}(\bar{x}, \bar{g}, y)(x, g, y)\, s &= (\bar{x}, \bar{g}yxg, y)\, s \\ &= (\bar{x}, \bar{g}, y)(x, g', y') = (\bar{x}, \bar{g}yxg', y').\end{aligned} \tag{33}$$

On setting $\bar{g} = (yx)^{-1}$ we have

$$(\bar{x}, g, y)\, s = (\bar{x}, g', y'). \tag{34}$$

Lemma 5. *Under the assumptions of Lemma 1, the stationary measure $\alpha(x, y)$ of the right random walk*

$$\sum_{g,y} \alpha(x, y)\, \nu((x, g, y)^{-1}(x, g', y')) = \alpha(x, y') \tag{35}$$

can be taken to be independent of x and if so we shall call $\alpha(x, y)$ simply $\alpha(y)$ Similarly the stationary measure $\beta(x, y)$ of the left random walk

$$\sum_{g,x} \beta(x, y)\, \nu((x', g', y)(x, g, y)^{-1}) = \beta(x', y) \tag{36}$$

can be taken to be independent of y and we shall call it $\beta(x)$.

Again it will be enough to give the argument for the right random walk since the discussion for the left random walk is similar. The corollary implies that under the assumptions of Lemma 1 a sigma-finite stationary measure is concentrated on the kernel K of the semigroup. Consider a stationary measure $\alpha(x, g, y)$ on the right ideal kS, $k = (x, g, y)$, which is an irreducible closed set of recurrent states for the right random walk. Standard results in the theory of Markov chains [see Chung (1960)] imply that a stationary sigma-finite measure on a closed irreducible set of recurrent states exists and is uniquely determined up to a multiplicative constant. Lemma 3 implies that the stationary sigma-finite measure for the process on a subgroup $H = \{x\} \times G \times \{y\}$ of kS is constant. However the stationary measure $\alpha(x, g, y)$ on kS restricted to H agrees with the stationary measure for the process on H [see Harris (1956)]. Therefore $\alpha(\mathrm{x}, g, y)$ does not depend on g and can be written $\alpha(x, y)$. Further, since (31) holds by Lemma 4, the stationary measure $\alpha(x, y)$ can be taken to be independent of x.

Lemma 6. *Let*

$$_xI = \{k = (x, g, y), g \in G, y \in Y\}, \qquad I_y = \{k = (x, g, y), x \in X, g \in G\}$$

be right and left ideals in K. Then under the assumptions of Lemma 1

$$\begin{aligned} \nu^{(n)}(_xI) \uparrow \gamma(x) > 0, \qquad \sum_x \gamma(x) = 1, \\ \nu^{(n)}(I_y) \uparrow \delta(y) > 0, \qquad \sum_y \delta(y) = 1, \end{aligned} \tag{37}$$

as $n \to \infty$.

Now

$$\nu^{(n+1)}(_xI) \geqslant \sum_{\substack{s \in _xI \\ s' \in S}} \nu^{(n)}(s)\, \nu(s') \geqslant \nu^{(n)}(_xI) \tag{38}$$

so that $\nu^{(n)}(_xI)$ is a monotone increasing function of n. Let $\nu^{(n)}(_xI) \to \gamma(x) > 0$ as $n \to \infty$. Since all the mass contracts onto the kernel semigroup K as $n \to \infty$, it is clear that $\sum_x \gamma(x) = 1$.

Lemma 7. *Let* $z_n(w_n)$, $n = 1, 2, \ldots,$ *be the right (left) random walks on S with transition probability* $\nu(s^{-1}s')(\nu(s's^{-1}))$ *and initial distribution* ν. *Then if the assumptions of Lemma* 1 *are satisfied and*

$$\begin{aligned} a_n(k) = P(z_n = k = (x, g, y);\, z_j \neq k, j < n) \\ (b_n(k) = P(w_n = k = (x, g, y);\, w_j \neq k, j < n)) \end{aligned} \tag{39}$$

it follows that

$$\sum_{n=1}^{\infty} a_n(k) = \gamma(x) \qquad \left(\sum_{n=1}^{\infty} b_n(k) = \delta(y)\right). \tag{40}$$

Notice that $\sum_{n=1}^{\infty} a_n(k) = \gamma(x)$ $(\sum_{n=1}^{\infty} b_n(k) = \delta(y))$ follows immediately from the fact that kS (Sk) is an irreducible closed set of recurrent states for the right (left) random walk on S and that all the probability mass contracts onto K. The proof of Lemma 7 is complete.

Since ${}_xI$ is an irreducible closed set of recurrent states for the right random walk

$$\frac{\sum_{j=1}^{n} \nu^{(j)}((x, g, y)^{-1}(x, g', y'))}{\sum_{j=1}^{n} \nu^{(j)}((x, \bar{g}, \bar{y})^{-1}(x, \bar{g}', \bar{y}'))} \to \frac{\alpha(y')}{\alpha(\bar{y}')} \tag{41}$$

as $n \to \infty$ [see Chung (1960)]. However,

$$\begin{aligned} \nu^{(n)}((x, g, y)) &= \sum_{j=1}^{n} a_j((x, g, y))\, \nu^{(n-j)}((x, g, y)^{-1}(x, g, y)) \\ \nu^{(n)}((x, g', y')) &= \sum_{j=1}^{n} a_j((x, g', y'))\, \nu^{(n-j)}((x, g', y')^{-1}(x, g', y')) \end{aligned} \tag{42}$$

with

$$\sum_{j=1}^{\infty} a_j((x, g, y)) = \sum_{j=1}^{\infty} a_j((x, g', y')) = \gamma(x). \tag{43}$$

Therefore

$$\begin{aligned} &\frac{\sum_{j=1}^{n} \nu^{(j)}((x, g, y))}{\sum_{j=1}^{n} \nu^{(j)}((x, g', y'))} \\ &\quad = \frac{\sum_{m=0}^{n-1} (\sum_{j=1}^{n-m} a_j((x, g, y)))\, \nu^{(m)}((x, g, y)^{-1}(x, g, y))}{\sum_{m=0}^{n-1} (\sum_{j=1}^{n-m} a_j((x, g', y')))\, \nu^{(m)}((x, g', y')^{-1}(x, g', y'))} \\ &\quad \to \frac{\alpha(y)}{\alpha(y')} \end{aligned} \tag{44}$$

as $n \to \infty$ because of (41) and (43). A similar argument in terms of the left random walk implies that

$$\frac{\sum_{j=1}^{n} \nu^{(j)}((x, g, y))}{\sum_{j=1}^{n} \nu^{(j)}((x', g', y))} \to \frac{\beta(x)}{\beta(x')} \tag{45}$$

as $n \to \infty$. Both (44) and (45) then indicate that

$$\begin{aligned} \frac{\sum_{j=1}^{n} \nu^{(j)}((x, g, y))}{\sum_{j=1}^{n} \nu^{(j)}((x', g', y'))} &= \frac{\sum_{j=1}^{n} \nu^{(j)}((x, g, y))}{\sum_{j=1}^{n} \nu^{(j)}((x', g', y))} \frac{\sum_{j=1}^{n} \nu^{(j)}((x', g', y))}{\sum_{j=1}^{n} \nu^{(j)}((x', g', y'))} \\ &\to \frac{\alpha(y)\, \beta(x)}{\alpha(y')\, \beta(x')} \end{aligned} \tag{46}$$

as $n \to \infty$. We would now like to show that we can set $\alpha(y) = \delta(y)$, $\beta(x) = \gamma(x)$. It is clear that

$$\frac{\sum_{j=1}^{n} \nu^{(j)}((x, g, y))}{\sum_{j=1}^{n} \nu^{(j)}((x', g, y))}$$

$$= \frac{\sum_{m=0}^{n-1} (\sum_{j=1}^{n-m} a_j((x, g, y)))\, \nu^{(m)}((x, g, y)^{-1}(x, g, y))}{\sum_{m=0}^{n-1} (\sum_{j=1}^{n-m} a_j((x', g, y)))\, \nu^{(m)2}(x', g, y)^{-1}(x', g, y))}.$$

Because of (31) and (40) it follows that (47) approaches $\gamma(x)/\gamma(x')$ as $n \to \infty$. But this implies that we can set $\beta(x) = \gamma(x)$. A similar argument with left random walks indicates that one can set $\alpha(y) = \delta(y)$.

Theorem 1. *Let ν be a probability measure on the countable semigroup S. Assume that S is generated by the support $\sigma(\nu)$ of ν and that there is an $s \in S$ such that $\sum_{j=1}^{\infty} \nu^{(j)}(s) = \infty$. Then S contains a minimal twosided completely simple ideal K whose elements are the recurrent states of the right (left) random walk on S generated by ν. Further*

$$\frac{\sum_{j=1}^{n} \nu^{(j)}((x, g, y))}{\sum_{j=1}^{n} \nu^{(j)}((x', g', y'))} \to \frac{\gamma(x)\, \delta(y)}{\gamma(x')\, \delta(y')} > 0$$

as $n \to \infty$ for elements $k = (x, g, y)$, $k' = (x', g', y) \in K$.

Notice that all elements $s \notin K$ of the semigroup S are transient states of both the left and right random walks on S generated by ν. Since $\sum_{j=0}^{\infty} \nu^{(j)}(s) < \infty$ for such elements, it follows that

$$\frac{\sum_{j=0}^{n} \nu^{(j)}(s)}{\sum_{j=0}^{n} \nu^{(j)}(k)} \to 0$$

as $n \to \infty$ for $s \notin K$, $k \in K$. Lemma 5 and Theorem 1 directly imply the following result.

Theorem 2. *Under the assumptions of Theorem 1 there is a unique sigma-finite measure (up to a multiplicative constant) stationary for both the left and right random walks on S induced by ν. The measure η has the kernel K of S as its support and is given by*

$$\eta(k) = \gamma(x)\, \delta(y)$$

where $k = (x, g, y) \in K$.

It is of some interest to see what kind of semigroups S can support a measure ν such that (17) holds for some element $s \in S$. The proof of Lemma 3 yields some information in this direction which we summarize in the following theorem.

Theorem 3. *Let ν be a probability measure on the countable semigroup S whose support $\sigma(\nu)$ generates S. If there is an $s \in S$ with $\sum_{j=1}^{\infty} \nu^{(j)}(s) = \infty$, then S must have a minimal two-sided completely simple ideal K. Further,* (17) *is valid if and only if $\tilde{\nu}(h, h') = \tilde{\nu}(h^{-1} h')$* [see formula (30)] *is the transition probability of a recurrent random walk on $H = \{x\} \times G \times \{y\}$. Thus G* (as a group) *must be able to support a recurrent random walk.*

Much is known about Abelian groups that can support recurrent random walks [see Kesten and Spitzer (1965)]. However, little is known about noncommutative groups.

REFERENCES

Chung, K. L. (1960). Markov Chains with Stationary Transition Probabilities." Springer, Berlin.

De Leeuw, K., and I. Glicksberg (1961). Applications of almost periodic compactifications. *Acta Math.* **105**, 63–97.

Grenander, U. (1963). "Probabilities on Algebraic Structures." Almqvist and Wiksell, Stockholm.

Halmos, P. R. (1958). "Measure Theory." Van Nostrand. Princeton, New Jersey.

Harris, T. E. (1956). The existence of stationary measures for certain Markov processes. *Proc. Symp. Math. Statist. and Probability, 3rd, Berkeley* **2**, 113–124.

Heble, M., and Rosenblatt, M. (1963). Idempotent measures on a compact topological semigroup. *Proc. Amer. Math. Soc.* **14**, 177–184.

Kesten, H., and Spitzer, F. (1965). Random walk on countably infinite groups. *Acta Math.* **114**, 237–265.

Ljapin, E. S. (1963). "Semigroups" (transl.) (Math. Monograph, No. 3). Amer. Math. Soc., Providence, Rhode Island.

Martin-Löf, P. (1965). Probability theory on discrete semigroups. *Z. Wahrscheinlichkeitstheorie und Verw. Gebiete* **4**, 78–102.

Pym, J. S. (1962). Idempotent measures on semigroups. *Pacific J. Math.* **12**, 685–698.

Rosen, W. G. (1956). On invariant means over compact semigroups. *Proc. Amer. Math. Soc.* **7**, 1076–1082.

Rosenblatt, M. (1960). Limits of convolution sequences of measures on a compact topological semigroup. *J. Math. Mech.* **9**, 293–306.

Rosenblatt, M. (1964). Equicontinuous Markov operators. *Teor. Verojatnost. i Primenen* **9**, 205–222.

Tortrat, A. (1966). Lois tendues μ sur un demi-groupe topologique complètement simple *X, Z. Wahrscheinlichkeitstheorie und Verw. Gebiete* **6**, 145–160.

Wallace, A. D. (1956). The Rees-Suschkewitsch structure theorem for complete simple semigroups. *Proc. Nat. Acad. Sci. U.S.A.* **42**, 430–432.

*The Study of Closets and Free Contents Related to Semilattice Decomposition of Semigroups**

TAKAYUKI TAMURA
Department of Mathematics
University of California
Davis, California

Introduction

The greatest semilattice decomposition of a semigroup is one of the important concepts in the structure theory of semigroups because a semigroup can be decomposed into the union of a special type of semigroups, i.e., semilattice indecomposable semigroups. The author found in 1964 that the concept of (free) contents plays a great part in the discussion of semilattice decompositions and semilattice-indecomposable semigroups. However, the structure of (free) contents has not been studied much.

The structure of semilattice-indecomposable semigroups has been studied to some extent in the case of idempotent semigroups, commutative semigroups, or medial semigroups. In such cases the minimal ideal, if it exists, has the property that each element of the ideal is divided by every power of every element of the semigroup. This ideal will be called a closet. This concept will be generalized to arbitrary semigroups and will allow us to derive larger classes of semilattice-indecomposable semigroups.

In Scction I, we will state the known results concerning the theory of decompositions and semilattice-indecomposable semigroups and will

* This paper contains the results of the research supported by NSF Grants GP5988 and GP7608.

The main results on closets and contents were presented at the International Symposium on Semigroups and Application, Smolenice, Czechoslovakia, June 1968 and in the Symposium on Semigroups, Wayne State University, Detroit, June 1968.

explain what is the motive of considering the concepts "content" and "closet." In Section II, we will discuss the structure of free contents and answer the question: When are two free contents isomorphic? In Section III, we will study the concept of closets and will discuss how the closets are connected with the structure of a semigroup and with band decompositions of a semigroup. In particular, the semigroups with constant closet will be of greatest interest, and quite a few examples will be given in which use is made of free contents.

Of course there still remain many problems with respect to contents and closets. This paper is, however, the first step toward further development in the future.

I. Decomposition of a Semigroup and $\mathscr{S}$-Indecomposable Semigroups

1. Greatest Decomposition

Let $\mathscr{T}$ be a system of a finite number of identities

$$f_i(x_1, \ldots, x_n) = g_i(x_1, \ldots, x_n), \qquad i = 1, \ldots, k. \tag{1.1}$$

Let ρ be a congruence on a semigroup S. If S/ρ satisfies $\mathscr{T}$, ρ is called a $\mathscr{T}$ congruence on S and S/ρ is called a $\mathscr{T}$ homomorphic image of S. For a fixed $\mathscr{T}$ there is a smallest $\mathscr{T}$ congruence ρ_0 on S, i.e.,

$$\rho_0 \text{ is a } \mathscr{T} \text{ congruence on } S \tag{1.2}$$

$$\text{if } \rho \text{ is a } \mathscr{T} \text{ congruence on } S, \text{ then } \rho_0 \subseteq \rho. \tag{1.3}$$

The existence of such a smallest $\mathscr{T}$ congruence was discussed by Tamura and Kimura (1955), Kimura (1958a), Clifford and Preston (1961), Tamura (1965), and Yamada (1955). The partition of S which is induced by the smallest $\mathscr{T}$ congruence ρ_0 is called the greatest $\mathscr{T}$ decomposition of S. A semigroup which is isomorphic with S/ρ_0 is called the greatest $\mathscr{T}$-homomorphic image of S. The universal relation $\{(x, y) : x \in S, y \in S\}$ is denoted by ω or ω_S; the equality relation $\{(x, x) : x \in S\}$ is denoted by ι or ι_S. If ρ_0 is the smallest $\mathscr{T}$ congruence on S and if $\rho_0 = \omega_S$, i.e., $|S/\rho_0| = 1$, then S is called $\mathscr{T}$ indecomposable; otherwise S is called $\mathscr{T}$ decomposable. The simplest examples of $\mathscr{T}$ are

$$\mathscr{C} = \{xy = yx\}, \qquad \mathscr{I} = \{x^2 = x\}, \qquad \mathscr{S} = \{xy = yx, x^2 = x\}.$$

Let $\mathscr{B}$ be the set of all binary relations on a semigroup D. We define unary operations in $\mathscr{B}$. The capital letters R, S, T, C_r, C_l denote the operations: Let $\xi \in \mathscr{B}$.

$$\xi R = \xi \cup \iota$$

$$\xi S = \xi \cup \xi^{-1}, \qquad \xi^{-1} = \{(y, x) : (x, y) \in \xi\}$$

$$\xi T = \bigcup_{i=1}^{\infty} \xi^i$$

$$\xi C_r = \xi \cup \{(xa, ya) : a \in D, (x, y) \in \xi\}$$

$$\xi C_l = \xi \cup \{(ax, ay) : a \in D, (x, y) \in \xi\}$$

Then we have

$$\begin{aligned} &R^2 = R, \quad S^2 = S, \quad T^2 = T, \quad RS = SR, \quad RT = TR, \\ (1.4) \quad &STS = TST = ST, \\ &C_l^2 = C_l, \quad C_r^2 = C_r, \quad C_lC_r = C_rC_l. \end{aligned}$$

Let $C = C_lC_r$.

$$(1.5) \quad C^2 = C, \qquad RC = CR, \qquad SC = CS, \qquad CTC = TCT = CT.$$

Let $Q = RST$, $N = RSCT = QCT$. Then ξQ and ξN are the equivalence relation and the congruence relation on D generated by ξ respectively. Let

$$\begin{aligned} \xi P_c &= \xi \cup \{(xy, yx) : x, y \in D\} \\ \xi P_d &= \xi \cup \{(x^2, x) : x \in D\} \\ \xi P_s &= \xi P_c \cup \xi P_d . \end{aligned}$$

(1.6) *$\xi P_c N$ is the $\mathscr{C}$ congruence on D generated by ξ, $\xi P_d N$ is the $\mathscr{I}$ congruence on D generated by ξ, and $\xi P_s N$ is the $\mathscr{S}$ congruence on D generated by ξ, respectively. In particular, $\iota P_c N$, $\iota P_d N$, and $\iota P_s N$ are the smallest $\mathscr{C}$, $\mathscr{I}$, $\mathscr{S}$ congruences, respectively.*

For a system of identities

$$\mathscr{T}: \; f_i(x_1, \ldots, x_n) = g_i(x_1, \ldots, x_n), \qquad i = 1, \ldots, k,$$

let $\xi P_i = \xi \cup \{(f_i(x_1, \ldots, x_n), g_i(x_1, \ldots, x_n)) : x_1, \ldots, x_n \in D\}$. Then $\xi(P_1 \cup \cdots \cup P_k)N$ is the smallest $\mathscr{T}$ congruence on D generated by ξ where $P_1 \cup \cdots \cup P_k$ is defined by $\xi(P_1 \cup \cdots \cup P_k) = \xi P_1 \cup \cdots \cup \xi P_k$.

By the way, for an implication "$f = g \Rightarrow h = k$"

$$\xi P = \xi \cup \{(h(x_1, \ldots, x_n), k(x_1, \ldots, x_n)) : f(x_1, \ldots, x_n)\, \xi g(x_1, \ldots, x_n)\}.$$

The smallest congruence of this type is given by

$$\iota \left(\bigcup_{i=1}^{\infty} (PN)^i \right).$$

Let ρ_D, σ_D, τ_D denote the smallest $\mathscr{S}$, $\mathscr{C}$, $\mathscr{I}$ congruences on D, respectively.

$$P_s N = (P_c N)(P_d N) = (P_d N)(P_c N). \tag{1.7}$$

In other words, the greatest $\mathscr{S}$-homomorphic image of D is obtained by the greatest $\mathscr{I}$-homomorphic image of D/σ_D or by the greatest $\mathscr{C}$-homomorphic image of D/τ_D.

REMARK. (1.7) can be extended to the case for more than two identities, but it is not valid for implications. For example, let $\mathscr{T}_1$ be an identity and $\mathscr{T}_2$ be an implication. Then

$$(P_1 \cup P_2)\, N = (P_1 N)(P_2 N) = (P_2 N)(P_1 N)(P_2 N)$$

but $(P_1 N)(P_2 N) \neq (P_2 N)(P_1 N)$ in general.

The proof of the results on operations on relations can be seen in the author's paper (1965).

2. Attainability

Let S be a semigroup and $S = \bigcup_{\alpha \in \Gamma} S_\alpha$ be an $\mathscr{S}$ decomposition of S, specifically, Γ is a semilattice,

$$S_\alpha \cap S_\beta = \emptyset \qquad (\alpha \neq \beta)$$
$$S_\alpha{}^2 \subseteq S_\alpha, \qquad S_\alpha S_\beta \subseteq S_{\alpha\beta}, \qquad S_\beta S_\alpha \subseteq S_{\alpha\beta} \qquad \text{for all} \quad \alpha, \beta \in \Gamma.$$

In this case we say that S is a semilattice union of semigroups S_α, $\alpha \in \Gamma$, or a semilattice of semigroups S_α, $\alpha \in \Gamma$.

The author proved the following theorem (Tamura 1956):

(1.8) **Theorem.** *In the greatest $\mathscr{S}$ decomposition Δ_0 of a semigroup S, $S = \bigcup_{\lambda \in L} S_\lambda$, each congruence class S_λ is $\mathscr{S}$ indecomposable. Conversely, if a decomposition Δ_0 is an $\mathscr{S}$ decomposition of S and if each congruence class S_λ is $\mathscr{S}$ indecomposable, then Δ_0 is the greatest $\mathscr{S}$ decomposition of S.*

We sketch the key point of the proof.

(1.9) *Let I be an ideal of a semigroup S. If σ is an $\mathscr{S}$ congruence on I, then there is an $\mathscr{S}$ congruence ρ on S such that the restriction $\rho|I$ of ρ to I is σ.*

This can be proved using the fact that a translation semigroup of a semilattice is a semilattice and if a semigroup S is homomorphic onto a semilattice L, a right translation of S induces a translation of L.

(1.10) *Let η be an $\mathscr{S}$ congruence on a semigroup S. Let S_α be one of the congruence classes modulo η and let σ be an $\mathscr{S}$ congruence on S_α. Then there is an $\mathscr{S}$ congruence ρ on S such that $\rho|S_\alpha = \sigma$.*

Using (1.9) and (1.10), Theorem 1.8 is proved in the author's paper (1956). As a corollary to (1.9) we have:

(1.11) *If a semigroup S is $\mathscr{S}$ indecomposable, then an ideal of S is $\mathscr{S}$ indecomposable.*

Petrich (1964) proved equivalent statements of Theorem 1.8 and (1.11) in terms of prime ideals and faces.

A nonempty subset I of a semigroup S is called a prime ideal if I is an ideal and if $S\backslash I$ is a nonempty subsemigroup of S. $S\backslash I$ is called a face. S is $\mathscr{S}$ indecomposable if and only if S has no prime ideal. Let $N(x)$ denote the smallest face of S containing x and call the set $N_x = \{y \in S : N(y) = N(x)\}$ an N class of S associated with x.

(1.12) **Theorem** (Petrich, 1964). *The set of all distinct N classes of S is the greatest $\mathscr{S}$ decomposition of S and $N_xN_y = N_{xy}$. Further any ideal of each N_x has no prime ideal.*

An $\mathscr{S}$ indecomposable semigroup is called "𝔭 simple" since it has no prime ideal. We will use "𝔭 simple" as a synonym of "$\mathscr{S}$ indecomposable." The former one is a shorter word than the latter, but the latter is based on the type of decomposition as in the case "$\mathscr{I}$ indecomposable" or "$\mathscr{C}$ indecomposable" and so on.

The third proof of Theorem 1.8 was obtained by Tamura (1964) using the property of "contents" which will be explained in Section I.3.

By Theorem 1.8 every semigroup is a semilattice union of a special type of semigroups, i.e., $\mathscr{S}$ indecomposable semigroups. Is there any system of identities of special types except "semilattice" for which every semigroup is the set union of a special type of subsets? In fact "semilattice" is a unique system of identities with such a property in the following sense:

Let $\mathscr{T}$ be a system of identities, and let S be any semigroup. S has a greatest $\mathscr{T}$ decomposition. Suppose that each congruence class of S in the greatest $\mathscr{T}$ decomposition—if it is a subsemigroup—is $\mathscr{T}$ indecomposable for all S. Then $\mathcal{T}$ is called an *attainable* system of identities on all semigroups.

Both $\{x = x\}$ and $\{x = y\}$ are attainable. These are called trivial. Theorem 1.8 tells us that $\{xy = yx, x^2 = x\}$ is nontrivially attainable. However:

(1.13) **Theorem** (Tamura, 1966). *If $\mathcal{T}$ is a nontrivial attainable system of identities on all semigroups, then $\mathcal{T}$ is equivalent to "semilattice": $\{xy = yx, x^2 = x\}$.*

This shows the important significance of the $\mathcal{S}$ decomposition of semigroups.

Related to (1.10) we define "extendability" of a system of identities as follows:

Let $\mathcal{T}$ be a system of identities. Let S be any semigroup and S_α be a congruence class, which is a subsemigroup, in a $\mathcal{T}$ decomposition Δ of S. Suppose that any $\mathcal{T}$ decomposition of S_α can be extended to a $\mathcal{T}$ decomposition of S. In other words, for all semigroups S and for every $\mathcal{T}$ congurence σ on S_α there is a $\mathcal{T}$ congruence ρ on S such that $\rho|S_\alpha = \sigma$. Then $\mathcal{T}$ is called an *extendable* system of identities.

The semilattice $\{xy = yx, x^2 = x\}$ is nontrivially extendable. It is obvious that extendability implies attainability. By (1.10) and Theorem 1.13 we have the following.

(1.14) **Theorem.** *As far as systems of identities are concerned, the concept of extendability is equivalent to attainability.*

3. Contents and $\mathcal{S}$ Decomposition

Let S be a semigroup. Let $a_1, \ldots, a_n$ be a finite number of elements of S. All the elements x of S each of which is the product of *all* of $a_1, \ldots, a_n$ (admitting repeated use) form a subsemigroup of S. We denote it by C_S or $C_S(a_1, \ldots, a_n)$ and it is called the content of $a_1, \ldots, a_n$ in S. We notice that $a_1, \ldots, a_n$ are not required to be distinct, but for example $C_S(a)$ is different from $C_S(a, a)$ in general: $C_S(a) = \{a^i : i \geqslant 1\}$ while $C_S(a, a) = \{a^i : i \geqslant 2\}$.

Let $\mathcal{F}_0$ be the free semigroup generated by distinct letters $a_1, \ldots, a_n$. $\mathcal{F}_0 = \mathcal{F}_0(a_1, \ldots, a_n)$. The content $C_{\mathcal{F}_0}(a_1, \ldots, a_n)$ is called the free content of $a_1, \ldots, a_n$. The letters $a_1, \ldots, a_n$ are called the generators of $C_{\mathcal{F}_0}(a_1, \ldots, a_n)$. Clearly $C_S(a_1, \ldots, a_n)$ is the homomorphic image of $C_{\mathcal{F}_0}(a_1, \ldots, a_n)$.

(1.15) **Theorem.** *A free content is $\mathfrak{p}$ simple, and hence a content is $\mathfrak{p}$ simple.*

The free semigroup $\mathscr{F}_0(a_1, \ldots, a_n)$ is a semilattice union of $2^n - 1$ free contents and this is the greatest $\mathscr{S}$ decomposition of $\mathscr{F}_0$. Accordingly Theorem 1.15 is an immediate consequence of Theorem 1.8. However, the author (1964) proved directly the former half of Theorem 1.15 without using Theorem 1.8, and then obtained Theorem 1.8 as the consequence of Theorem 1.15. The following lemmas, (1.16)–(1.18), can be used to prove Theorem 1.15.

Let $\mathscr{F} = C_{\mathscr{F}_0}(a_1, \ldots, a_n)$ and let ξ be an $\mathscr{S}$ congruence on $\mathscr{F}$. Let $x_1x_2 \cdots x_i \cdots x_m$ be an element of $\mathscr{F}$ where each x_i is one of $a_1, \ldots, a_n$.

(1.16) $x_1 \cdots x_{i-1}x_ix_{i+1} \cdots x_m \,\xi\, x_ix_{i+1} \cdots x_mx_1 \cdots x_{i-1}, \qquad 1 \leqslant i \leqslant m.$

(1.17) *If $A, B \in \mathscr{F}$ and $x \in \{a_1, \ldots, a_n\}$, then $A \,\xi\, B$ implies $Ax \,\xi\, Bx$ and $xA \,\xi\, xB$.*

(1.18) $$Ax \,\xi\, A \quad \text{and} \quad xA \,\xi\, A.$$

The smallest $\mathscr{S}$ congruence on a semigroup S can be described in terms of contents:

(1.19) *The following three statements are equivalent*:

(1.19.1) *ρ_0 is the smallest $\mathscr{S}$ congruence on S.*

(1.19.2) *$a\,\rho_0 b$ if and only if there is a finite sequence of elements of S*

$$a = a_0, \qquad a_1, \ldots, a_{n-1}, \qquad a_n = b$$

such that a_i and a_{i+1} are related in one of the following fashions

$$\left.\begin{array}{lll} \text{(i)} & a_i = c_ix_iy_id_i, & a_{i+1} = c_iy_ix_id_i \\ \text{(ii)} & a_i = c_ix_id_i, & a_{i+1} = c_ix_i^2d_i \\ \text{(iii)} & a_i = c_ix_i^2d_i, & a_{i+1} = c_ix_id_i \end{array}\right\} \quad \begin{array}{l} c_i, d_i \in S^1 = S \cup \{1\} \\ x_i, y_i \in S \end{array}$$

(1.19.3) *$a\,\rho_0 b$ if there is a finite sequence of contents in S*

$$C_1, C_2, \ldots, C_k$$

such that $a \in C_1$, $b \in C_k$, and $C_i \cap C_{i+1} \neq \emptyset$ $(i = 1, \ldots, k-1)$.

Since $\iota P_S N$ is the smallest $\mathscr{S}$ congruence by (1.6) we have:

(1.19.1) $\Rightarrow$ (1.19.2). The proof of (1.19.2) $\Rightarrow$ (1.19.3) is easy.

(1.19.3) $\Rightarrow$ (1.19.1) is proved by checking the conditions in the definition of the smallest $\mathscr{S}$ congruence.

Let $S = \bigcup_{\lambda \in L} S_\lambda$ be the greatest $\mathscr{S}$ decomposition of S induced by the smallest $\mathscr{S}$ congruence ρ_0 on S. Let σ be an $\mathscr{S}$ congruence on S_λ.

Let $a, b \in S_\lambda$, i.e., $a\rho_0 b$. By using (1.19.2) and Theorem 1.15, we can prove that $a\rho_0 b$ implies $a\sigma b$, that is, $\sigma = \omega_{S_\lambda}$ (Tamura, 1964). We notice that if $a, b \in S_\lambda$, then $C_1, C_2, \ldots, C_k$ mentioned in (1.19.3) are contained in S_λ because each C_i is $\mathfrak{p}$ simple.

As a corollary to (1.19) we have the following, (1.20), which includes a condition for S to be $\mathfrak{p}$ simple.

(1.20) *Let T be a subsemigroup of a semigroup S. T is $\mathfrak{p}$ simple if and only if for every two elements a, b of T there is a finite sequence of contents $C_1, \ldots, C_k$ in S such that $a \in C_1$, $b \in C_k$, $C_1, \ldots, C_k \subseteq T$, and $C_i \cap C_{i+1} \neq \emptyset$ $(i = 1, \ldots, k-1)$.*

As an application of (1.20) we can prove (1.11):

An ideal of a $\mathfrak{p}$-simple semigroup is $\mathfrak{p}$ simple.

Incidentally we add the following proposition:

(1.21) *Let S be a semigroup. For each $a \in S$ there is a greatest $\mathfrak{p}$-simple subsemigroup T of S containing a. (T is a maximal $\mathfrak{p}$-simple subsemigroup of S.) T is a maximal $\mathfrak{p}$-simple subsemigroup of S if and only if T is a congruence class of S modulo the smallest $\mathscr{S}$ congruence of S.*

In Section II we will discuss the internal structure of free contents.

Kimura and the author (1954) determined the greatest $\mathscr{S}$ decomposition of commutative semigroups; McLean (1954) did the same for idempotent semigroups. We now notice that both are obtained as an application of (1.19.3) (Shafer and Tamura, 1966).

Let S be a commutative semigroup. Define a relation η as follows.

(1.22) *$a\eta b$ iff $a^m = bx$, $b^n = ay$ for some $x, y \in S$ and some $m, n > 0$.*

ρ_0 is defined by (1.19.3). We can prove that (i) η is transitive, (ii) $\rho_0 \subseteq \eta$, (iii) $\eta \subseteq \rho_0$.

(1.23) *If S is a commutative semigroup, then $\rho_0 = \eta$.*

Let S be a band, i.e., an idempotent semigroup.

(1.24) *A content in a band is a rectangular band.*

We may prove (1.24) in a free band by induction on the length of words. Define two relations β and ρ_0' as follows:

(1.25) (McLean) $a\beta b$ iff $aba = a$ and $bab = b$.

(1.26) $a\rho_0' b$ iff a and b are in a same content.

Then

(1.27) if S is a band, then $\rho_0 = \rho_0' = \beta$.

By (1.24) and (1.27) McLean's result is readily obtained.

A commutative semigroup S is called Archimedean if for every $a, b \in S$, there are $m, n > 0$ and $x, y \in S$ such that

$$a^m = bx \quad \text{and} \quad b^n = ay.$$

(1.28) **Theorem** (Kimura and Tamura, 1954). *A commutative semigroup is $\mathscr{S}$ indecomposable if and only if it is Archimedean.*

(1.29) **Theorem** (McLean, 1954). *A band is $\mathscr{S}$ indecomposable if and only if it is a rectangular band.*

A semigroup is called unipotent if and only if it contains a unique idempotent.

(1.30) **Corollary.** *A finite commutative semigroup is Archimedean if and only if it is unipotent.*

A semigroup S is called medial if S satisfies the identity $xyzu = xzyu$. We define a relation η' on a medial semigroup S.

(1.31) a $\eta' b$ iff there are $x, y, z, u \in S$ and $m, n > 0$ such that

$$a^m = xby, \qquad b^n = zau.$$

A medial semigroup S is called Archimedean if for every $a, b \in S$ there are $x, y, z, u \in S$ and $m, n > 0$ such that

$$a^m = xby, \qquad b^n = zau.$$

Then:

(1.32) *If S is a medial semigroup, $\rho_0 = \eta'$.*

(1.33) **Theorem** (Chrislock, 1966). *A medial semigroup is $\mathscr{S}$ indecomposable if and only if it is Archimedean.*

This is a generalization of Theorem 1.28.

4. $\mathfrak{p}$-Simple Semigroups

By (1.7), Theorems 1.28 and 1.29, we have the following.

(1.34) **Proposition.** *The following are equivalent:*

(1.34.1) *S is $\mathscr{S}$ indecomposable.*

(1.34.2) *The greatest $\mathscr{I}$-homomorphic image of S is rectangular band.*

(1.34.3) *The greatest $\mathscr{C}$-homomorphic image of S is Archimedean.*

We can classify all $\mathscr{S}$-indecomposable semigroups into the following cases:

(1.35.1) $\mathscr{C}$ indecomposable and $\mathscr{I}$ indecomposable.

(1.35.2) $\mathscr{C}$ indecomposable and $\mathscr{I}$ decomposable.

(1.35.3) $\mathscr{C}$ decomposable and $\mathscr{I}$ indecomposable.

(1.35.4) $\mathscr{C}$ decomposable and $\mathscr{I}$ decomposable.

Another important classification is based on (0) simplicity.

(1.36) *A simple semigroup is* $\mathfrak{p}$*-simple.*

(1.37) *The following conditions on* 0*-simple semigroups* S *are equivalent.*

(1.37.1) S *has at least one zero devisor.*

(1.37.2) S *is* $\mathscr{S}$ *indecomposable.*

(1.37.3) S *is* $\mathscr{I}$ *indecomposable.*

(1.37.4) S *is* $\mathscr{C}$ *indecomposable.*

We can construct some nonsimple $\mathscr{S}$-indecomposable semigroups by means of ideal extensions. The basic proposition is stated in more general form.

Let $\mathscr{T}$ be a system of identities which is consistent with the property "having zero." This means that there is a nontrivial semigroup with zero which satisfies $\mathscr{T}$. Clearly a homomorphic image of a $\mathscr{T}$-indecomposable semigroup is also $\mathscr{T}$ indecomposable.

(1.38) **Proposition.** *Let* I *be a* $\mathscr{T}$*-indecomposable semigroup and* T *be a* $\mathscr{T}$*-indecomposable semigroup with zero. Then every ideal extension* S *of* I *by* T *is* $\mathscr{T}$ *indecomposable if it exists.*

Finite $\mathfrak{p}$-simple semigroups are constructed by successive ideal extensions. Let S be a finite nonsimple $\mathfrak{p}$-simple semigroup. If S has no zero, let I be the minimal ideal of S; if S has a zero, let I be the union of all 0-minimal ideals of S. All finite nonsimple $\mathfrak{p}$-simple semigroups S are classified into the 16 classes according to the properties of I, S/I, the greatest $\mathscr{C}$-, and $\mathscr{I}$-homomorphic images of S. [see Tamura, (1967).] In particular see Tamura (1954, 1958), Yamada (1964), and Tamura and Yamada (unpublished paper) with respect to finite unipotent semigroups and finite nil semigroups. By "a nil semigroup" we mean a unipotent semigroup with 0 in which some power of every element is 0.

It is known that a commutative Archimedean semigroup S is one of the following types

(1.39.1) A commutative nil semigroup.

(1.39.2) An ideal extension of an Abelian group G, $|G| > 1$, by a commutative nil semigroup Z, $|Z| \geqslant 1$.

(1.39.3) A commutative Archimedean torsion-free semigroup.

S is of type (1.39.1) if and only if S is a set union of an ascending chain of ideals S_i of S

$$S = \bigcup_{i=1}^{\infty} S_i , \qquad S_1 \subseteq S_2 \subseteq \cdots \subseteq S_i \subseteq \cdots$$

such that S_1 and S_i/S_{i-1} $(i = 2, 3, \ldots)$ satisfy the identity $x^2 = 0$. It is easy to construct the semigroups of type (1.38.2) when G and Z are given (Tamura, 1954).

Let $C = \bigcap_{n=1}^{\infty} Sa^n$. As seen in Tamura (1957, 1968) and Clifford and Preston (1961) C is independent of a and is either the minimal ideal of S or the empty set. In detail

$$C = \begin{cases} \{0\} & \text{for } (1.39.1) \\ G & \text{for } (1.39.2) \\ \emptyset & \text{for } (1.39.3). \end{cases}$$

We define a relation $\leqslant$ on a commutative Archimedean semigroup S by divisibility, that is,

$$a \leqslant b \quad \text{iff either} \quad a = b \quad \text{or} \quad a = bx \qquad \text{for some } x \in S.$$

Then the relation $\leqslant$ is a partial ordering if and only if either $C = \{0\}$ or $C = \emptyset$.

This is generalized to medial semigroups. A part of the following are due to Chrislock (1966, 1969).

(1.40) **Theorem.** *A medial Archimedean semigroup is one of the following types*:

(1.40.1) *A medial nil semigroup.*

(1.40.2) *A medial ideal extension of the direct product D, $|D| > 1$, of an Abelian group and a rectangular band by a medial nil semigroup.*

(1.40.3) *A medial Archimedean torsion-free semigroup.*

If we define C by $C = \bigcap_{n=1}^{\infty} Sa^nS$, then it is independent of a and

$$C = \begin{cases} \{0\} & \text{for } (1.40.1) \\ D & \text{for } (1.40.2) \\ \emptyset & \text{for } (1.40.3) \end{cases}$$

Remark. $C = \emptyset$ in the medial case can be proved by using $C = \emptyset$ in the commutative case (Tamura, 1957, 1968).

Thus we see that $C = \bigcap Sa^nS$ has an interesting property in medial Archimedean semigroups. However we can define the concept C for any semigroup S which need not be $\mathscr{S}$ indecomposable although C then depends on the element a. In Section III we will call C the closet of a and will discuss what relationships there are between the closets, the structure, and the band decomposition of S. The study of the closets from a general point of view may suggest a new class of $\mathfrak{p}$-simple semigroups.

II. Free Contents

Content and free content are defined in Section I.3. It goes without saying that a free content is left and right cancellative.

1. Characterization by Homomorphisms

(2.1) **Theorem.** *The following three statements are equivalent* :

(2.1.1) *C is a free content.*

(2.1.2) *C is a maximal $\mathfrak{p}$-simple subsemigroup of a finitely generated free semigroup.*

(2.1.3) *A positive integer n can be chosen in the following way: For every semigroup S generated by $a_1, \ldots, a_n$ there are a homomorphism φ of C into S and a semigroup D generated by $a'_1, \ldots, a'_n$ such that C can be embedded into D as a maximal $\mathfrak{p}$-simple subsemigroup of D and φ is extended to a homomorphism $\bar{\varphi}$ of D onto S carrying a'_i to a_i ($i = 1, \ldots, n$).*

Proof. (2.1.1) $\rightleftarrows$ (2.1.2). Let $C = \mathscr{F} = C_{\mathscr{F}_0}(a_1, \ldots, a_n)$ (see Section I.3). $\mathscr{F}$ is a congruence class in the greatest $\mathscr{S}$ decomposition of the free semigroup $\mathscr{F}_0(a_1, \ldots, a_n)$. By Theorem 1.15 $\mathscr{F}$ is $\mathfrak{p}$-simple. The maximality is assured by (1.21). The converse is obvious.

(2.1.1) $\rightarrow$ (2.1.3). Let $C = \mathscr{F} = C_{\mathscr{F}_0}(a_1, \ldots, a_n)$ and $D = \mathscr{F}_0(a_1, \ldots, a_n)$. C is a maximal $\mathfrak{p}$-simple subsemigroup of D by (2.1.2). Let S be a semigroup generated by $a_1, \ldots, a_n$. D is homomorphic onto S in the natural way. Let $\bar{\varphi}$ be the homomorphism $D \rightarrow S$ and φ be the restriction $\bar{\varphi}|C$. Then we have (2.1.3).

(2.1.3) $\rightarrow$ (2.1.1). Assume (2.1.3). Let $S = \mathscr{F}_0(a_1, \ldots, a_n)$. By the assumption $\bar{\varphi}$ is a homomorphism of a semigroup $D(a'_1, \ldots, a'_n)$ generated by $a'_1, \ldots, a'_n$ onto $\mathscr{F}_0(a_1, \ldots, a_n)$ such that $a'_i\varphi = a_i$ ($i = 1, \ldots, n$). It is easy to prove that $\bar{\varphi}$ is an isomorphism since S is a free semigroup. Therefore we have (2.1.2), hence (2.1.1).

If a free content C can be embedded into $\mathscr{F}_0(a_1, \ldots, a_n)$, then C also can be embedded into $\mathscr{F}_0(a_1, \ldots, a_m)$ for all $m \geqslant n$.

The positive number n of a free content $C_{\mathscr{F}_0}(a_1, \ldots, a_n)$ is called the rank of $C_{\mathscr{F}_0}(a_1, \ldots, a_n)$.

Naturally a question is raised.

Is the rank of a free content C the minimum of m's for which C can be embedded into a free semigroup $\mathscr{F}_0(a_1, \ldots, a_m)$ as a maximal $\mathfrak{p}$-simple subsemigroup?

The answer is affirmative. However, to prove this we need to prove that a free content of rank n can not be isomorphic onto a free content of rank m if $n \neq m$. We will prove this in Section II.3.

2. Primes and Minimal Elements

From now on a free content will be denoted by $\mathscr{F}$, and let n be the rank of $\mathscr{F}$:

$$\mathscr{T} = C_{\mathscr{F}_0}(a_1, \ldots, a_n) \qquad \text{where} \quad \mathscr{F}_0 = \mathscr{F}_0(a_1, \ldots, a_n).$$

Capital letters will denote words, i.e., elements, of $\mathscr{F}$ or $\mathscr{F}_0$, and small letters will denote some of $a_1, \ldots, a_n$.

If $X = x_1 \cdots x_m$ and $Y = y_1 \cdots y_k$, then $XY = x_1 \cdots x_m y_1 \cdots y_k$. Hence if $W \in \mathscr{F}$ and $V \in \mathscr{F}_0$, then WV, VW are in $\mathscr{F}$. An element W of $\mathscr{F}$ is called a prime if $W \in \mathscr{F} \backslash \mathscr{F}^2$.

Let $W \in \mathscr{F}$.

$$W = x_1 x_2 \cdots x_k \qquad \text{where} \quad \{x_1, \ldots, x_k\} = \{a_1, \ldots, a_n\}. \tag{2.2}$$

Each W has a unique expression (2.2) since each element of $\mathscr{F}_0$ has. $\mathscr{L}(W)$ is defined by

$$\mathscr{L}(W) = x_1 x_2 \cdots x_l$$

where $l \leqslant k$ and $\{x_1, \ldots, x_l\} = \{a_1, \ldots, a_n\}$ but $\{x_1, \ldots, x_{l-1}\} \neq \{a_1, \ldots, a_n\}$. $\mathscr{L}(W)$ is called the left main of W. Likewise the right main $\mathscr{R}(W)$ of W is defined by

$$\mathscr{R}(W) = x_r x_{r+1} \cdots x_k$$

where $r \geqslant 1$ and $\{x_r, \ldots, x_k\} = \{a_1, \ldots, a_n\}$ but $\{x_{r+1}, \ldots, x_n\} \neq \{a_1, \ldots, a_n\}$. It is obvious that if $X = YZ$, $Y, Z \in \mathscr{F}$, then

$$\mathscr{L}(X) = \mathscr{L}(Y) \qquad \text{and} \qquad \mathscr{R}(X) = \mathscr{R}(Z).$$

Clearly $\mathscr{L}(W)$ and $\mathscr{R}(W)$ are primes.

W is called left minimal if $\mathscr{L}(W) = W$; W is called right minimal if $\mathscr{R}(W) = W$. W is called minimal if $\mathscr{L}(W) = \mathscr{R}(W) = W$. The positive number k of (2.2) is called the length $|W|$ of W; $|a_i|_W$ is the number of the letter a_i's which appear in W, for example, if $W = a_1{}^2a_2a_1a_3{}^2$, then $|a_1|_W = 3$. W is called a permutation if $|W| = n$, n the rank of $\mathscr{F}$; equivalently $|a_i|_W = 1$ for all i.

The length is also defined for elements of a free semigroup.

Let $W_1 = x_1x_2 \cdots x_s$ and $W_2 = y_ty_{t+1} \cdots y_m$. If

$$x_i = y_t, \quad x_{i+1} = y_{t+1}, \quad \ldots, \quad x_s = y_{t+s-i}$$

then we say W_1 intersects W_2. The intersection part $x_ix_{i+1} \cdots x_s$ is denoted by $W_1 \wedge W_2$.

(2.3) **Proposition.** *W is a prime if and only if $\mathscr{L}(W)$ intersects $\mathscr{R}(W)$.*

PROOF. Suppose $\mathscr{L}(W)$ does not intersect $\mathscr{R}(W)$. Then

$$W = \mathscr{L}(W) \cdot A \cdot \mathscr{R}(W) \qquad \text{for some} \quad A \in \mathscr{F}_0, \quad |A| \geqslant 1,$$

and $\mathscr{L}(W) \cdot A \in \mathscr{F}$, $\mathscr{R}(W) \in \mathscr{F}$. Hence W is not a prime. Suppose that W is not a prime: $W = UV$, U, $V \in \mathscr{F}$. Then $\mathscr{L}(W) = \mathscr{L}(U)$ and $\mathscr{R}(W) = \mathscr{R}(V)$; $\mathscr{L}(W)$ does not intersect $\mathscr{R}(W)$.

(2.4) **Proposition.** *Every element of $\mathscr{F}$ is factorized into the product of primes.*

PROOF. Let $W \in \mathscr{F}$. We prove this by induction on $|W| \geqslant n$. If $|W| = n$, W is a permutation, hence a prime. Assume the statement is true for W', $|W'| < |W|$. We may assume that W is not a prime.

$$\begin{aligned} W &= LUR \qquad \text{where } L = \mathscr{L}(W), \quad R = \mathscr{R}(W) \\ &= LV \qquad \text{where } V = UR. \end{aligned}$$

L is a prime and $V \in \mathscr{F}$ and $|V| < |W|$. By the assumption of induction, V can be factorized into the product of primes. This completes the proof.

The factorization of an element into the product of primes is called a prime factorization. W is called uniquely factorizable if W has a unique prime factorization, in other words, if $W = P_1 \cdots P_k = Q_1 \cdots Q_l$, $k \geqslant 1$, $l \geqslant 1$ where P_i $(i = 1, \ldots, k)$, Q_i $(i = 1, \ldots, l)$ are primes, then $k = l$ and $P_1 = Q_1, \ldots, P_k = Q_k$. W is called two-prime factorizable or we say W has a two-prime factorization if $W = P_1P_2$, where P_1 and P_2 are primes. If W has a unique two-prime factorization, W is called uniquely two-prime factorizable.

(2.5) **Proposition.** *W is uniquely factorizable if and only if W is either a prime or $W = W_1W_2$ where W_1 is left minimal and W_2 is right minimal.*

PROOF. First assume W is uniquely factorizable. By Proposition 2.3 we may assume that $\mathscr{L}(W)$ does not intersect $\mathscr{R}(W)$. Let $W = L_1W'R_1$, where $L_1 = \mathscr{L}(W)$, $R_1 = \mathscr{R}(W)$. Suppose $| W' | > 0$. W' is factorized into the product of elements V_1, V_2 of $\mathscr{F}_0$:

$$W' = V_1V_2, \qquad 0 < | V_1 | < n, \qquad | V_2 | \geqslant 0,$$

such that L_1V_1 is a prime. Also $V_2R_1 \in \mathscr{F}$ and V_2R_1 can be factorized into the product of primes, say $V_2R_1 = P_1 \cdots P_l$, where P_i $(i = 1, \ldots, l)$ are primes. Accordingly we have a prime factorization of W:

$$W = (L_1V_1)\, P_1 \cdots P_l, \qquad 1 \leqslant | V_1 | < n. \tag{2.6}$$

On the other hand, by a prime factorization of $W'R_1$ we have another prime factorization of W:

$$W = L_1P_1' \cdots P_t' \quad \text{where} \quad W'R_1 = P_1' \cdots P_t'. \tag{2.7}$$

Thus (2.6) and (2.7) are different prime factorizations of W, a contradiction to the assumption. Therefore $| W' | = 0$, that is, $W = L_1R_1$, L_1 is left minimal, R_1 is right minimal.

Next we will prove the converse. If W is a prime, it is obvious. Assume $W = W_1W_2$, $\mathscr{L}(W) = W_1$, $\mathscr{R}(W) = W_2$. Suppose W has another factorization

$$W = W_1W_2 = W_1'W_2', \qquad W_1', W_2' \in \mathscr{F}$$

in which W_1' and W_2' are not assumed to be prime.

Suppose $W_1 \neq W_1'$. Then since $W_1 = \mathscr{L}(W_1) = \mathscr{L}(W_1')$,

$$W_1' = W_1V, \qquad | V | \geqslant 1$$

and

$$W_2 = VW_2', \qquad W_2 = \mathscr{R}(W_2) = \mathscr{R}(W_2').$$

This is a contradiction to the assumption that W_2 is right minimal. Therefore $W_1 = W_1'$, hence $W_2 = W_2'$, W is uniquely factorizable.

REMARK. From the proof of Proposition 2.5, it follows that if W is uniquely factorizable, it is uniquely two-prime factorizable. However the converse is not true. For example, $W = (abcdba)(abcdba)(abcdba)$ is uniquely two-prime factorizable but not uniquely factorizable.

(2.8) **Proposition.** *W^2 is uniquely factorizable if and only if W is minimal. If W is minimal, W^3 is two-prime factorizable.*

PROOF. The former half is an immediate consequence of Proposition 2.5. We will prove the latter half. Let $W = UV$ in which $U, V \in \mathscr{F}_0$. Then WU and VW are primes since $W = \mathscr{L}(WU)$ intersects $\mathscr{R}(WU)$, and $\mathscr{L}(VW)$ intersects $W = \mathscr{R}(VW)$. Therefore W^3 is two-prime factorizable $W^3 = (WU)(VW)$.

(2.9) **Proposition.** *L is left minimal if and only if there is a nonprime, uniquely factorizable element W such that*

$$W = LV \qquad \text{for some} \quad V \in \mathscr{F}.$$

PROOF. Suppose that L is left minimal. Let R be an arbitrary right-minimal element. Let $W = LR$. Then W is nonprime uniquely factorizable by Proposition 2.5. Conversely suppose that $W = LR$ is a nonprime and uniquely factorizable. By Proposition 2.5 $W = L_1R_1$, where L_1 is left minimal, R_1 is right minimal. Since $W = LR = L_1R_1$

$$\mathscr{L}(L) = \mathscr{L}(W) = L_1, \qquad \mathscr{R}(R) = \mathscr{R}(W) = R_1;$$

hence $L = L_1X$, $R = YR_1$ for some $X, Y \in \mathscr{F}_0$. This is impossible unless $|X| = |Y| = 0$. Therefore $L = L_1$, left minimal.

(2.10) **Proposition.** *Given a left minimal element L and a right minimal element R there is at most one prime W such that $\mathscr{L}(W) = L$, $\mathscr{R}(W) = R$. Such a W exists if and only if L intersects R.*

PROOF. Assume that L intersects R:

$$L = x_1 \cdots x_{k-1} b_k b_{k+1} \cdots b_m, \qquad 1 \leqslant k, \quad k \leqslant m, \quad m \leqslant t$$

$$R = b_k b_{k+1} \cdots b_m y_{m+1} \cdots y_t, \qquad n \leqslant m, \quad n \leqslant t - k + 1.$$

We will prove that the intersection $b_k \cdots b_m$ is uniquely determined by L and R. Suppose this were not true. Without loss of generality we may assume

$$x_l = b_k, \quad x_{l+1} = b_{k+1}, \ldots$$

that is, $x_l \cdots x_{k-1} b_k \cdots b_m = b_k \cdots b_m y_{m+1} \cdots y_s$ for some l, s with $1 \leqslant l < k \leqslant m < s \leqslant t$. It follows that $x_1 \cdots x_{k-1} b_k \cdots b_{m-1} \in \mathscr{F}$.

This contradicts the assumption that L is left minimal. Thus we have proved the uniqueness of the intersection. The uniqueness of W immediately follows from this.

(2.11) **Proposition.** *W is a permutation if and only if W^2 is uniquely* *factorizable, and the number of two-prime factorizations of W^3 is the minimum of the numbers of the two-prime factorizations of all elements X^3 such that X^2 is uniquely factorizable.*

PROOF. Assume that W is a permutation, $|W| = n$, n the rank of $\mathscr{F}$. Since W is minimal, W^2 is uniquely factorizable and W^3 is two-prime factorizable by Proposition 2.8. Let $W = UV$, $|U| \geqslant 1$, $|V| \geqslant 1$, $|U| + |V| = n$, $U, V \in \mathscr{F}_0$. Then WU and VW are primes and $W^3 = (WU)(VW)$. All the two-prime factorizations of W^3 are obtained in this way. Therefore we have $n - 1$ factorizations of W^3. In general if W' is minimal, we have $|W'| - 1$ two-prime factorizations of W'^3 in the same reason. Hence $n - 1$ is the minimum. We will prove the converse. Since W^2 is uniquely factorizable, W is minimal. Then the number of two-prime factorizations of W^3 is $|W| - 1$. This number is the minimum if and only if $|W| = n$. Hence W is a permutation.

Thus we have characterized primes, (left) minimal elements, and permutations in terms of prime factorizations.

3. Isomorphisms and Homomorphisms between Free Contents

Let $\mathscr{F}_m$ and $\mathscr{F}_n$ denote the free contents of rank m and n, respectively.

(2.12) **Theorem.** *$\mathscr{F}_m$ is isomorphic onto $\mathscr{F}_n$ if and only if $m = n$.*

PROOF. Let $\mathscr{W}_m$ be the set of all minimal elements of $\mathscr{F}_m$ and $\mathscr{W}_n$ be the set of all those of $\mathscr{F}_n$. Suppose $\mathscr{F}_m$ is isomorphic onto $\mathscr{F}_n$. The primes are mapped to the primes and unique prime factorizability is invariant by the isomorphism. By Proposition 2.8, $\mathscr{W}_m$ is mapped onto $\mathscr{W}_n$. According to Proposition 2.11, the number $m - 1$ is the minimum of the numbers of two-prime factorizations of W^3, $W \in \mathscr{W}_m$. This number should be invariant under the isomorphism: $m - 1 = n - 1$. Hence we have $m = n$. The converse is clear.

(2.13) **Theorem.** *$\mathscr{F}_m$ is isomorphic into $\mathscr{F}_n$ if and only if $n > 1$.*

The statement is equivalent to (2.14) and (2.15) below:

(2.14) *$\mathscr{F}_m$ is isomorphic into $\mathscr{F}_{m+1}$ ($m = 1, 2, 3, \ldots$).*

(2.15) *If $m > 2$, $\mathscr{F}_m$ is isomorphic into $\mathscr{F}_2$.*

Let $a_1, \ldots, a_m$ be the generators of $\mathscr{F}_m$; and $a_1, \ldots, a_m, a_{m+1}$ the generators of $\mathscr{F}_{m+1}$; and a, b be the generators of $\mathscr{F}_2$.

PROOF OF (2.14). We denote each element W of $\mathscr{F}_m$ by

$$W(a_1, \ldots, a_m).$$

Consider a mapping $\varphi_{m,m+1} : \mathscr{F}_m \to \mathscr{F}_{m+1}$ defined by

$$(2.16) \qquad [W(a_1, \ldots, a_m)]\, \varphi_{m,m+1} = W(a_1, \ldots, a_{m-1}, a_m a_{m+1}).$$

Then it is easy to show that $\varphi_{m,m+1}$ is an isomorphism of $\mathscr{F}_m$ into $\mathscr{F}_{m+1}$.

PROOF OF (2.15). Define $\psi_{m,2} : \mathscr{F}_m \to \mathscr{F}_2$ by

$$(2.17) \qquad [W(a_1, a_2, \ldots, a_m)]\, \psi_{m,2} = W(aba, ab^2a, \ldots, ab^m a).$$

Then $\psi_{m,2}$ is an isomorphism of $\mathscr{F}_m$ into $\mathscr{F}_2$.

We have the isomorphisms $\varphi_{m,n}$ of $\mathscr{F}_m$ into $\mathscr{F}_n$ as follows:

$$\text{if } m < n, \quad \varphi_{m,n} = \varphi_{m,m+1}\varphi_{m+1,m+2} \cdots \varphi_{n-1,n},$$

$$\text{if } m > n \geqslant 2, \quad \varphi_{m,n} = \psi_{m,2}\varphi_{2,3} \cdots \varphi_{m-1,n}.$$

(2.18) **Proposition.** *If $m > n$, $\mathscr{F}_m$ is homomorphic onto $\mathscr{F}_n$.*

PROOF. Let $a_1, \ldots, a_n$ be the generators of $\mathscr{F}_n$ and $a_1, \ldots, a_n$, $a_{n+1}, \ldots, a_m$ be the generators of $\mathscr{F}_m$.

Let

$$W = W(a_1, \ldots, a_n, a_{n+1}, \ldots, a_m)$$

be an element of $\mathscr{F}_m$. For $W \in \mathscr{F}_m$ a new element $W' \in \mathscr{F}_n$

$$W' = W(a_1, \ldots, a_n, \hat{a}_{n+1}, \ldots, \hat{a}_m)$$

is defined by the word obtained by eliminating the letters $a_{n+1}, \ldots, a_m$ form the word $W(a_1, \ldots, a_n, a_{n+1}, \ldots, a_m)$ with the remaining unchanged. For example, if $m = 4$, $n = 2$, and $W(a, b, c, d) = a^2cbadacb^2$, then $W'(a, b, \check{c}, \check{d}) = a^2ba^2b^2$. If $\pi_{m,n}$ is defined by

$$[W(a_1, \ldots, a_n, a_{n+1}, \ldots, a_m)]\, \pi_{m,n} = W(a_1, \ldots a_n, \check{a}_{n+1}, \ldots, \check{a}_m),$$

then it can be easily shown that $\pi_{m,n}$ is a homomorphism of $\mathscr{F}_m$ onto $\mathscr{F}_n$.

The following problem is unsolved.

(2.18) **Problem.** *If $m < n$, is $\mathscr{F}_m$ homomorphic onto $\mathscr{F}_n$?*

4. Idempotent Decomposition of Free Contents

In this section $\mathscr{F}$ denotes a free content of rank n. Since $\mathscr{F}$ is $\mathscr{S}$ indecomposable, the greatest $\mathscr{I}$ decomposition of $\mathscr{F}$ coincides with the greatest rectangular band decomposition of $\mathscr{F}$. (See Section I.4.)

Let σ be the relation on $\mathscr{F}$ defined by

$$X \sigma Y \quad \text{iff} \quad \mathscr{L}(X) = \mathscr{L}(Y) \text{ and } \mathscr{R}(X) = \mathscr{R}(Y).$$

(2.19) **Theorem.** *σ is the smallest idempotent congruence on $\mathscr{F}$.*

PROOF. σ is certainly an equivalence. Let $X \sigma Y$ and $Z \in \mathscr{F}$. Then $\mathscr{L}(XZ) = \mathscr{L}(X) = \mathscr{L}(Y) = \mathscr{L}(YZ)$ and $\mathscr{R}(XZ) = \mathscr{R}(Z) = \mathscr{R}(YZ)$. Hence $XZ \sigma YZ$. Likewise $ZX \sigma ZY$. Thus σ is a congruence. Since $\mathscr{L}(XYX) = \mathscr{L}(X)$ and $\mathscr{R}(XYX) = \mathscr{R}(X)$, σ is a rectangular band congruence. Let τ be any rectangular band congruence. We will prove $\sigma \subseteq \tau$. Assume $X \sigma Y$ and let $L = \mathscr{L}(X) = \mathscr{L}(Y)$, $R = \mathscr{R}(X) = \mathscr{R}(Y)$. Then if we put $X = LX_1 = X_2R$, then

$$X \tau X^3 = XXX = LX_1XX_2R \tau LR$$

since $X_1XX_2 \in \mathscr{F}$. In the same way $Y \tau LR$. Hence $X \tau Y$. This completes the proof.

Let ξ_l be the relation on $\mathscr{F}$ defined by

$$X \xi_l Y \quad \text{iff} \quad \mathscr{L}(X) = \mathscr{L}(Y).$$

(2.20) **Theorem.** *ξ_l is the smallest left-zero congruence on $\mathscr{F}$.*

PROOF. ξ_l is clearly an equivalence. Let $Z \in \mathscr{F}$. $\mathscr{L}(X) = \mathscr{L}(Y)$ implies $\mathscr{L}(XZ) = \mathscr{L}(X) = \mathscr{L}(Y) = \mathscr{L}(YZ)$ and $\mathscr{L}(ZX) = \mathscr{L}(Z) = \mathscr{L}(ZY)$. Clearly ξ_l is a left-zero congruence. Let ξ_l' be a left-zero congruence. We will prove $\xi_l \subseteq \xi_l'$. Suppose $X \xi_l Y$ and let $L = \mathscr{L}(X) = \mathscr{L}(Y)$. Then $XY = LX'$ for some $X' \in \mathscr{F}$ and

$$X \xi_l' XY = LX' \xi_l' L.$$

Likewise $Y \xi_l' L$. Therefore $X \xi_l' Y$.

Similarly we have the smallest right-zero congruence on $\mathscr{F}$.

$$X \xi_r Y \quad \text{iff} \quad \mathscr{R}(X) = \mathscr{R}(Y).$$

The following problem is unsolved.

(2.21) **Problem.** Find the greatest $\mathscr{C}$ decomposition of $\mathscr{F}_n$. Since $\mathscr{F}_n$ is $\mathscr{S}$ indecomposable, the greatest $\mathscr{C}$-homomorphic image of $\mathscr{F}_n$ is archimedean. On the other hand, $\mathscr{F}_n$ is homomorphic onto the additive semigroup S_n of n-dimensional positive integer vectors, hence the greatest $\mathscr{C}$-homomorphic image of $\mathscr{F}_n$ is torsion free. Clearly each prime element consists of a singleton class in the greatest $\mathscr{C}$ decomposition.

5. Free Content and General Product

Let S be a set and $\mathfrak{B}_S$ be the set of all binary operations defined on S. The equality in $\mathfrak{B}_S$ is defined by $\theta, \eta \in \mathfrak{B}_S$, $\theta = \eta$ if and only if $x \theta y = x \eta y$ for all $x, y \in S$. For each $a \in S$ the two binary operations a^* and $^*a$ on $\mathfrak{B}_S$ are defined as follows:
Let $\theta, \eta \in \mathfrak{B}_S$. Then $\theta\, a^*\, \eta \in \mathfrak{B}_S$, $\theta\, {}^*a\, \eta \in \mathfrak{B}_S$ are defined by

$$\begin{aligned} x(\theta\, a^*\, \eta)\, y &= (x\, \theta\, a)\, \eta y, \\ x(\theta\, {}^*a\, \eta)\, y &= x\, \theta\, (a\, \eta\, y). \end{aligned} \qquad x, y \in S.$$

Let T be a semigroup. Consider a mapping Θ of $T \times T$ into $\mathfrak{B}_S$:

$$(\alpha, \beta)\, \Theta = \theta_{\alpha,\beta}, \qquad (\alpha, \beta) \in T \times T$$

subject to

$$\theta_{\alpha,\beta}\, a^*\, \theta_{\alpha\beta,\gamma} = \theta_{\alpha,\beta\gamma}\, {}^*a\, \theta_{\beta,\gamma} \tag{2.22}$$

for all $\alpha, \beta, \gamma \in T$, all $a \in S$.

Given S, T, Θ satisfying (2.22), a binary operation is defined on $S \times T = \{(x, \alpha): x \in S, \alpha \in T\}$ as follows:

$$(x, \alpha)(y, \beta) = (x\, \theta_{\alpha,\beta}\, y, \alpha\beta). \tag{2.23}$$

Then $X \times \Theta$ is a semigroup with respect to (2.23).

The semigroup $S \times T$ with (2.23) is called a general product of a set S by a semigroup T with respect to Θ and it is denoted by

$$S \otimes_\Theta T \qquad \text{or} \qquad S \otimes T.$$

The author will discuss general product in detail in his forthcoming paper.

Let $\mathscr{F}_0$ be the free semigroup generated by $a_1, \ldots, a_n$, and $\mathscr{F}_0{}^1$ be the free semigroup $\mathscr{F}_0$ with identity element 1 adjoined. The void word acts as the identity element.

Let $\mathscr{F} = C_{\mathscr{F}_0}(a_1, \ldots, a_n)$ be the free content of $a_1, \ldots, a_n$.

For each $\alpha \in \mathscr{F}_0{}^1$ the two transformations φ_α and ψ_α of $\mathscr{F}$ are defined:

$$\begin{aligned} X \in \mathscr{T}, \qquad X\varphi_\alpha &= X\alpha, \\ \psi_\alpha X &= \alpha X, \end{aligned}$$

where αX, α, $X\alpha$ are regarded as words.

Clearly

$$X\varphi_\alpha\varphi_\beta = X\varphi_{\alpha\beta}, \qquad \psi_\beta\psi_\alpha X = \psi_{\beta\alpha}X.$$
$$\psi_\beta(X\varphi_\alpha) = (\psi_\beta X)\,\varphi_\alpha.$$

Let $\Phi = \{\varphi_\alpha ; \alpha \in \mathscr{F}_0^{\,1}\}$, $\Psi = \{\psi_\alpha : \alpha \in \mathscr{F}_0^{\,1}\}$. Then $\mathscr{F}_0^{\,1}$ is isomorphic onto Φ and Ψ under $\alpha \to \varphi_\alpha$ and $\alpha \to \psi_\alpha$, respectively.

Let $\mathscr{L}$ be the set of all left minimal elements of $\mathscr{F}$. Each $X \in \mathscr{F}$ has a unique expression

$$X = A\varphi_\alpha \qquad \text{for some} \quad A \in \mathscr{L}, \quad \alpha \in \mathscr{F}_0^1.$$

(2.24) **Theorem.** *Suppose $\mathscr{F}$ is a free content. Let $\mathscr{L}$ be the left zero semigroup defined on the set of all left minimal elements of $\mathscr{F}$. For each $A \in \mathscr{L}$ we define a binary operation θ_A on $\mathscr{F}_0^{\,1}$ by*

$$\alpha\,\theta_A\,\beta = \alpha\,A\,\beta, \qquad \alpha, \beta \in \mathscr{F}_0^1.$$

Let $\Theta = \{\theta_A : A \in \mathscr{L}\}$. Then $\mathscr{F}$ is isomorphic onto $\mathscr{F}_0^{\,1} \otimes_\Theta \mathscr{L}$, that is,

$$\mathscr{F}_0^1 \times \mathscr{L} = \{(\alpha, A) : \alpha \in \mathscr{F}_0^1, A \in \mathscr{L}\}$$

in which the operation is defined by

$$(2.25) \qquad (\alpha, A)(\beta, B) = (\alpha\,\theta_B\,\beta, A).$$

PROOF. A mapping $A\varphi_\alpha \to (\alpha, A)$ is an isomorphism of $\mathscr{F}$ onto $\mathscr{F}_0^{\,1} \otimes \mathscr{L}$.

REMARK. We have treated free contents in this paper. However the problems on contents in a semigroup are also important and interesting.

The rank of content $C_S(a_1, \ldots, a_n)$ in S is defined to be n. According to the author's recent result (unpublished) if S satisfies an identity of the form

$$xy = y^{m_1}x^{n_1} \cdots y^{m_k}x^{n_k}$$

then every content of rank greater than 1 is a group.

Problems

1. Can we characterize free contents in terms of general products?
2. Determine all the automorphisms of the free content $\mathscr{F}_m$.

3. Study the following: k-prime factorization, unique k-prime factorization, and so on.

4. Study the relationship between the system of contents in a semigroup S and the structure of S in particular the structure of $\mathscr{S}$-indecomposable semigroup S.

III. Closets in Semigroups

1. Basic Results

Let S be a semigroup and let $a \in S$.

(3.1) **Definition.** $C_l(a) = \bigcap_{n=1}^{\infty} Sa^n$ is called the left closet of a in S.

(3.2) $C_r(a) = \bigcup_{n=1}^{\infty} a^n S$ is called the right closet of a in S.

(3.3) $C(a) = \bigcap_{n=1}^{\infty} Sa^n S$ is called the closet of a in S.

$C_l(a)$, $C_r(a)$, $C(a)$ could be empty. If not empty, $C_l(a)$ is a left ideal, $C_r(a)$ is a right ideal, $C(a)$ is an ideal of S.

If $|C_l(a)| = 1$, i.e., $C_l(a) = 0_l$, then 0_l is a right zero of S;
if $|C_r(a)| = 1$, i.e., $C_r(a) = 0_r$ then 0_r is a left zero of S;
if $|C(a)| = 1$, i.e., $C(a) = 0$, then 0 is a zero of S.

If an element a is of finite order, then $C_l(a) = Sa^n$, $C_r(a) = a^n S$, and $C(a) = Sa^n S$ for some $n > 0$.

In particular if e is an idempotent, $C_l(e) = Se$, $C_r(e) = eS$, $C(e) = SeS$. These contain e.

(3.4) *If* $a \in C_l(b)$, $C_l(a) \subseteq C_l(b)$; *if* $a \in C_r(b)$, $C_r(a) \subseteq C_r(b)$.
If $a \in C(b)$, $C(a) \subseteq C(b)$.

Let $\mathbb{C}_l = \{C_l(a): a \in S\}$, $\mathbb{C}_r = \{C_r(a): a \in S\}$, $\mathbb{C} = \{C(a): a \in S\}$. These are partially ordered sets with respect to the inclusion relation.

If $C_0 = C_l(a_0) \neq \emptyset$ and if $C_l(a) \subseteq C_0$ implies either $C_l(a) = C_0$ or $C_l(a) = \emptyset$, then C_0 is called a minimal element of $\mathbb{C}_l$. Likewise a minimal emelent of $\mathbb{C}_r$ or $\mathbb{C}$ can be defined.

(3.5) $\mathbb{C}_l$ $(\mathbb{C}_r)$ *contains a minimal element* C_0 *if and only if* C_0 *is a minimal left (right) ideal of* S, *hence* C_0 *is left (right) simple.*

Proof. Let $C_0 = C_l(a_0)$ and let I be a left ideal of S such that $I \subseteq C_l(a_0)$. For $a \in I$, $C_l(a) = \bigcap Sa^n \subseteq I \subseteq C_l(a_0)$. Since $C_l(a_0)$ is minimal in $\mathbb{C}_l$, $C_l(a) = C_l(a_0)$, hence $I = C_l(a_0)$. The last statement is proved in Clifford and Preston's book (1967).

(3.6) *$\mathbb{C}$ contains a minimal element C_0 if and only if C_0 is the kernel (i.e., the smallest ideal) of S, hence C_0 is simple.* [See Clifford and Preston (1967).]

The terminology "minimal ideal" may be used as a synonym of "smallest ideal."

(3.7) $$C_l(a) = C_l(a^n), \qquad C_r(a) = C_r(a^n), \qquad C(a) = C(a^n)$$

for all $a \in S$ and all positive integers n.

PROOF. By the definition $C_l(a) \subseteq Sa^{in}$ for all $i > 0$. Hence $C_l(a) \subseteq C_l(a^n)$. For each m there is i_m such that $m \leqslant i_m n$. Then $C_l(a^n) \subseteq Sa^{i_m n} \subseteq Sa^m$; hence $C_l(a^n) \subseteq C_l(a)$.

(3.8) $$C(ab) = C(ba) \qquad \text{for all} \quad a, b \in S.$$

PROOF. This obtained by

$$S(ab)^n S = Sa(ba)^{n-1}bS \subseteq S(ba)^{n-1}S \qquad \text{and} \qquad S(ba)^n S \subseteq S(ab)^{n-1}S.$$

(3.9) $$C_l(a) \subseteq C(a), \; C_r(a) \subseteq C(a) \qquad \text{for all} \quad a.$$

(3.10) $$C_l(a) \cdot C_r(a) \subseteq C(a), \; C_r(a) \cdot C_l(a) \subseteq C_r(a) \cap C_l(a) \quad \text{for all } a \in S.$$

PROOF OF (3.9) The first one follows from $Sa^n \subseteq Sa^{n-1}S$.

PROOF OF (3.10). $C_l(a) \cdot C_r(a) \subseteq Sa^n \cdot a^m S = Sa^{n+m}S$ for $n + m = 1, 2, \ldots$. The second one is obvious since $C_r(a)$ is a right ideal and $C_l(a)$ is a left ideal.

(3.11) *If $C_l(a) = S$ ($C_r(a) = S$), then $C(a) = S$.*
If $C(a) = \emptyset$, then $C_l(a) = \emptyset$, $C_r(a) = \emptyset$.

(3.12) **Definition.** A semigroup S is called left (right) concentric if $C_l(a)$ ($C_r(a)$) is constant, i.e., $C_l(a) = C_l(b)$ for all $a, b \in S$. ($C_r(a) = C_r(b)$ for all $a, b \in S$.) S is called concentric if $C(a)$ is constant.

If S is concentric, and if S has a nonempty closet, $C(a)$ is a minimal ideal; if S is left (right) concentric, and if S has a nonempty left (right) closet, $C_l(a)$ ($C_r(a)$) is a minimal left (right) ideal.

(3.13) *If S is a concentric semigroup and if $C = C(a) \neq \emptyset$ for all $a \in S$, then $C = C_l(a) \cdot C_r(a)$ for all $a \in S$.*

PROOF. By (3.10) $C_l(a) \cdot C_r(a) \subseteq C$. Since $C_l(a) \cdot C_r(a)$ is an ideal and C is minimal, $C = C_l(a) \cdot C_r(a)$.

(3.14) *If a semigroup S is left (right) concentric and $C_l = \{0_l\}$ ($C_r = \{0_r\}$), then 0_l (0_r) is a zero of S.*

PROOF. If $C_l(a) = 0$ for all $a \in S$, 0 is a right zero of S. The set of all right zeros is an ideal, but S has a unique right zero: If $0'$ is a right zero, $0 = C_l(0) = C_l(0') = 0'$. Consequently $\{0\}$ is an ideal, i.e., 0 is a zero of S.

(3.15) *The following are equivalent.*

(3.15.1) *A semigroup S is simple.*

(3.15.2) *A semigroup S is concentric and $C = S$.*

(3.15.3) *A semigroup S satisfies $C_l(a) \cdot C_r(a) = S$ for all $a \in S$.*

PROOF. (3.15.1) → (3.15.2) is obvious. (3.15.2) → 3.15.1): Let I be an ideal of S, and let $a \in I$. Then $S = C(a) \subseteq I \subseteq S$; hence $I = S$. (3.15.2) → (3.15.3) is by (3.13).

(3.15.3) → (3.15.2). We have $C = S$ by (3.10).

(3.16) *If $x = xy$ $(x = yx)$, then $x \in C_l(y)$ $(x \in C_r(y))$.*
If $x = zxy$, then $x \in C(y) \cap C(z)$.

PROOF. If $x = xy$, $x = xy = xy^2 = \cdots = xy^n = \cdots =$, hence $x \in C_l(y)$. If $x = zxy$, $x = zxy = z^2xyy = z^3xy^2y = \cdots = z^nxy^{n-1}y = \cdots$, hence $x \in C(y)$. Similarly we have $x \in C(z)$.

Immediately we have the following.

(3.17) *If S is left (right) concentric and if $C_l = \{0\}$ $(C_r = \{0\})$ then $x = xy$ $(x = yx)$ implies $x = 0$.*

If S is concentric and $C = \{0\}$, then $x = xy$ implies $x = 0$; $x = yx$ implies $x = 0$; $x = zxy$ implies $x = 0$.

(3.18) *If S is left (right) concentric and $C_l = \emptyset$ $(C_r = \emptyset)$, then $x \neq xy$ $(x \neq yx)$ for all $x, y \in S$.*

If S is concentric and $C = \emptyset$, then $x \neq xy$, $x \neq yx$, $x \neq zxy$ for all $x, y \in S$.

(3.19) *Let S be a (right, left) concentric semigroup with (right, left) closet C. We define a quasiorder $a \leqslant b$ by $(a = by, a = xb)$ $a = xby$ for some $x, y \in S^1$. The quasi-order $\leqslant$ is a partial ordering if and only if either $C = \{0\}$ or $C = \emptyset$.*

PROOF. Suppose $C = \{0\}$ or $\emptyset$, and suppose $a = xby$ and $b = zau$. Then we have $a = xzauy$. By (3.17) and (3.18), antisymmetry is derived. Suppose $C \neq \{0\}$ and $C \neq \emptyset$. Then C is the minimal ideal of S by (3.6); hence C is a simple semigroup: $CxC = C$ for all $x \in C$. If $a, b \in C$ $(a \neq b)$, $a = xby$ and $b = zau$, antisymmetry does not hold. In the case of right concentric semigroups, we can prove it in the same way as the above since a minimal right ideal is right simple. [See (3.5).]

2. Finite Convergence and Concentricity

In this section we introduce the concept of finite convergence and we will discuss the relationships among the three concepts: concentricity, finite convergence and $\mathfrak{p}$ simplicity.

(3.20′) **Definition.** An element a of a semigroup S is called finitely l convergent (finitely r convergent) if $C_l(a) = Sa^m$ ($C_r(a) = a^mS$) for some m and finitely convergent if $C(a) = Sa^mS$ for some m. S is called finitely convergent (finitely l convergent, finitely r convergent) if all elements of S are finitely convergent (finitely l convergent, finitely r convergent). a is called divergent (l divergent, r divergent) if $C(a) = \emptyset$ ($C_l(a) = \emptyset$, $C_r(a) = \emptyset$). S is called divergent (l divergent, r divergent) if all elements are divergent (l divergent, r divergent). S is called $*$-finitely convergent if each element of S is either divergent or finitely convergent.

(3.20) *The following are equivalent:*

(3.20.1) *An element a is finitely convergent.*

(3.20.2) *$a^n \in C(a)$ for some $n > 0$.*

(3.20.3) *There is $n > 0$ such that $a^n \in Sa^mS$ for all $m \geqslant n$.*

Proof. (3.20.1) → (3.20.2). Since $C(a) = Sa^kS$ for some k, we have $a^{k+2} \in C(a)$.

(3.20.2) → (3.20.1). Since $C(a)$ is an ideal, $a^n \in C(a)$ implies $Sa^nS \subseteq C(a)$. Immediately $C(a) = Sa^nS$.

(3.20.2) ⇄ (3.20.3). Obvious.

(3.21) *The following are equivalent:*

(3.21.1) *An element a is finitely l convergent.*

(3.21.2) *$a^n \in C_l(a)$ for some $n > 0$.*

(3.21.3) *There is $n > 0$ such that $a^n \in Sa^m$ for all $m \geqslant n$.*

The similar statements hold for r convergence.

(3.22) *If an element a is finitely l convergent and finitely r convergent, then a is finitely convergent and*

$$C(a) = C_l(a) \cdot C_r(a).$$

Proof. Let $C_l(a) = Sa^m$, $C_r(a) = a^nS$. By (3.10) $C(a) \subseteq Sa^{m+n}S = C_l(a) \cdot C_r(a) \subseteq C(a)$. Hence $C(a) = C_l(a)C_r(a) = Sa^{m+n}S$.

A $\mathfrak{p}$-simple finitely convergent semigroup need not be concentric.

(3.23) Example. Finite 0-simple semigroup S with zero divisors. If a is nilpotent, $C(a) = \{0\}$; otherwise $C(a) = S$.

A $\mathfrak{p}$-simple concentric semigroup need not be finitely convergent.

(3.24) EXAMPLE. Free content. $C(a) = \emptyset$.

(3.25) EXAMPLE. Let $\mathscr{F}$ be the free content generated by a, b. Let I be the ideal of $\mathscr{F}$ generated by a^2b^2. Let $S = \mathscr{F}/I$. Then it can be shown that $C(x) = \{0\}$ for all $x \in S$; 0 is finitely convergent but $x \neq 0$ is not finitely convergent.

A concentric semigroup need not be $\mathfrak{p}$ simple.

(3.26) EXAMPLE. Free semigroup generated by more than one generator. $C(x) = \emptyset$ for all x, but S is not $\mathfrak{p}$ simple.

(3.27) EXAMPLE. Let A be a group, $B = \{1, 2, 3, \ldots\}$ be the additive semigroup of all positive integers. Let S be the semilattice union of A and B such that

$$S = A \cup B, \qquad AB \subseteq A, \quad BA \subseteq A$$

in which AB and BA are defined as follows: Let $a_0 \in A$.

$$x \in A, \quad b \in B \qquad x \cdot b = xa_0{}^b, \quad b \cdot x = a_0{}^b x.$$

It is easy to show that S is a semigroup.

If $a \in A$, $A \supseteq Sa^nS \supseteq Aa^nA = A$ hence $C(a) = A$.

If $b \in B$, $Sb^nS = Ab^nA \cup Ab^nB \cup Bb^nA \cup Bb^nB = A \cup Bb^nB$ since $Ab^nA = A$, $Ab^nB \subseteq A$, $Bb^nA \subseteq A$.

Then $C(b) = \bigcap_n Sb^nS = \bigcap_n(A \cup Bb^nB) = A \cup \bigcap_n Bb^nB = A$ because $\bigcap_n Bb^nB = \emptyset$. Every $a \in A$ is finitely convergent but $b \in B$ is not.

(3.28) **Theorem.** *A semigroup S is concentric and finitely convergent if and only if S is an ideal extension of a simple semigroup by a nil semigroup.*

PROOF. Suppose that S is concentric and finitely convergent. Let $C(a) = I$ for all $a \in S$. Since S is finitely convergent, $I \neq \emptyset$ and I is simple. By (3.20) $a^n \in I$ for some n. Therefore S/I is a nil semigroup. Conversely suppose that S is an ideal extension of a simple semigroup I by a nil semigroup. Let $a \in S$. There is $n_0 > 0$ such that $a^{n_0} \in I$. Then if $n \geqslant n_0$, $I = Ia^nI \subseteq Sa^nS \subseteq SIS \subseteq I$, hence $Sa^nS = I$ for all $n \geqslant n_0$. Thus $C(a) = I = Sa_nS$ for all $a \in S$.

(3.29) **Corollary.** *A concentric finitely convergent semigroup S is $\mathfrak{p}$ simple.*

PROOF. By Theorem 3.28 it is an extension of a simple semigroup I by a nil semigroup. Let a_0 be a fixed element of I and x be any element of S. Let ρ be an $\mathscr{S}$ congruence on S. Recall that a simple semigroup I is $\mathfrak{p}$ simple. For some $n > 0$, $x^n \in I$ and $x \,\rho\, x^n \,\rho\, a_0$; hence $x \,\rho\, a_0$ for all $x \in S$.

The following theorem is a characterization of a class of $\mathfrak{p}$-simple semigroups.

(3.30) **Theorem.** *Let $\mathfrak{S}$ be a class of semigroups. Suppose that $\mathfrak{S}$ satisfies*

(3.30.1) *If $S \in \mathfrak{S}$, every Rees-factor semigroup of S is*† *in $\mathfrak{S}$.*

Assuming (3.30.1) *the following two conditions on $\mathfrak{S}$ are equivalent.*

(3.30.2) *Every semigroup in $\mathfrak{S}$ is concentric and $*$-finitely convergent.*

(3.30.3) *If $S \in \mathfrak{S}$ and if S has a zero, S is a nil semigroup.*

We notice that (3.20.2) is equivalent to the following.

(3.30.2′) *Every semigroup in $\mathfrak{S}$ is either divergent or concentric, finitely convergent.*

Proof. Assume (3.30.1) and (3.30,2′). Let $S \in \mathfrak{S}$ be a semigroup with zero. S is concentric, finitely convergent and the closet is $\{0\}$. By (3.20) or Theorem 3.28, for each element a there is $n > 0$ such that $a^n = 0$. We have (3.30.3).

Conversely assume (3.30.1) and (3.30.3). If $S \in \mathfrak{S}$ has a minimal ideal I, then I is simple and $S/I \in \mathfrak{S}$ by (3.30.1) and S/I has a zero, hence S/I is nil by (3.30.3). By Theorem 3.28, S is concentric, finitely convergent. In case where $S \in \mathfrak{S}$ has no minimal ideal, let $\mathfrak{J} = \{I_\alpha \colon \alpha \in \Xi\}$ be the set of all ideals of S. Then $\bigcap_{\alpha \in \Xi} I_\alpha = \emptyset$. Let $x \in S$, and let I_α be any ideal of S. By (3.30.3) S/I_α is nil, hence $x^n \in I_\alpha$ for some $n > 0$; $Sx^nS \subseteq I_\alpha$. Accordingly $C(x) \subseteq I_\alpha$ for all ideals I_α; therefore we have $C(x) = \emptyset$ for all $x \in S$.

From now on let $\mathfrak{S}$ denote a class satisfying (3.30.1) and (3.30.2), equivalently (3.30.1) and (3.30.3). The following is the generalization of Corollary 3.29.

(3.31) *Every semigroup in a class $\mathfrak{S}$ is $\mathfrak{p}$ simple.*

Proof. Suppose that $S \in \mathfrak{S}$ is not $\mathscr{S}$ indecomposable. Then we may assume there is an $\mathscr{S}$ decomposition of S such that

$$S = S_0 \cup S_1 , \qquad S_0 \neq \emptyset, \quad S_1 \neq \emptyset$$

and

$$S_0^2 \subseteq S_0 , \qquad S_1^2 \subseteq S_1 , \qquad S_0S_1 \subseteq S_0 , \qquad S_1S_0 \subseteq S_0 .$$

S_0 is an ideal of S. By (3.30.1) $S/S_0 \in \mathfrak{S}$ and S/S_0 must be nil by (3.30.3). However it is a contradiction.

(3.32) *If S is a concentric semigroup then an ideal I of S is also concentric.*

† We mean that $\mathfrak{S}$ contains a semigroup isomorphic onto a Rees-factor semigroup of S.

If S is finitely convergent, then I is also finitely convergent. If S is divergent, I is divergent.

PROOF. Let $a \in I$. The three statements are obtained from

$$Sa^{n+2}S = Saa^naS \subseteq Ia^nI \subseteq Sa^nS.$$

(3.33) *An ideal of each S in $\mathfrak{S}$ is concentric and $*$-finitely convergent.*

(3.34) *A homomorphic image of S in $\mathfrak{S}$ is concentric and $*$-finitely convergent.*

PROOF. Let S be homomorphic onto S'. We consider the two possible cases.

(i) In the case where S' has a minimal ideal M'. Let M be the preimage of M' under the homomorphism $S \to S'$. It is easy to see that S/M is homomorphic onto S'/M'. By (3.30.1) and (3.30.3), S/M is nil, and hence S'/M' is nil. In other words, S' is an ideal extension of a simple semigroup M' by a nil semigroup. Therefore by Theorem 3.28, S' is concentric and finitely convergent.

(ii) In the case where S' has no minimal ideal. The intersection of all ideals of S' is empty. Let I' be an ideal of S' and I be the preimage of I'. I is an ideal of S. Since S/I is nil, S'/I' is nil. For any $x' \in S'$ there is $n > 0$ that $x'^n \in I'$ which implies

$$C'(x') \subseteq S'x'^nS' \subseteq I' \qquad \text{for all ideals } I' \text{ of } S'.$$

Therefore $C'(x') = \emptyset$ for all $x' \in S'$; that is, S' is divergent. Together (i) and (ii) (3.34) has been proved.

(3.34′) *A homomorphic image of a concentric, finitely convergent semigroup is concentric finitely convergent.*

PROOF. This is an immediate consequence of (3.34): Since S is concentric, S has a minimal ideal; therefore a homomorphic image S' of S has a minimal ideal. (3.34′) is contained in the case (i) of the proof of (3.34). However we show the direct proof of (3.34′).

We notice that S is concentric and finitely convergent if and only if for every $a, b \in S$ there are positive integers m and n (depending on a and b)

$$Sa^mS = Sa^{m+1}S = Sb^nS = Sb^{n+1}S.$$

This is certainly preserved by homomorphisms.

(3.35) *A homomorphic image of a finitely convergent semigroup is finitely convergent.*

PROOF. S is finitely convergent if and only if for every $a \in S$

$$Sa^mS = Sa^{m+1}S \qquad \text{for some} \quad m > 0.$$

This is preserved by homomorphisms.

REMARK. A homomorphic image of a divergent semigroup need not be divergent, nor convergent.

EXAMPLE. Free semigroup.

Consider a class $\mathfrak{T}$ of semigroups which satisfies the following conditions:

(3.36.1) If $S \in \mathfrak{T}$, every homomorphic image of S is in $\mathfrak{T}$.

(3.36.2) If $S \in \mathfrak{T}$, every ideal of S is in $\mathfrak{T}$.

(3.36.3) The same as (3.30.2).

Clearly $\mathfrak{T}$ satisfies (3.30.1).

By (3.33) and (3.34) the following is obtained.

(3.37) **Theorem.** *Given $\mathfrak{S}$ there is a smallest $\mathfrak{T}$ which contains $\mathfrak{S}$ as a subclass.*

3. Closets and Decompositions

In this section we will discuss the relationship between the closets of a semigroup and the band decompositions of a semigroup. Let S be a semigroup.

(3.38) **Definition.** Let $a, b \in S$. Two sequences $\{Sa^mS\}_{m=1,2,\ldots}$ and $\{Sb^nS\}_{n=1,2,\ldots}$ are called equivalent if for any m there is n such that $Sb^nS \subseteq Sa^mS$ and for any n there is m such that $Sa^mS \subseteq Sb^nS$.

The condition in Definition 3.38 is equivalent to the following.

(3.39) For any $m > 0$ there are $x, y \in S$ and $n > 0$ such that

$$b^n = xa^my$$

and for any $k > 0$ there are $z, u \in S$ and $l > 0$ such that

$$a^l = zb^ku.$$

The equivalence of $\{Sa^m\}$ and $\{Sb^n\}$, the equivalence of $\{a^mS\}$ and $\{b^nS\}$ are defined in the similar way, and we have similar restatements to (3.39).

(3.40) **Definition.**

$$a \ \rho \ b \quad \text{iff} \quad \{Sa^m S\} \quad \text{and} \quad \{Sb^n S\} \text{ are equivalent.}$$
$$a \ \rho_l \ b \quad \text{iff} \quad \{Sa^m\} \quad \text{and} \quad \{Sb^n\} \text{ are equivalent.}$$
$$a \ \rho_r \ b \quad \text{iff} \quad \{a^m S\} \quad \text{and} \quad \{b^n S\} \text{ are equivalent.}$$

These are equivalence relations.

(3.41) If $a \rho b$, then the following are true.

(3.41.1) $C(a) = C(b)$

(3.41.2) a is finitely convergent if and only if b is finitely convergent; a is divergent if and only if b is divergent.

The similar statements are true for ρ_l and ρ_r.

(3.42) **Theorem.** *The congruence $\bar{\rho}$ generated by ρ is the smallest $\mathscr{S}$ congruence on S.*

Proof. Since $a^2 \rho a$ and $ab \rho ba$, $a^2 \bar{\rho} a$ and $ab \bar{\rho} ba$ for all $a, b \in S$. Certainly $\bar{\rho}$ is an $\mathscr{S}$ congruence on S. Let σ be an $\mathscr{S}$ congruence on S. We will prove $\rho \subseteq \sigma$. Then $\bar{\rho} \subseteq \sigma$ and this will complete the proof. Suppose $a \rho b$. By (3.39)

$$b^l = ya^n z, \qquad a^k = ub^m v.$$

Then

$$a \ \sigma \ a^k = ub^m v \ \sigma \ b^m uv \ \sigma \ bs \ \sigma \ b^2 s \ \sigma \ ba, \qquad s = uv$$
$$b \ \sigma \ b^l = ya^n z \ \sigma \ a^n yz \ \sigma \ at \ \sigma \ a^2 t \ \sigma \ ab \ \sigma \ ba, \qquad t = yz.$$

Therefore $a \sigma b$.

(3.43) **Definition.**

$$a \ \eta \ b \quad \text{iff} \quad a^k = ubv \quad \text{and} \quad b^l = yaz \qquad \text{for some } k > 0, l > 0$$
$$\text{some } u, v, y, z \in S.$$
$$a \ \tau \ b \quad \text{iff} \quad C(a) = C(b)$$
$$a \ \beta \ b \quad \text{iff} \quad a = aba \quad \text{and} \quad bab = b.$$

(3.44) *If S is medial then $\bar{\rho} = \rho = \eta$.*

Proof. Suppose $a \rho b$. $b^l = ya^n z$ where we may assume $l > n + 1$. By using mediality

$$(bc)^l = b^l c^l = ya^n zc^l = ya^n c^n c^{l-n-1} zc = y(ac)^n z'$$

where $z' = c^{l-n-1} zc$. Also we have $(cb)^l = y'(ca)^n z$. Similarly $a^k = ab^m v$

implies $(ac)^k = u(bc)^m v'$ and $(ca)^k = u'(cb)^m v$. Consequently ρ is a congruence, hence $\bar{\rho} = \rho$.

According to Chrislock (1966), η is the smallest $\mathscr{S}$ congruence on S, and $\rho \subseteq \eta$ is obvious from the definition. Only we need is to prove $\eta \subseteq \rho$. Assume $a \, \eta \, b$: $b^l = yaz$, $a^k = ubv$. For any $n > 0$, $a^{kn} = u^n b^n v^n$, $b^{ln} = y^n a^n z^n$. Hence $a \, \rho \, b$. Thus we have proved $\eta = \rho$. Since ρ is a congruence, $\bar{\rho} = \rho = \eta$.

(3.45) *If S is a band, then $\bar{\rho} = \rho = \tau = \beta$.*

PROOF. By McLean's theorem (1954) each congruence class of S modulo $\bar{\rho}$ is a rectangular band: if $a \, \bar{\rho} \, b$, then $aba = a$ and $bab = b$, so $SaS = SabaS \subseteq SbS$ and similarly $SbS \subseteq SaS$. Therefore $C(a) = C(b)$. We have $\bar{\rho} \subseteq \tau$. On the other hand, assume $a \, \tau \, b$. $SaS = SbS$ implies $b = yaz$, $a = ubv$, hence $a \, \rho \, b$. Thus $\tau \subseteq \rho$, $\bar{\rho} \subseteq \tau \subseteq \rho$; finally $\bar{\rho} = \rho = \tau$. We know that β is the smallest $\mathscr{S}$ congruence on S (McLean, 1954), i.e., $\beta = \bar{\rho}$. On the other hand, ρ is given by $a \, \rho \, b$ iff $a = ubv$, $b = xay$ for some x, y, u, v. Accordingly $\bar{\rho} = \beta \subseteq \rho$, hence $\bar{\rho} = \rho = \beta$.

REMARK. $\rho = \bar{\rho} = \tau$ in bands but $\rho = \bar{\rho} \subseteq \tau$ in commutative semigroups. For example, $\rho = \bar{\rho} \subset \tau$ if S is a semilattice union of two finite Abelian groups.

For any relation ξ, $\bar{\xi}$ denotes the congruence generated by ξ.

(3.46) **Theorem.** *$\overline{\rho_l \cap \rho_r}$ is the smallest $\mathscr{I}$ congruence.*

PROOF. Since $a \, \rho_l \, a^2$ and $a \, \rho_r \, a^2$ for all a,

$$a(\rho_l \cap \rho_r) \, a^2 \qquad \text{for all } a.$$

Hence $\overline{\rho_l \cap \rho_r}$ is an $\mathscr{I}$ congruence. Let ζ be any $\mathscr{I}$ congruence. We will prove $\rho_l \cap \rho_r \subseteq \zeta$. Let $x(\rho_l \cap \rho_r) y$. By the definition

$$x^l = zy^n, \quad y^k = ux^m; \qquad x^{l'} = y^{n'}z', \quad y^{k'} = x^{m'}u'.$$

From these

$$y \, \zeta \, y^k = ux^m \, \zeta \, ux, \qquad x \, \zeta \, x^{l'} = y^{n'}z' \, \zeta \, yz';$$

we have $y \, \zeta \, ux$ and $x \, \zeta \, yz'$, and then $yx \, \zeta \, ux^2 \, \zeta \, ux \, \zeta \, y$, $yx \, \zeta \, y^2z' \, \zeta \, yz' \, \zeta \, x$; therefore $x \, \zeta \, y$. Accordingly $\rho_l \cap \rho_r \subseteq \zeta$, hence $\overline{\rho_l \cap \rho_r} \subseteq \zeta$.

(3.47) **Definition.** A semigroup is called a left-regular band if it satisfies the identities $x = x^2$, $xyx = xy$, and a right-regular band if $x = x^2$ and $xyx = yx$. [This definition is due to Kimura (1958b).]

Let $\gamma = \rho_l \cap \rho_r$. We define δ_r by

$$a \, \delta_r \, b \qquad \text{iff} \quad ab \, \bar{\gamma} \, b \quad \text{and} \quad ba \, \bar{\gamma} \, a.$$

Since $x^2 \bar{\delta}_r x$ for all x and $\bar{\gamma}$ is smallest of such, $\bar{\gamma} \subseteq \bar{\delta}_r$.

Now

$$(aba)(ab) = aba^2b \,\bar{\gamma}\, abab \,\bar{\gamma}\, ab,$$
$$(ab)(aba) = (ab)^2a \,\bar{\gamma}\, aba,$$

hence $aba \,\bar{\delta}_r\, ab$. Thus $\bar{\delta}_r$ is a left-regular band congruence. Let ξ be any left-regular band congruence. Let $a \,\delta_r\, b$. Since $a \,\bar{\gamma}\, ba$, $ab \,\bar{\gamma}\, b$, and $\bar{\gamma} \subseteq \xi$,

$$a \,\xi\, ba \,\xi\, bab \,\xi\, b^2 \,\xi\, b$$

and so $a \,\xi\, b$, $\delta_r \subseteq \xi$ and hence $\bar{\delta}_r \subseteq \xi$. Thus we have proved the following.

(3.48) $\bar{\delta}_r$ *is the smallest left-regular band congruence.*

(3.49) **Theorem.** $\bar{\rho}_r$ *is the smallest left-regular band congruence, i.e.,* $\bar{\rho}_r = \bar{\delta}_r$.

PROOF. First we will prove $\bar{\gamma} \subseteq \bar{\rho}_r \subseteq \bar{\delta}_r$. $\bar{\gamma} \subseteq \bar{\rho}_r$ is obvious by the definition of γ. To show $\bar{\rho}_r \subseteq \bar{\delta}_r$, suppose $a \,\rho_r\, b$. Then we have the following implications:

$$\left.\begin{array}{l} a^k = b^m v \rightarrow a \,\bar{\gamma}\, a^k = b^m v \,\bar{\gamma}\, bv \rightarrow ba \,\bar{\gamma}\, a \\ b^l = a^n z \rightarrow b \,\bar{\gamma}\, b^l = a^n z \,\bar{\gamma}\, az \rightarrow ab \,\bar{\gamma}\, b \end{array}\right\} \rightarrow a \,\delta_r\, b.$$

Hence $\bar{\rho}_r \subseteq \bar{\delta}_r$. To prove $\bar{\rho}_r = \bar{\delta}_r$ we may prove that $S/\bar{\rho}_r$ is a left-regular band. For this, since $\bar{\gamma} \subseteq \bar{\rho}_r$, we may prove that if S' is a band, $S'/\bar{\rho}_r$ satisfies the identity $xyx = xy$. Assume S' is a band, $x, y \in S'$.

$$xyxS' \subseteq xyS' \qquad \text{and} \qquad xyS' = xyxyS' \subseteq xyxS'$$

hence $xyxS' = xyS'$. We have $xyx \,\bar{\rho}_r\, xy$ for all $x, y \in S'$. This completes the proof.

(3.48′) $\bar{\rho}_l$ *is the smallest right-regular band congruence, i.e.,* $\bar{\rho}_l = \bar{\delta}_l$.

We define various relations

$b \underset{\rho_r}{<} a$ iff $\forall n \, \exists k \, \exists y : b^k = a^n y$.

$b \underset{\rho_l}{<} a$ iff $\forall n \, \exists k \, \exists y' : b^k = y' a^n$.

$b \,\rho_r\, a$ iff $b \underset{\rho_r}{<} a$ and $a \underset{\rho_r}{<} b$.

$b \,\rho_l\, a$ iff $b \underset{\rho_l}{<} a$ and $a \underset{\rho_l}{<} b$.

$b \underset{\rho}{<} a$ iff $\forall n \, \exists k \, \exists y,\ z\!: b^k = y a^n z$.

$b \,\rho\, a$ iff $b \underset{\rho}{<} a$ and $a \underset{\rho}{<} b$.

$b \,\eta_l\, a$ iff $b \underset{\eta_l}{<} a$ and $a \underset{\eta_l}{<} b$.

$b \underset{\eta}{<} a$ iff $\exists k \, \exists y,\ z\!: b^k = yaz$.

$b \,\eta\, a$ iff $b \underset{\eta}{<} a$ and $a \underset{\eta}{<} b$.

$b \underset{\tau_r}{<} a$ iff $C_r(b) \subseteq C_r(a)$.

$b \underset{\tau_l}{<} a$ iff $C_l(b) \subseteq C_l(a)$.

$b \,\tau_r\, a$ iff $C_r(b) = C_r(a)$.

$b \underset{\eta_r}{\prec} a$ iff $\exists k \exists y\colon b^k = ay$. $\qquad b\,\tau_l\,a$ iff $C_l(b) = C_l(a)$.

$b \underset{\eta_l}{\prec} a$ iff $\exists k \exists z\colon b^k = za$. $\qquad b \underset{\tau}{\prec} a$ iff $C(b) \subseteq C(a)$.

$b\,\eta_r\,a$ iff $b \underset{\eta_r}{\prec} a$ and $a \underset{\eta_r}{\prec} b$. $\qquad b\,\tau\,a$ iff $C(b) = C(a)$.

(3.50) $\eta_r = \underset{\eta_r}{\prec} \cap \underset{\eta_r}{\prec}^{-1}$, $\eta_l = \underset{\eta_l}{\prec} \cap \underset{\eta_l}{\prec}^{-1}$, $\eta = \underset{\eta}{\prec} \cap \underset{\eta}{\prec}^{-1}$,

$\rho_r = \underset{\rho_r}{\prec} \cap \underset{\rho_r}{\prec}^{-1}$, $\rho_l = \underset{\rho_l}{\prec} \cap \underset{\rho_l}{\prec}^{-1}$, $\rho = \underset{\rho}{\prec} \cap \underset{\rho}{\prec}^{-1}$,

$\tau_r = \underset{\tau_r}{\prec} \cap \underset{\tau_r}{\prec}^{-1}$, $\tau_l = \underset{\tau_l}{\prec} \cap \underset{\tau_l}{\prec}^{-1}$, $\tau = \underset{\tau}{\prec} \cap \underset{\tau}{\prec}^{-1}$,

$\underset{\rho_r}{\prec} \subseteq \underset{\eta_r}{\prec}$, $\underset{\rho_r}{\prec} \subseteq \underset{\tau_r}{\prec}$, $\underset{\rho_l}{\prec} \subseteq \underset{\eta_l}{\prec}$, $\underset{\rho_l}{\prec} \subseteq \underset{\tau_l}{\prec}$, $\underset{\rho}{\prec} \subseteq \underset{\eta}{\prec}$, $\underset{\rho}{\prec} \subseteq \underset{\tau}{\prec}$,

$\rho_r \subseteq \eta_r$, $\rho_r \subseteq \tau_r$, $\rho_l \subseteq \eta_l$, $\rho_l \subseteq \tau_l$, $\rho \subseteq \eta$, $\rho \subseteq \tau$,

$\underset{\rho_r}{\prec} \subseteq \underset{\rho}{\prec}$, $\underset{\rho_l}{\prec} \subseteq \underset{\rho}{\prec}$, $\rho_r \subseteq \rho$, $\rho_l \subseteq \rho$,

$\underset{\rho}{\prec} \subseteq \underset{\eta_r}{\prec} \cdot \underset{\eta_l}{\prec}$, $\underset{\rho}{\prec} \subseteq \underset{\eta_l}{\prec} \cdot \underset{\eta_r}{\prec}$, $\underset{\eta}{\prec} \subseteq \underset{\eta_r}{\prec} \cdot \underset{\eta_l}{\prec}$, $\underset{\eta}{\prec} \subseteq \underset{\eta_l}{\prec} \cdot \underset{\eta_r}{\prec}$.

(3.51) $\overline{\rho_l \cap \rho_r} = \overline{\underset{\rho_l}{\prec} \cap \underset{\rho_r}{\prec}^{-1}} = \overline{\underset{\rho_r}{\prec} \cap \underset{\rho_l}{\prec}^{-1}}$.

Proof. $\rho_r \subseteq \underset{\rho_r}{\prec}$, $\rho_l \subseteq \underset{\rho_l}{\prec}$ and $\rho_l = \rho_l^{-1} \subseteq \underset{\rho_l}{\prec}^{-1}$, $\rho_r = \rho_r^{-1} \subseteq \underset{\rho_r}{\prec}^{-1}$. Let ζ be any $\mathscr{I}$ congruence. In Theorem 3.46 we used only $x \underset{\rho_r}{\prec} y$ and $y \underset{\rho_l}{\prec} x$ to prove $x\,\zeta\,y$, i.e., $\underset{\rho_l}{\prec} \cap \underset{\rho_r}{\prec}^{-1} \subseteq \zeta$.

Here $\rho_l \cap \rho_r \subseteq \underset{\rho_l}{\prec} \cap \underset{\rho_r}{\prec}^{-1} \subseteq \zeta$ and $\overline{\rho_l \cap \rho_r} \subseteq \overline{\underset{\rho_l}{\prec} \cap \underset{\rho_r}{\prec}^{-1}} \subseteq \bar{\zeta} = \zeta$ for all $\mathscr{I}$ congruences ζ. If we put $\zeta = \overline{\rho_l \cap \rho_r}$, we have

$$\overline{\rho_l \cap \rho_r} = \overline{\underset{\rho_l}{\prec} \cap \underset{\rho_r}{\prec}^{-1}}.$$

By symmetry of r and l we have the remaining part.

(3.52) *Let S be a semigroup satisfying $(xy)^n = x^n y^n$ for all $x, y \in S$ and all $n > 0$.*

(3.52.1) $\underset{\rho_r}{\prec} = \underset{\eta_r}{\prec}$, $\underset{\rho_l}{\prec} = \underset{\eta_l}{\prec}$, $\underset{\eta_l}{\prec} \cdot \underset{\eta_r}{\prec} \subseteq \underset{\eta}{\prec}$, $\underset{\eta_r}{\prec} \cdot \underset{\eta_l}{\prec} \subseteq \underset{\eta}{\prec}$,

$\rho_l = \eta_l$, $\rho_r = \eta_r$.

(3.52.2) $\underset{\rho}{\prec} = \underset{\eta_l}{\prec} \cdot \underset{\eta_r}{\prec} = \underset{\eta_r}{\prec} \cdot \underset{\eta_l}{\prec} = \underset{\rho_l}{\prec} \cdot \underset{\rho_r}{\prec} = \underset{\rho_r}{\prec} \cdot \underset{\rho_l}{\prec} = \underset{\eta}{\prec}$, $\rho = \eta$, $\bar{\rho} = \bar{\eta}$.

Proof. To show $\underset{\eta_r}{\prec} \subseteq \underset{\rho_r}{\prec}$, $b^l = ay \to \forall n \quad b^{ln} = (ay)^n = a^n y^n$. To show $\underset{\eta_r}{<} \cdot \underset{\eta_l}{<} \subseteq \underset{\eta}{<}$, $b \underset{\eta_r}{<} c$, $c \underset{\eta_l}{<} a \to b^l = cz$, $c^s = ua \to b^{ls} = c^s z^s = uaz^s$. The other equalities are easily obtained.

(3.53) *If S is medial, $\underset{\eta}{<}$ is compatible, hence $\bar{\rho} = \eta$.*

4. Closets and Structure

In this section we will characterize some semigroups in terms of (right, left) closets. In particular we will find the structure of concentric semigroups.

Let S be a semigroup.

(3.54) *S is a group if and only if $C_l(x) = C_r(x) = S$ for all $x \in S$.*

(3.55) *S is left (right) simple if and only if $C_l(a) = S$ ($C_r(a) = S$) for all $a \in S$.*

We have already characterized simple semigroups by (3.15).

(3.56) *S is completely simple if and only if $C(x) = S$ for all $x \in S$ and* $\mathbb{C}_l$ and $\mathbb{C}_r$ contain minimal elements.

(3.57) *A semigroup S is a semilattice if and only if $\tau = \iota$, that is, $C(a) = C(b)$ implies $a = b$.*

PROOF. Since $\rho \subseteq \tau$, $\rho = \iota = \bar{\rho}$. Therefore S is a semilattice by Theorem 3.42. Conversely if S is a semilattice, $\tau = \bar{\rho} = \iota$ by (3.45.)

ANOTHER PROOF. Use (3.7) and (3.8). Then $a^2 = a$ and $ab = ba$ for all $a, b \in S$. Conversely prove if S is a semilattice, $Sa = Sb$ implies $a = b$.

(3.58) *A semigroup is a band if and only if $\tau_l \cap \tau_r = \iota$, that is, $C_l(a) = C_l(b)$ and $C_r(a) = C_r(b)$ imply $a = b$.*

PROOF. If $\tau_l \cap \tau_r = \iota$, then $\rho_l \cap \rho_r = \iota$; hence $\overline{\rho_l \cap \rho_r} = \iota$ [see (3.50)]. S is a band by Theorem 3.46. Conversely suppose S is a band and suppose

$$C_r(a) = C_r(b), \qquad C_l(a) = C_l(b), \qquad \text{namely} \quad aS = bS, \qquad Sa = Sb.$$

It follows that $a = bx$, $b = ua$ for some x, u. Then

$$a = bx = ba = ua = b.$$

(3.59) **Theorem.** *The following are equivalent.*

(3.59.1) *A semigroup S is a semilattice union of left-zero semigroups.*

(3.59.2) *S is a band and satisfies the identity $xyx = xy$.*

(3.59.3) *$\tau_r = \iota$, that is, $C_r(a) = C_r(b)$ implies $a = b$.*

PROOF. (3.59.1) → (3.59.2) (Kimura, 1958b). Let $S = \bigcup_{\alpha\in\Gamma} S_\alpha$, where Γ is a semilattice and each S_α is a left-zero semigroup. Let $x_\alpha \in S_\alpha$, $y_\beta \in S_\beta$. Since S is a band and $x_\alpha y_\beta$, $y_\beta x_\alpha \in S_{\alpha\beta}$, we have

$$x_\alpha y_\beta x_\alpha = (x_\alpha y_\beta)(y_\beta x_\alpha) = x_\alpha y_\beta .$$

(3.59.2) → (3.59.1). S is a semilattice union of rectangular bands (McLean's theorem): $S = \bigcup_{\alpha\in\Gamma} S_\alpha$. Suppose some S_α is

$$S_\alpha = L \times R, \quad L \text{ a left-zero semigroup}$$
$$R \text{ a right-zero semigroup and } |R| > 1.$$

Let (a, b), $(a, c) \in S_\alpha$ where $a \in L$, $b, c \in R$ but $b \neq c$. Then

$$(a, c)(a, b)(a, c) = (a, c) \neq (a, b) = (a, c)(a, b),$$

a contradiction to the identity $xyx = xy$. Therefore $|R| = 1$ for all S_α. S is a semilattice union of left-zero semigroups.

(3.59.2) → (3.59.3). Recall that $\bar{\rho}_r$ is the smallest left-regular band congruence. Since S is a left-regular band, $\bar{\rho}_r = \iota$. From $\iota \subseteq \rho_r \subseteq \bar{\rho}_r$ it follows that $\rho_r = \iota$. Immediately

$$C_r(a) = aS = bS = C_r(b) \quad \text{implies} \quad a = b.$$

(3.59.3) → (3.59.2). The assumption says $\tau_r = \iota$. Since $\rho_r \subseteq \tau_r$, $\rho_r = \iota$, hence $\bar{\rho}_r = \iota$. S is a left-regular band by Theorem 3.49.

(3.60) **Corollary.** *S is a semilattice if and only if $\tau_l = \tau_r = \iota$, that is, $C_l(a) = C_l(b)$ implies $a = b$ and $C_r(a) = C_l(b)$ implies $a = b$.*

PROOF. Suppose $\tau_l = \tau_r = \iota$. By Theorem 3.59 and its dual statements, each congruence class of S in the greatest $\mathscr{S}$ decomposition must be singleton. Hence S is a semilattice. The converse is clear.

(3.61) *S is a rectangular band if and only if S is a concentric band.*

PROOF. By (3.45).

(3.62) *The following are equivalent.*

(3.62.1) *S is a left-zero semigroup.*

(3.62.2) *S is concentric and $\tau_r = \iota$.*

(3.62.3) *$C_l(a) = S$ for all a and $\tau_r = \iota$.*

(3.62.4) *S is a band and $|C_r(a)| = 1$ for all a.*

PROOF. (3.62.2) → (3.62.1). Use Theorem 3.59 and (3.45) $\bar{\rho} = \rho = \tau$.

(3.62.3) → (3.62.1). Use (3.55) and Theorem 3.59.

(3.62.4) $\to$ (3.62.1) Since S is a band, $|C_r(a)| = |aS| = 1$. This implies $aS = a$ for all $a \in S$.

The converses are obvious.

The remaining part will be devoted to the discussion on concentric, right-concentric semigroups.

(3.62′) **Theorem.** *S is a concentric semigroup with closet C $(\neq \emptyset)$ if and only if S is an ideal extension of a simple semigroup C by a concentric semigroup Z with zero.*

PROOF. Suppose S is a concentric semigroup with closet C. C is the minimal ideal, hence a simple semigroup. Let $S' = S/C$, and let $a \in S$ and a' be the homomorphic image of a under f: $S \to S'$. f is ono-to-one, $x \to x'$, for $x \notin C$ and $x' \neq 0$. Suppose

$$0 \neq C'(a') = \bigcap_{n=1}^{\infty} S'a'^n S' \qquad \text{for some} \quad a' \in S', \quad a' \neq 0.$$

Let $x' \in C'(a')$, $x' \neq 0$. For each positive integer n there are z_n', $u_n' \in S'$ such that

$$x' = z_n' a'^n u_n' \qquad (n = 1, 2, \ldots)$$

where $z_n' \neq 0$, $u_n' \neq 0$, $a' \neq 0$ since $x' \neq 0$. Since f is a homomorphism and f is one-to-one outside C, we have

$$x = z_n a^n u_n \qquad (n = 1, 2, \ldots),$$

that is, $x \in C(a) = C$. This is, however, a contradiction to $x' \neq 0$, $x \notin C$. Therefore $C'(a') = \{0\}$ for all $a' \in S'$.

Conversely suppose S is an ideal extension of a simple semigroup C by a concentric semigroup Z with closet $\{0\}$. Let $a \in S$. Ca^nC is an ideal of S and $Ca^nC \subseteq C$. Since C is simple, $C = Ca^nC$ for all $a \in S$. Then

$$C = \bigcap_{n=1}^{\infty} Ca^nC \subseteq \bigcap_{n=1}^{\infty} Sa^nS \subseteq C$$

where the last inequality is obtained by the assumption on Z. Therefore $C(a) = \bigcap Sa^nS = C$ for all $a \in S$.

(3.63) **Theorem.** *A semigroup S is right concentric, $C_r(a) = T \neq \emptyset$ for all $a \in S$ if and only if the following conditions are met.*

(3.63.1) *T is an ideal of S and right simple, and*

(3.63.2) *S/T is a right-concentric semigroup with zero.*

PROOF. Assume that S is right concentric.

(i) *T is the smallest right ideal of S.* Needless to say, T is a right ideal of S. Let R be a right ideal of S and let $x \in R$. Then $T = C_r(x) \subseteq xS \subseteq R$.

(ii) *$T = T^2 = tS = TS$ for all $t \in T$.* T^2, tS, and TS are right ideals of S and these are contained in T. By (i) we have (ii).

(iii) *T is right simple, $tT = T$ for all $t \in T$.* T is a minimal right ideal by (i), and hence right simple [see Lemma 8.13, p. 89, of Clifford and Preston (1967)].

(iv) *ST is the smallest ideal of S. ST is simple.* For all $t \in T$, $C(t) = \bigcap St^nS = \bigcap ST = ST$ because $t^nS = T$ by (ii); for all $x \in S$, $C(x) = \bigcap Sx^nS \supseteq \bigcap ST = ST$ because $T \subseteq x^nS$ by (i). Hence $C(t) = ST$ is the smallest ideal of S [see (3.6)].

(v) *T is the smallest right ideal of ST, hence a unique minimal right ideal of ST.* By (ii) and (i),

$$TST = T^2 = T \subseteq ST.$$

This shows that T is a right ideal of ST. Let J be a right ideal of ST. Let $t' \in J$. By (i) $T \subseteq t'S$ and

$$T = T^2 \subseteq t'ST \subseteq J.$$

We need now the following lemma which is given by Clifford and Preston (1967, p. 89).

Lemma. *Let D be a simple semigroup containing a minimal right ideal. Then D is the disjoint union of its minimal right ideals.*

Applying this lemma to ST, by (iv) and (v) we have $ST = T$. T is an ideal by (iv), and right simple by (iii). This proves (3.63.1).

We will prove (3.63.2). Let $S' = S/T$ and $C_r'(a') = \bigcap_{n=1}^{\infty} a'^n S'$, $a' \in S'$. Certainly $0 \in C_r'(a')$, but suppose that $C_r'(a')$ contains a nonzero element b' of S'.

$$b' = a'x_1' = a'^2x_2' = \cdots = a'^n x_n' = \cdots \tag{3.64}$$

where b', a', x_i' $(i = 1, 2, \ldots) \neq 0$. Let b, a, x_i be the preimage of b', a', x_i', respectively. Then $b \in S$ but $b \notin T$ and

$$b = ax_1 = a^2x_2 = \cdots = a^n x_n = \cdots \tag{3.65}$$

holds in S, that is, $C_r(a) \neq T$, which is a contradiction. Therefore $C_r'(a') = \{0\}$ for all $a' \in S'$.

Conversely assume (3.63.1) and (3.63.2). Let $V = S \backslash T$, and $a \in S$.

To prove $\bigcap a^n V \subseteq T$, suppose $b \in \bigcap a^n V$ and $b \notin T$. Then we get (3.65) which implies (3.64): $C_r'(a') \neq \{0\}$ contradiction. Hence we have proved $\bigcap a^n V \subseteq T$. Since T is right simple, $yT = T$ for $y \in S$.

$$C_r(x) = \bigcap x^n S = \bigcap (x^n T \cup x^n V) = \bigcap (T \cup x^n V) = T \cup \bigcap_{n=1}^{\infty} x^n V = T.$$

The proof of the theorem is completed.

(3.66) **Corollary.** *A semigroup S is right concentric and left concentric if and only if S is an ideal extension of a group T by a right- and left-concentric semigroup with zero.*

(3.67) *If S is a (right-, left-) concentric semigroup with nonempty closet, then every Rees-factor semigroup of S is a (right-, left-) concentric semigroup with zero.*

PROOF. Let C be a (right) closet $\neq \emptyset$, and let I be an ideal of S. By (Theorem 3.63) Theorem 3.62, C is the kernel, and $C \subseteq I$. Let $S' = S/I$. With a slight modification of the proof of the theorem we can prove that $(C_r'(a') = \{0\})$ $C'(a') = \{0\}$ for all $a' \in S'$.

Let S be a (right-) concentric semigroup with (right) closet C.

(3.68.1) If $|C| = 1$, i.e., $C = \{0\}$, then 0 is the zero which is a unique idempotent.

(3.68.2) If $C \neq \{0\}$, S contains C as the kernel, C is (right) simple and S/C is of type (3.68.1).

(3.68.3) If $C = \emptyset$, S has neither idempotent element nor minimal (right) ideal.

In particular if S is (right) concentric finitely (r) convergent, the semigroups of type (3.68.1) are nil.

We give an example of concentric $\mathfrak{p}$-simple semigroup with zero which is not a nil semigroup.

(3.69) **Example.** Let $A = C_{\mathscr{F}_0}(a_1, \ldots, a_m, b_1, \ldots, b_k)$ be the free content (of rank $m + k$), and $B = \mathscr{F}_0(b_1, \ldots, b_k)$ be the free semigroup. $A \cup B \cup \{0\}$ is regarded as a subsemigroup of

$$\{0\} \cup \mathscr{F}_0(a_1, \ldots, a_m, b_1, \ldots, b_k).$$

Let $\bar{\rho}$ be the congruence on $A \cup B \cup \{0\}$ generated by ρ defined below: For fixed $n_1, n_2, \ldots, n_k > 0$,

$$\rho = \{(b_1^{n_1}, 0), (b_2^{n_2}, 0), \ldots, (b_k^{n_k}, 0)\}.$$

Let $S = (A \cup B \cup \{0\})/\bar{\rho}$. Then S is a concentric $\mathfrak{p}$-simple semigroup and $C(x) = \{0\}$ for all $x \in S$.

We have just begun the study of closets of semigroups. Many problems remain.

Problems

1. Is a homomorphic image of a concentric semigroup also concentric?

2. Let $\mathfrak{S}_1$ be the class of $\mathfrak{p}$-simple semigroups satisfying a permutation identity ($x_1 x_2 \cdots x_n = x_{\pi(1)} \cdots x_{\pi(n)}$, π a permutation). Does $\mathfrak{S}_1$ satisfy the conditions of Theorem 3.30?

3. Problem 2 replacing "permutation identity" by "identity."

4. Study the structure of concentric (finitely convergent) semigroups with zero.

REFERENCES

Chrislock, J. (1966). The structure of archimedean semigroups. Dissertation, University of California, Davis, California.

Chrislock, J. (1969). On medial semigroups. *J. Algebra* **12**, 1–9.

Clifford, A., and Preston, G. (1961). "The Algebraic Theory of Semigroups." Vol. 1 (Math. Surveys, No. 7). Amer. Math. Soc., Providence, Rhode Island.

Clifford, A., and Preston, G. (1967). "The Algebraic Theory of Semigroups." Vol. 2.

Kimura, N. (1958a). On some existence theorems on multiplicative system, I, Greatest quotient, *Proc. Japan Acad.* **34**, 305–309.

Kimura, N. (1958b). The structure of idempotent semigroups (1), *Pacific J. Math.* **8**, 257–275.

Kimura, N., and Tamura, T. (1954). On decomposition of a commutative semigroup. *Kodai Math. Sem. Rep.* **4**, 182–225.

Kimura, N., and Tamura, T. (1955). Existence of greatest decomposition of a semigroup. *Kodai Math. Sem. Rep.* **7**, 83–84.

McLean, D. (1954). Idempotent semigroups. *Amer. Math. Monthly* **61**, 110–113.

Petrich, M. (1964). The maximal semilattice decomposition of a semigroup. *Math. Z.* **85**, 68–82.

Shafer, J., and Tamura, T. (1966). Another proof of two decomposition theorems of semigroups. *Proc. Japan. Acad.* **42**, 685–687.

Tamura, T. (1954). Note on unipotent inversible semigroups. *Kodai Math. Sem. Rep.* **3**, 93–95.

Tamura, T. (1956). The theory of construction of finite semigroups, 1. *Osaka Math. J.* **8**, 243–261.

Tamura, T. (1957). Commutative nonpotent archimedean semigroup with cancellation law. *J. Gakugei Tokushima Univ.* **8**, 5–11.

Tamura, T. (1958). The theory of construction of finite semigroups. III, *Osaka Math. J.* **10**, 191–204.

Tamura, T. (1964). Another proof of a theorem concerning the greatest semilattice-decomposition of a semigroup. *Proc. Japan. Acad.* **40**, 777–780.

Tamura, T. (1965). The theory of operations on binary relations. *Trans. Amer. Math. Soc.* **120**, 343–358.

Tamura, T. (1966). Attainability of system of identities on semigroups. *J. Algebra* **3**, 261–276.

Tamura, T. (1967). Decomposability of extensions and its application to finite semigroups. *Proc. Japan. Acad.* **43**, 93–97.

Tamura, T. (1968). Construction of trees and commutative archimedean semigroups. *Math. Nachr.* **36**, 255–287.

Tamura, T. Unpublished paper. The basic study of general product.

Tamura, T. Semigroups satisfying $xy = f(x, y)$. *Pacific J. Math.* to be published.

Yamada, M. (1955). On the greatest semilattice decomposition of a semigroup. *Kodai Math. Sem. Rep.* **7**, 59–62.

Yamada, M. (1964). Construction of finite commutative s-semigroups. *Proc. Japan. Acad.* **40**, 94–98.

Yamada, M., and Tamura, T. Note on finite commutative nil semigroups. *Portugal. Math. (Lisbon)* to be published.

Recent Results on Binary Topological Algebras

ALEXANDER DONIPHAN WALLACE

Department of Mathematics
University of Florida
Gainsville, Florida

Exception being made of Day and Wallace [2], the results in question remain, as yet, unpublished and, indeed, unsubmitted as of this date. In the order of their appearance here they are due to my colleagues K. N. Sigmon, E. N. Ferguson, and D. P. Stadtlander, and I am grateful to these mathematicians for the opportunity of reading their manuscripts and for their permission to openly discuss their results prior to publication.

In some instances the notation and terminology of the monumental "Elements" of Hofmann and Mostert [5] will be used, but perhaps Paalman-de Miranda [7] will be a surer guide. In this respect we adhere to more familiar language and do not employ such words and phrases as *catena*, *elephant grabbing doughnut*, *hofmos* (pl. *hofmoi*), *nautilus Mississippi*, and so on.

1. Cancellative Medial Means on an *n* Cell Are Arithmetic

Suppose that C is a convex subset of some real linear topological space and for $x, y \in C$ write

$$x \circ y = (x + y)/2.$$

This binary operation is clearly continuous and satisfies

$$x \circ x = x$$
$$x \circ y = y \circ x$$

(is a *mean*)

$$(x \circ y) \circ (z \circ w) = (x \circ z) \circ (y \circ w)$$

(is *medial*)

$$x \circ a = y \circ a \quad \text{implies} \quad x = y$$

(is *cancellative*).

Aczel [1] gives a voluminous bibliography on means and related matter, stretching from 1747 to 1965, and running to over 100 pages. The references on pp. 278 and 279 are germane here and the latter of these cites some 30 papers. Additionally, there should be mentioned Aumann's and Eckmann's work (cited by Aczel [1]) and Eckmann *et al.* [3]. Though no contact is made with Sigmon's theorem it is not possible to forego mentioning the beautiful result that no mean exists on an n sphere, which these papers prove and extend.

Theorem (Sigmon [8]). If $(x, y) \to x \circ y$ is a cancellative medial mean on the n cell E^n, then there is a homeomorphism into

$$f: E^n \to R^n$$

such that

$$f(x \circ y) = [f(x) + f(y)]/2, \qquad x, y \in E^n.$$

The n cell may be either open or closed, and the above statement does not encompass all that is proved. The theorem may be regarded as residing in the domain of nonassociative topological algebra, or as being a contribution to the theory of composite functional equations. In any event, it is a major contribution to either, only the case $n = 1$ having been previously treated with success. Its proof is, in part, a reduction to theorems on semigroups, and relies on the use of topologized direct limits.

It goes without saying that there is much interest in knowing which continua admit a mean. P. Bacon has shown (sharpening a result of Sigmon's) that any continuum admitting a mean must be unicoherent, and has given an example of a contractible continuum which admits no mean, contrary to what had been supposed.

There is now sufficient evidence to indicate rather clearly that the ancient and honorable theory of functional equations is amenable to that very modern discipline, binary topological algebra.

2. The Skin Problem for $n = 2$

As usual, a semigroup is a nonvoid Hausdorff space together with a continuous associative multiplication, denoted by juxtaposition. As in the case of means, it is interesting to know what spaces admit what continuous associative multiplications. In 1950 essentially nothing was known, but now, thanks to the diligent efforts of many mathematicians, many excellent results have been discovered and proved, as may be seen by consulting Hofmann and Mostert [5] and Paalman-de Miranda [7]. But one of the problems which had defied assault for over 10 years by the combined armamentaria thus assembled has recently fallen to the attack of Ferguson [4].

If, as usual, S denotes a semigroup, then E will be its set of idempotents,

$$E = \{x \mid x \in S \quad \text{and} \quad x^2 = x\}.$$

Theorem (Ferguson [4]). There does not exist on the closed two-cell a continuous associative multiplication with the set of idempotents being precisely the bounding circle.

Although tedious, the proof is delicate and subtle in places and employs a variety of modes inherited from earlier workers. Among these are those use by Anne Lester (Hudson) in her papers on n cells, the parameterization technique of Mostert and Shields, Koch's arc theorem, and plane topology (for references see Hofmann and Mostert [5] and Paalman-de Miranda [7]). Assuming the proposition false, any element admits at least one nth root, and taking $p \in S\backslash E$, there is constructed a thread through p which meets E in the zero of S (which may be assumed) and some idempotent $e \in E$. (A *thread* is here a semigroup topologically a closed interval, with one endpoint being a zero and the other a unit.) It may be shown that either eS or Se has an empty interior, and, letting it be the latter, it follows that Se is a tree (acyclic continuous curve) and so is uniquely arcwise connected. It must contain the thread constructed earlier and is simultaneously in the boundary (E) and contains p, a contradiction.

The situation for $n > 2$ remains as obscure as ever, but it is not implausible that progress could be made if something was known about two-dimensional clans, a problem very much worth attacking for many reasons. In a different direction, my earlier approach using a sweeping-out theorem may do the job.

3. Actions on Irreducible Continua

There are many very good reasons for considering *acts*, such being maps

$$S \times X \to X$$

with S a semigroup, X a nonvoid Hausdorff space, with the value of the anonymous function at (s, x) denoted by sx, and satisfying

$$s(s'x) = (ss')\, x.$$

Among other reasons, there is the sheer mathematical exuberance of just plain generalizing whatever has been done in terms of semigroups, since a semigroup clearly acts on itself.

Acts are sometimes termed *automata* (in this case, topological), and then S is termed the *input* semigroup and X the *state space.* Although we shall have nothing to do with them here, a *machine* is an act together with an additional map (the *output* function)

$$T \overset{\circ}{\leftarrow} S \times X$$

satisfying

$$(ss') \circ x = (s \circ (s'x))(s' \circ x),$$

T being the *output* semigroup. Think of a vending machine in the ordinary usage of this phrase, and suppose that it has just been serviced, and so is in its virgin state. If a coin is deposited, the machine grumbles, accepts the coin, and emits a candy bar. It is thus in a new state, with one less candy bar and one more coin. So much for the use of *input* and *state.*

At this distant date I cannot recall who first used the word *act*, but it was either R. J. Koch or myself. It is undecided which will prevail, act or automaton—most probably the latter, since it has the sound of greater pomposity and orotundity, and has the possible virtue of greater dignity. I recall the time when Koch presented his dissertation, titled "Theorems on Mobs," to the august Office of the Graduate Dean, which the dean promptly rejected with the statement that he would not read such a title at graduation exercises. After some persuasion "semigroup" was found an acceptable substitute for "mob," and the hooding was completed. So much for brevity.

As earlier, there is the question of what semigroups act on what spaces. Any semigroup can act on any space X by putting $sx = x$ uniformly, or $sx = z$, uniformly for a fixed $z \in X$. Leaving to one side these trivial actions, it appears that the answer is—just as a semigroup acts on itself, or as a group acts on a space.

This answer is, of course, too brief to be useful. However the following result will show what is meant. (Incidentally, a *bing* is a compact connected semigroup, and the action is *unitary* if x is always a member of Sx.)

Theorem (Stadtlander [9]). Let the bing S act unitarily on the continuum X irreducible between two points, and denote by K the minimal ideal of S.

(1) X/KX is either an arc or a point, where X/KX is gotten by collapsing KX to a point.

(2) If B is a component of $X\backslash KX$, then the closure of B "is" an Abelian clan and its minimal ideal coincides with the boundary of B.

(3) KX is either a continuum irreducible between two points or "is" an Abelian group, the latter if it has an empty interior.

(4) K consists entirely of homeomorphisms, or of constant maps, on KX.

The "is" requires some explanation, but could be replaced by "admits the structure of." Here is the explanation, and in part the reason why the result is true. But this "reason" conceals many details.

Suppose that T and X are compact (or discrete) spaces and that we are given a map

$$T \times X \to X$$

denoted as usual by juxtaposition, and suppose also that we have a surmap

$$\emptyset\colon\ S \to X.$$

Out of these data we wish to construct an operation of X on itself. We have the following.

(i) $\emptyset(s) = \emptyset(t)$ implies $sx = tx$ for all $x \in X$ iff there is an operation $\circ$ for which the diagram

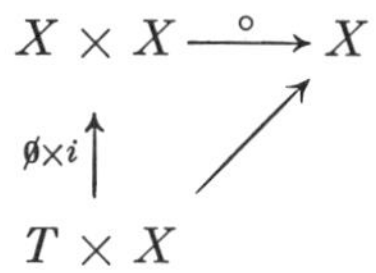

$$\begin{array}{ccc} X \times X & \xrightarrow{\ \circ\ } & X \\ {\scriptstyle \emptyset \times i}\uparrow & \nearrow & \\ T \times X & & \end{array}$$

is analytic,

$$\emptyset(s) \circ x = sx, \qquad s \in S, \qquad \text{and} \qquad x \in X.$$

(ii) Given (i), the operation $\circ$ is associative iff $\emptyset(s) = t\emptyset(t')$ implies $sx = t(t'x)$ for all $x \in X$.

The immediately preceding stems from papers by Hosszu, by Aczel and myself, and slightly more generally [10]. Getting back to the case at hand with a compact *commutative* semigroup acting on a compact space and with $Sq = X$ for some $q \in X$, we fabricate the surmap by letting $\emptyset(s) = sq$ and we observe at once that this gives the desired associative operation of X on itself. This operation is commutative and q is the unit for it.

It is easier to see why the "reason" is a reason in another instance than in Stadtlander's result. However, this proposition is included in Stadtlander's, which was obtained later.

Theorem (Day and Wallace [2]). Let the bing S act unitarily on the compact space X, which contains a dense open half-line W whose complement C is nondegenerate, with $SC \subset C$, and suppose also that

$$\square \neq Q = \{x \mid Sx = X\} \neq X.$$

There is then a commutative bing T acting on X with $Tq = X$ for some $q \in Q$, and putting $\emptyset(t) = tq$ there derives accordingly a continuous commutative associative multiplication $\circ$ on X satisfying

$$x \circ (tq) = tx$$

with q as unit.

It may be remarked that actually crd $Q = 1$ and that the instance in which we do not have $SC \subset C$ is rather trivial.

The proof goes along these lines. First reduce S by the effectivity congruence $\mathscr{C}$, $(s, t) \in \mathscr{C}$ iff $sx = tx$ for all $x \in X$, so that $S/\mathscr{C}$ acts unitarily and effectively on X. So, suppose that the initial action is effective. Then let T be the subsemigroup of S which is minimal relative to having the same orbits as S, $Tx = Sx$ for all $x \in X$. There being an idempotent e with $eq = q$, eTe is a clan with unit e, and turns out to be just T. The ideal

$$I = \{t \mid tX \subset C \quad \text{and} \quad t \in T\}$$

has the property that $T \setminus I$ is a dense subsemigroup of T and that T/I is a thread, and thus T/I is Abelian, using Koch's arc theorem. It may be shown that T itself is Abelian, and proof comes to an end.

The above has something in common with Koch and Wallace [6], as has Stadtlander's proof of his result. He also generalizes some results and notions which were given in my lectures of about 1956, for which R. J. Koch kindly made the notes.

ACKNOWLEDGMENT

The author extends his gratitude to The Department of Mathematics of Wayne State University for its invitation to participate in the Conference, and to the National Science Foundation for support under GP-8729.

REFERENCES

1. Janos Aczel, "Lectures on Functional Equations." Academic Press, New York, 1966.
2. J. M. Day and A. D. Wallace, Multiplication induced in the state space of an act, *Math. Systems Theory* **1**, 305–310 (1967).
3. B. Eckmann, T. Ganea, and P. J. Hilton, "Generalized Means" (Studies in Analysis). Stanford Univ. Press, Stanford, California, 1962.
4. E. N. Ferguson, Semigroups on the two cell with idempotent boundary, *Duke Math. J.* to appear.
5. K. H. Hofmann and P. S. Mostert, "Elements of Compact Semigroups." Merrill, Columbus, Ohio, 1966.
6. R. J. Koch and A. D. Wallace, Admissibility of semigroup structures on continua, *Trans. Am. Math. Soc.* **88**, 177–287 (1958).
7. A. B. Paalman-de Miranda, "Topological Semigroups." Math. Centrum, Amsterdam, 1964.
8. K. N. Sigmon, Cancellative medial means are arithmetics, *Duke Math. J.* to appear.
9. D. P. Stadtlander, Actions with topologically restricted state spaces, *Duke Math. J.* to appear.
10. A. D. Wallace, Recursions with semigroup state-spaces, *Rev. Roumaine Math. Pures Appl.* **12**, 1411–1415 (1967).

Author Index

Numbers in parentheses are reference numbers and indicate that an author's work is referred to, although his name is not cited in the text. Numbers in italics show the page on which the complete reference is listed.

Y

Z

Subject Index

T

U

W